# Particle Size

Fog bank off the California Coast near San Francisco.

# PARTICLE SIZE

*Theory and Industrial Applications*

RICHARD D. CADLE
National Center for Atmospheric Research
Boulder, Colorado

REINHOLD PUBLISHING CORPORATION, *New York*
*Chapman & Hall, Ltd., London*

Copyright © 1965 by
REINHOLD PUBLISHING CORPORATION

Library of Congress Catalog Card Number 65-28529
Printed in the United States of America

# Preface

With few exceptions, the sizes and size distributions of the particles in systems of finely divided materials are of importance only as they relate to other properties of the systems. For example, the sizes of particles in city smog are of importance as they affect the haziness of city air, the depth of penetration of the particles into human lungs, and the amount of deposition of the particles on various surfaces before winds disperse the smog. The sizes of the particles in the pigments and fillers used in paints have marked effects on the covering power of the paints, and on the color, gloss, and protection which they impart to a surface.

Merely to describe the relationship between particle size and some other property of a powder or suspension is of limited usefulness unless it is considered in connection with a particular practical situation. Thus the effect of particle size on the rate of deposition of aerosol particles on the walls of a tube through which they are flowing is of theoretical interest, but becomes of practical importance when the tube is a passage in the human respiratory system. And the study of the importance of particle size to deposition in the lungs is of increased significance when related to the deposition of specific types of substances which may have greatly different effects on the human body. For example, the deposition of sodium chloride in the lungs may have no harmful effects while the deposition of radioactive particles may produce cancer.

This book is devoted to the practical importance of particle size. For the reasons just described much of the book is devoted to setting the stage, to showing the general nature of the problem or industry to which fine particle behavior is important. In this way the information concerning particle size effects, which all too often is of a rather isolated or fragmentary nature, can be related to a major problem.

No attempt has been made to achieve completeness in describing the literature of a particular field. Many important topics have been ignored, and the references have been selected as examples or to emphasize a point rather than to provide a thorough review. Nonetheless, it is hoped that this book will provide the scientist or engineer faced with problems in the fine-particle field with general concepts of the relationships between particle size and other properties of disperse systems, with a review of current knowledge concerning particle-size effects on a number of practical problems, and with indications of methods for attacking problems involving fine particles.

Obviously, much remains to be learned concerning the effects of particle size. It is intended that this book will help to point up such deficiencies in our knowledge and to stimulate research on systems of particles.

A large number of references, both to the original literature and to various books and reviews, have been listed. This will permit the serious reader to obtain more complete information than could be included here. The book has been written primarily for a skilled scientist or engineer who is not an expert in the fine-particle field. However, it may also have some value as a reference book for those experienced in some aspect of particle technology.

Numerous other books have been written about fine-particle behavior, including works on particle size determination, such as one written by the author, on aerosols, on particle technology in general, and at least one devoted to the statistics of fine particles. It is hoped that the present volume has a legitimate claim to being unique in its emphasis on the practical importance of particle size and thus will help satisfy an important requirement of workers with fine particles.

I wish to thank the many organizations which supplied illustrative material or gave permission to use it. These are acknowledged in the captions for the illustrations. I also wish to thank the University of Colorado for permitting extensive use of its library facilities and the National Center for Atmospheric Research for encouraging the preparation of this volume. In particular, I wish to acknowledge the help of my wife Edna for extensive aid in the preparation of the manuscript.

R. D. CADLE
NATIONAL CENTER FOR
ATMOSPHERIC RESEARCH

BOULDER, COLORADO
October, 1965

# Contents

# Chapter 1 Introduction

During the last few years major advances have been made in understanding the behavior of small particles and in our ability to use them to advantage. Many of the major advances in knowledge of particle behavior have been concerned with suspensions of solids and liquids in gases, the so-called aerosols. Much important information has been accumulated concerning light scattering by such particles. In particular, the Mie equations describing light scattering have been solved for particles of various shapes and complex refractive indices. They have been integrated over various size distributions, which is very helpful to the application of these equations, since the particles in a suspension are generally not all the same size. Knowledge of the mechanics of aerosol particles has also greatly advanced, particularly in respect to behavior during filtration, impaction, coagulation, and in temperature and concentration gradients.

The constantly increasing demand for greater reliability and closer tolerances in parts used for modern complex devices such as jet-propelled vehicles has brought a realization of the damage which dust can produce during the manufacturing process. Therefore, so-called clean rooms and white rooms, which are relatively free of dust, are increasingly used in various industries. Both the sizes and concentrations of particles in the air of such rooms must be monitored and compared with size and concentration limits. The setting of such limits may be a very important part of developing the specifications for a manufacturing operation.

The so-called aerosol industry with its canned spray deodorizers, hair sprays, insecticides, paints, and a host of other products is now of great economic importance and has greatly simplified many everyday operations.

The use of small particles in manufacturing has been greatly extended during recent years. Much of this increased use has been in such conventional fine-particle industries as the paint and cement industries. However, numerous new uses have recently been developed. Examples are magnetic tape for recording, products formed by powder metallurgy and

1

by pressure molding of powdered plastics, and powders consisting of sub-micron size particles for insulation.

The features characterizing small particles are size (by definition) and the properties particularly related to the size range of interest. Other properties, such as the nature of the material comprising the particles, may have a tremendous influence, of course, but these can be considered as being superimposed on the size effects. The purpose of this book is to discuss the effects of size on the properties of powders and suspensions of powders, with emphasis on the practical implications of these effects.

## DEFINITIONS OF PARTICLE SIZE

### Meaning of "particle"

The use of the term "particle size" generally implies that the user has answered two questions to his own satisfaction: What is meant by "particle"? and, What is meant by "particle size"? Superficially, the answers may seem obvious, but careful thought reveals that this is far from being so. Both terms are usually highly ambiguous unless they are carefully defined, and failure to define them properly has often seriously detracted from the usefulness of otherwise excellent reports of research and development.

The word "particle," in its most general sense, refers to any object having definite physical boundaries in all directions, without any limit with respect to size. Thus, broadly speaking, electrons, molecules, the solar system, and even complete galaxies can be considered to be particles. The concept that all matter is composed of particles is fundamental to science. However, the smaller particles are generally not uniformly distributed through a particular material but are associated as aggregates, aggregates of aggregates, etc., and it is this progression of complexity that so often leads to ambiguity.

The classic examples of this type of difficulty are samples of soil. These usually consist of relatively large aggregates which are certainly particles. Many properties of the soil may depend on their size. The action of organic soil conditioners is to stabilize such aggregates. But the aggregates in turn are comprised of grains which are also particles and are often referred to as ultimate particles of the soil. The differences among many soils, such as that between sand and clay, may be determined by the size of the ultimate particles. And the so-called ultimate particles are really far from ultimate. The individual grains, for instance, may contain two or more crystals or crystal fragments.

Another example is the difficulty in defining the particles in many gas-solid systems such as the so-called aerosols. The particles in stack gases often consist largely of loosely bound aggregates. When such particles are emitted into the atmosphere they decrease the visibility and may settle on vegetation, causing plant damage. The visibility decrease may result largely from light scattering by individual particles in the aggregates, while the rate of settling is generally controlled by the size and density of the aggregates. A common error in attempting to evaluate the potential hazards from particles in stack gases is to collect them by some bulk method, such as filtration through a thimble, and to determine the size distribution of the "ultimate" particles. The collection technique destroys the individuality of the aggregates and the size distribution obtained may have little or no relationship to the property of the suspension.

Therefore, it is of utmost importance for an investigator initiating a study of a particulate system, especially one involving aggregates, to select the definition of particle appropriate to his interests, and a method of measurement that will yield the sizes of the particles so defined.

For the purposes of this book the definition of particle will be limited by size; that is, only those particles will be considered whose diameters are in the range 0.05 to $10^4$ microns ($1\mu = 0.001$ mm). The lower end of this range overlaps slightly the colloid range while the upper end overlaps somewhat the range in which direct measurement of individual particles without magnification is possible. As pointed out by Herdan,[1] this is the region accessible to study by viewing, sedimentation, and observation by the optical, the electron, and the ultramicroscope. Particles in this size range are often referred to as "fine particles" or "small particles" and those in the submicron range are sometimes[2] called "ultrafine particles." The range of size treated in this book is so large that the simpler (as contrasted with general) forms of equations describing particle behavior often apply to only a portion of it. For example, the Rayleigh equation describing light scattering is valid only for particles smaller than about $0.1\mu$ diameter; for larger particles the more general Mie equations must be applied. Similarly, the unmodified Stokes equation describing sedimentation is applicable only in the range (approximate) 0.2 to $50\mu$ for particles of density about unity settling in air. The term particle, as used in this book, includes both the liquid and solid phase.

### Meaning of "size"

The terms "size," "radius," and "diameter" also need careful definition unless they are being used in a very general sense. The word "diameter" was originally defined in terms of circles and spheres, but it is useful also to define the term for irregular particles. Diameters of irregular particles may be defined in terms of the geometry of the individual particle. Such diameters are often called statistical diameters since large numbers of particles must be measured and the results averaged if the values are to have much significance.

A widely used definition of diameter was proposed by Martin.[3] It is the distance between opposite sides of the particle, measured crosswise of the particle and on a line bisecting the projected area, as drawn in Figure 1-1. Martin's diameters are generally used in connection with optical and electron microscopy. For the results to be statistically significant, it is important that some convention be chosen with respect to the direction in which

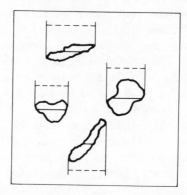

Figure 1-1. Martin's diameters (solid lines bisecting particles) and Feret's diameter (dashed lines). (*Courtesy of the Society of Chemical Industry* )

the diameters are measured. When a microscope is used, it is convenient to use the direction parallel to the bottom of the field. The relationship between Martin's diameter and the specific surface area (area per unit volume) has been given[4,5] by the equation

$$\text{Martin's diameter} = \frac{4}{D_p S_v}$$

where $D_p$ is the packing density and $S_v$ is the specific surface.

Another definition of particle diameter, attributed to Feret,[6] is the length of the distance between two tangents on opposite sides of the particle profile. The tangents must be parallel to an arbitrarily fixed direction (Figure 1-1). This diameter is somewhat more difficult to measure than Martin's and is probably used less frequently.

A definition of diameter which has been used extensively in Great Britain and is becoming increasingly popular in the United States is the diameter of a circle whose area is equal to the projected area of the particle. These diameters are conveniently measured with ocular micrometers (graticules) placed in the microscope eyepiece; on these are drawn a series of concentric circles. The diameter of a particle is that of the circle which appears to have an area closest to the projected area of the particle. Because of the simplicity of size determination techniques based on this definition and because of its increasing use, it is discussed below in considerable detail.

The globe and circle graticule is an invention of Patterson and Cawood,[7] designed to estimate rapidly the size distribution of smoke particles in the range 0.2 to $5.0\mu$ diameter. The graticule consists of a rectangle and two series of ten numbered circles as shown in Figure 1-2. The area enclosed by the circles in one series is blackened; hence the two series give rise to the term "globe and circle." The images of the circles and globes (more properly discs) correspond in size to particles ranging from 0.22 to $5.02\mu$ diameter when the deposit is viewed with a 2mm, 1.40 NA objective and a 12X eyepiece, using a tube length of 17 cm. The size of the rectangle under these conditions is $5 \times 10^{-3}$ cm. The microscopist may, by personal preference, choose to use either the globes or the circles. The limit of visibility of small particles lies considerably below the limit of resolution of the microscope. Therefore, the smallest particles are assigned a diameter of $0.22\mu$, although some of them may be smaller.

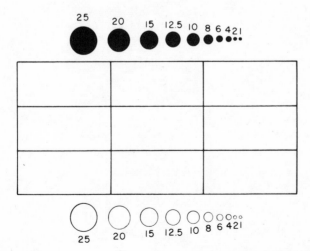

Figure 1-2. Patterson-Cawood[7] graticule. (*Courtesy of the Faraday Society*)

Fairs[8] developed the series of three micrometers shown in Figure 1-3. They consist of a central rectangle subdivided into small rectangles and bounded by or containing a series of graduated circles. They differ from the original Patterson design in that the series of three micrometers covers a range of 128:1, and that the size intervals except in the case of the two

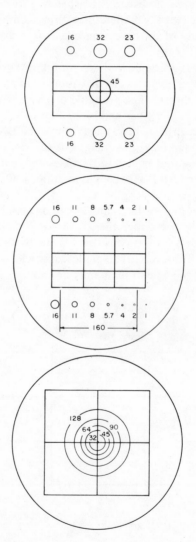

Figure 1-3. Fairs' graticule[8]. (*Courtesy of the Society of Chemical Industry*)

lowest, are arranged in a $\sqrt{2}$ progression. Fairs claimed that by using these size intervals the total error is "1.17 times the inevitable error of counting" and that the use of smaller intervals gives little improvement in the over-all accuracy of the size analysis.

Fairs' technique of sizing and counting the particles involved two observers, one performing the actual sizing, the other recording the results. Places were changed occasionally, since with trained personnel no appreciable "personal factor" was observed. The sizing and counting were carried out simultaneously by comparing with the reference circles every particle lying within the rectangle of the micrometer. Usually the particle size distribution was so great that it was necessary to size at two or three magnifications and in some cases to use two or three micrometers to include the largest particles. Data were expressed as cumulative weight percentages.

Fairs compared his method with two photosedimentation methods, one developed by Carey and Stairmand and the other a modified Richardson photoelectric turbidimeter. The results are shown in Tables 1-1 and 1-2. The agreement between the two sets of results shown in Table 1-1 was very close. The agreement between the two sets in Table 1-2 was not so close, although reasonable agreement was obtained except for the smallest particles. Fairs suggests that the high proportion of fines recorded by the Richardson turbidimeter was at least partially due to the presence of particles in the suspension less than $1\mu$ in diameter, which extinguish (scatter) a greater amount of light in proportion to their surface than would be expected from the Lambert-Beer law.

TABLE 1-1. COMPARISON OF PARTICLE SIZE DISTRIBUTIONS OF GROUND SAND AS OBTAINED BY FAIRS' TECHNIQUE AND BY THE CAREY AND STAIRMAND PHOTOSEDIMENTATION APPARATUS[8]

| Size Range ($\mu$) | Microscope | Weight %<br>Photo-sedimentation Apparatus |
|---|---|---|
| <5.0 | 5.4 | 6.4 |
| 5.0–10.0 | 11.1 | 11.2 |
| 10.0–20.0 | 18.5 | 18.4 |
| 20.0–30.0 | 16.0 | 16.0 |
| 30.0–40.0 | 16.0 | 13.4 |
| 40.0–40.0 | 15.0 | 15.6 |
| 53.0–66.0 | 5.5 ⎫ 18.0 | 19.0 |
| 66.0–120.0 | 12.5 ⎭ | — |

TABLE 1-2. COMPARISON OF PARTICLE SIZE DISTRIBUTIONS OF SIEVED LIMESTONE DUST AS OBTAINED BY FAIRS' TECHNIQUE AND BY THE RICHARDSON TURBIDIMETER[8]

| Size Range ($\mu$) | Weight % | |
|---|---|---|
| | Microscope, 1:1 Alcohol:Water Suspension | Turbidimeter, Alcohol Suspension |
| >3.0 | 5.8 | 11.3 |
| 3.9–5.0 | 7.5 | 9.4 |
| 5.0–10.0 | 23.2 | 15.2 |
| 10.0–15.0 | 16.5 | 14.1 |
| 15.0–15.0 | 10.5 | 10.5 |
| 20.0–30.0 | 11.5 | 15.0 |
| 30.0–40.0 | 9.6 | 11.5 |
| 40.0–53.0 | 9.7 | 9.3 |
| 53.0–66.0 | 5.7 | 3.8 |

In 1943 when Fairs published his method, many investigators had been instructed in this method of size analysis. The general technique is rapidly and easily acquired. The time for the analysis varies with the size range and the complexity of the sample, but in the most difficult cases the total time taken for the preparation of the sample, the sizing, and the calculation and plotting of the results is about three or four hours.

K. R. May[9] in 1945 published a paper describing the cascade impactor. This device produces four progressively finer aerosol jets impinging on glass slides in series, so that the collected sample is split into size-graded fractions in a form suitable for microscopic analysis. The collected particles appear as a single long trace on each slide. Since then, various modifications of this device have been developed, but the greatest efficiency of sampling by the original May device was achieved for particles in the range 1.5–50$\mu$ diameter.

May developed a modification of the globe and circle graticule for use with his impactor. He pointed out that the diameters of the circles of the Patterson and Cawood device do not increase in a regular series, and that this introduces considerable complication where two or more counts at different magnification have to be combined because, where the counts overlap, the size ranges are not the same, and each slide must be treated individually.

The May graticule consists of a rectangle, 200 units by 100 units, with numbered circles ranging from $\sqrt{2}$ units to $(\sqrt{2})^9$ units (22.6) in diameter.

Numbering the circles permits the microscopist to call out the sizes of the particles to an assistant as even numbers. The assistant records a stroke for each particle against the appropriate size range. The left half of the rectangle is divided into six rectangles for use with very small particles where it is convenient to keep the field stationary and count the particles in each small rectangle. The right half contains a number of vertical lines whose distance from the center line increases with the $\sqrt{2}$ progression. Each line is numbered with the appropriate power of $\sqrt{2}$.

The slide on which the sample is collected is mounted on the mechanical stage of the microscope so that the field as seen in the microscope moves perpendicularly to the length of the trace on the slide. May found when making a traverse of the trace, the best procedure is to move the stage slowly and continuously across, and deal with each particle as it crosses the chosen fraction of the center line. Each particle can then be measured when the left edge of the particle coincides with the center line, using the vertical lines in the right side of the rectangle. May suggests sizing by comparison with the globes or circles, making frequent checks with the vertical lines. Also, the latter increase the range of the micrometer which is essential when sizing the large particles frequently encountered on the first impactor slide.

Sharpe[10] has designed a circle micrometer for use with the Metropolitan-Vickers EM2 electron microscope. This avoids the need of preparing large numbers of electron micrographs to obtain a representative sampling of the particles. The micrometer is superimposed on the final image screen of the electron microscope and particle size can be read directly by matching the particles to the appropriate circles. Sharpe etched the circles on the surface of a brass plate coated with a fluorescent compound, zinc-cadmium sulfide. The circles are 2, 1, 0.5, 0.25, 0.1 and 0.05 cm diameter. The brass plate is placed in a camera casette in the position normally occupied by a photographic plate. If one uses a magnification of $10,000\times$, an image equal in area to the 1-cm circle corresponds to a particle of $1\mu$ diameter. Fairs[11] also mentions this micrometer, which was developed in his laboratory. He states that preliminary tests indicated good agreement between light microscope and electron microscope analyses. In view of the very small portion of the bulk fraction examined in electron microscope determinations, it is desirable to restrict them to samples whose size range is not greater than $50:1$ if reasonable accuracy is to be achieved.

Fairs[11] described the application of the globe and circle micrometer to projection microscope techniques. He stressed the importance of high-quality projection equipment and the use of monochromatic illumination when high magnifications are required. He obtained the latter by illuminating with a 250-watt high-pressure mercury vapor lamp used in conjunction with a Mercury Orange or Mercury Green filter.

The use of the projection microscope not only reduces eyestrain but permits incorporation of the micrometer in the projection screen. Fairs used a graticule consisting of a subdivided rectangle bounded by reference globes and circles. By adjusting the projection distance when changing from one magnification to another, a continuous progression of $\sqrt{2}$ intervals could be obtained from 76 to $0.3\mu$. Fairs chose the upper limit of $76\mu$, since it is the nominal aperture of the 240-mesh sieve in the British Standard fine series, permitting the sieve analysis of a powder sample to be simply extended to a size analysis by microscopic examination in the sub-sieve range. The graticule was prepared on a Kodak IV-0 Matte Gelatin plate. The surface was protected by a plain glass backing.

Fairs described in detail the procedure of making a count on a sample of flue dust with an over-all size range of 76 to $0.3\mu$ in which not more than 5 percent is expected to be in the size range $76-53\mu$. As usual, the sizing process is carried out by two observers, one counting and one re-recording, who change places frequently.

He also described[11] an investigation of the effect of irregular particle shape on the results obtained using ground limestone in which the particles were quite irregular. Four size ranges were used, namely 215–152, 152–105, 105–76, and $76-53\mu$. Sixty particles were selected to represent each size range by comparison with the reference circles. The two major dimensions of the projected area and the thickness were measured microscopically for each particle. A volume was then computed for each particle assuming ellipsoidal shape which was compared to the sphere of diameter equal to that of the corresponding reference circle on the micrometer. The ratio of these two volumes gave an indication of the shape factor, as shown in Table 1-3.

Fairs emphasized that his shape factor approached unity as the particle size dropped to $76\mu$. However, the significance of this approach seems questionable since matching projected areas to circles may be a more

TABLE 1-3. SHAPE FACTORS FOR GROUND DERBYSHIRE LIMESTONE

| Size Range (μ) | Shape Factor | | | |
|---|---|---|---|---|
| | Sample 1 | Sample 2 | Sample 3 | Average |
| 215–152 | 0.241 | 0.225 | 0.242 | 0.235 |
| 152–105 | 0.497 | 0.588 | 0.457 | 0.518 |
| 105–86 | 0.716 | 0.726 | 0.721 | 0.721 |
| 76–53 | 0.803 | 0.764 | 0.767 | 0.778 |

accurate method for estimating volumes than making the assumption that irregular particles are ellipsoids.

Watson[12] described a simplified eyepiece graticule for assessing dust samples collected with a thermal precipitator. The Pneumoconiosis Research Unit with which Watson was associated, at the beginning of its dust assessment with the thermal precipitator, decided to use a particle number concentration within the restricted size-range of 0.5 to $5\mu$ mean projected diameter as a measure of the hazardous fraction of airborne coal mine dust. For two years detailed size distributions were made with a Patterson-Cawood micrometer, the cumulative size distributions being plotted on log-probability paper. Watson's group used number of particles per $cm^3$ within four size groups, namely $<0.5$, 0.5 to 2, 2 to 5, and $>5\mu$ to indicate the fineness of the dust.

Much of the information produced by the detailed sizing was not used, so a simplified procedure using a new three-spot graticule was developed. It contains the conventional two rows of comparison circles, the diameters having the proportions 5:2:0.5. When using a 2-mm objective, the magnification is adjusted by altering the tube length of the microscope so that the circles correspond to diameters of 5, 2, and $0.5\mu$, respectively.

The rectangle of the graticule is 3.8 mm long and 1.9 mm wide, and the diameter of the largest circle is one-eighth the length of the rectangle. The open circles are drawn so that the diameters to the outside of the lines are equal to those of the respective "globes." The graticule was also reproduced on a ground-glass viewing screen for use with a projection microscope.

Watson found that with only four size groups in which to place particles, a keyboard recorder can easily be used by the microscopist himself to record the count. Watson pointed out that the calculations necessary to produce the final result are few and simple, and no graphical work is needed, resulting in a further saving of time compared with the old method.

Hamilton and his co-workers[13] also developed a simplified globe and circle device, this time for use by the British National Coal Board. The design they evolved was similar to that by Watson except that the circles corresponded to 0.5, 1, 2.5 and $5\mu$ when used with the usual 2-mm objective. The intermediate circle was chosen to be $2.5\mu$ so that the sizes 1 and $5\mu$ would still be indicated when the magnification was halved by changing from a 2-mm oil-immersion objective to a 4-mm dry objective. Also, an overlap of ranges could be obtained between the 0.5 and 1, and 2.5 and $5\mu$ ranges if the magnification was changed fivefold while measuring a sample of wide size distribution. The longer side of the rectangular grid was made equal to ten diameters of the largest circle, as in the Patterson-Cawood micrometer, to aid in attaining the correct magnification.

These authors used several observers, counting samples, to compare their new graticule with a line graticule similar to that used by May and with the Patterson-Cawood graticule. They concluded that although there were systematic differences among the mean counts by the observers, there was no evidence that these differences were altered by the type of graticule used for the size range 1 to $5\mu$. However, when the size range of $>1\mu$ was used, the parallel line graticule produced the largest counts, but the mean counts with the other two graticules were virtually the same. This new globe and circle graticule has been generally adopted for routine dust counting work in the National Coal Board. It is produced in two sizes with grid lengths of 4.0 mm and 3.5 mm to suit positive and negative types of eyepiece, respectively.

Watson and Mulford[14] have described the construction and application of hand-held test cards for training microscopists in the use of globe and circle techniques. The microscopist is asked to compare profiles representing particles with the globes or circles drawn on the cards. The results suggested that there is a tendency to oversize profiles and the cards can help a microscopist overcome this bias. Watson and Mulford also produced a profile test strip that can be viewed under a microscope to attain greater realism. Profiles of particles were traced on a paper strip and were numbered and filled in with black poster ink. The strip was then reduced photographically to a size suitable for low-power microscopy, cemented to a cover glass, and mounted on a microscope slide. The authors suggest that such strips will help eliminate bias.

Bovey[15] has given a historical survey of the use of graticules and fine scales in general, and has described a wide range of processes used in their manufacture. Optical, photographic, and mechanical requirements and their limitations are discussed. A number of special graticules and scales are described.

Several other definitions of size based on measurements of dimensions of individual particles have been suggested, but none of these has received the general acceptance accorded Martin's diameter and the globe and circle definition. At least two definitions are based on the assumption that the length ($l$), breadth ($b$), and thickness ($t$) of the particles can be measured. Thus the diameter can be defined as the arithmetic average of the three diameters:

$$d = (\tfrac{1}{3})(l + b + t) \tag{1.1}$$

or as the length of the side of a cube having a volume approximately equal to that of the particle:

$$\overline{d} = \sqrt[3]{lbt} \qquad (1.2)$$

Elongated particles are often described merely by length, or if the interest is in their behavior as fibers, by thickness.[16]

A number of automatic scanners have been developed based on the direct use of a microscope or on photomicrographs. Scanning may be achieved by placing a television rastor at the ocular of the microscope so that a minute spot of light scans the particle field. The transmitted light is detected by a photocell. Scanning may also be achieved by moving the specimen or photomicrograph. A major difficulty in the development of such techniques is handling the problem of counting large particles twice. One method of avoiding coincidence errors is to use a pair of spots which are separated by a distance less than the smallest diameter in the field of view.[17] Only those particles are measured which intercept the counting, but not the guard spot. Various modifications of this technique have been used.[18,19] The subject has been reviewed by Herdan, and by Orr and Dalla Valle.[20] The definition of particle size used for these devices will vary somewhat depending on the method used for avoiding coincidence errors, but in general it will be the distance across the particle which intercepts one of many evenly spaced parallel lines. The results, of course, are treated statistically by the electronic system of the instrument.

Diameters obtained by screening are also often described as statistical diameters, since the possibility of a particle passing through one of the openings depends directly on the dimensions of the particle. Whether a given particle passes through an opening in a screen may depend both upon shaking time and orientation of the particle when it reaches an opening. The fraction of a sample passing through a screen often approaches a final value asymptotically. The smaller the sample size the more rapidly this value is approached.[21] Sieving methods are generally preferred for particles larger than about $50\mu$ diameter. Sieves have been standardized in various countries.[22] Sieves with openings smaller than about $50\mu$ are seldom woven because of technical difficulties. However, "electroformed" screens are now available on special order with openings as small as a few microns* and membranes having pores of submicron size have been used to estimate the size of particles in colloidal suspensions.

Six basic operations are used in the production of the Buckbee Mears screens. First a negative is made by crossline ruling on a wax-coated

---

*Buckbee Mears Co., Toni Bldg., St. Paul, Minn. Pyramid Screen Corp., 181 Harvard St., Brookline, Mass.

glass plate with a ruling engine. Next the rulings are etched and filled to form a negative which is printed photographically on a nickel-covered copper plate. After development the plate is submerged in a nickel plating bath and the mesh is electrodeposited. The mesh is stripped from the copperplate, which can be used again. The fourth step, the preparation of the supporting grid, involves printing a grid pattern on both sides of photosensitized copper foil about 0.015 in. thick. The foil is then etched (step five) and the micromesh is drawn over the supporting grid. Hole sizes are checked with a tool-maker's microscope and the screen is soldered to a 3-in brass frame.

The application of electroformed screens to the determination of particle size distribution has been discussed by Doeschner, Seibert, and Peters.[23] They recommend that such screens be used as a primary standard for testing size distribution of cracking catalysts because of their highly precise openings, which can be reliably measured with a microscope, and because they are available in the size ranges that are of interest. Figure 1-4 shows some of their data comparing results obtained with electroformed sieves, woven-wire sieves, and a sedimentation technique.

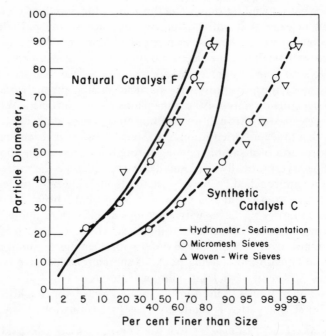

Figure 1-4. Particle size distributions by three methods for two synthetic catalyst samples.[23] (*Courtesy of the American Society for Testing and Materials*)

Particle size is also often defined in terms of the physical properties of the particles. In fact, most methods for determining particle size are tacitly based on such a definition. For example, diameters obtained with sedimentation techniques may be defined as the diameters of spherical particles having the same densities as the particles in question and settling at the same rate. Factors for converting from one definition of diameter to another are often applicable only to the class of powder for which they were determined. Therefore, just as the definition of particle for a given application is important, so is the definition of diameter used. An almost automatic way of choosing the appropriate diameter definition is to select a method for determining particle size that is closely related to the application of the results. For instance, if one is interested in the decrease in visibility produced by an aerosol, a method based on light scattering may be appropriate. A method based on the diffusion rate of particles might be especially appropriate if one were interested in studying their behavior upon entering the lung as an aerosol.

Of course, considerations other than the use of the result enter into choosing the size determination method. Cost of obtaining the results is often the determining factor in industrial applications where large numbers of particle size determinations must be routinely made. The results are generally of interest only as they relate to some useful property of the material, and empirical relationships between this property and the results of the particle size determinations must generally be obtained for each type of material. Some of the better-known methods for determining diameters defined in terms of physical properties are based on (a) sedimentation, (b) permeability, (c) light scattering, (d) adsorption, and (e) diffusion. Some of these techniques are discussed briefly in the next chapter, but a detailed discussion is beyond the scope of this book.

## SIZE DISTRIBUTIONS

### Classification of Data

Powders and suspensions of powders never consist of particles which are all exactly the same size. Therefore, they are excellent subjects for study and description by statistical methods. Information is required about both average particle sizes and distributions of sizes about the average. Microscopic techniques, for example, yield the sizes of large numbers of particles and the data must be arranged in such a way that its significance is apparent. Usually the first step is to obtain a frequency distribution or at least classes according to size. Data arranged in the latter manner are often called classified.[24,25]  There are many kinds of frequency distribution, only a few of which are applicable to fine particles.[26]

Frequency distributions are applicable either to populations which are finite in number, or to infinite populations.  When working with particles one is generally interested in the characteristics of a population that is essentially infinite; but one obtains a frequency distribution for a finite population in the hope that the finite population is a reasonably representative sample.  The results are then used to infer the frequency distribution for the particle population as a whole.  Fisher[26] has pointed out that the frequency distribution for an infinite population specifies the fraction of the population assigned to several classes.  These may be (1) a finite number of fractions adding up to unity, (2) an infinite series of finite fractions adding up to unity, or (3) a mathematical expression representing the size distribution.

Two types of essentially infinite particle populations may be considered, namely (1) that in which all the sizes of the powder are of interest and (2) that in which the population of interest is limited by setting upper or lower size limits, or both.  Type 1 populations generally have rather narrow size distributions, such as a batch of carbon black, while Type 2 populations usually have such wide distributions that they must be limited for convenient handling.  Examples of type 2 populations might be (a) air over cities, which contain particles ranging in size from that of atoms to airplanes and (b) rocky soils.

Consider a hypothetical sample selected from an infinite population of particles the diameters of which vary from zero to about 10 microns.  Size distribution data for this sample are obtained by microscopically determining Martin diameters for 250 particles chosen at random from the sample on a microscope slide.  The Martin diameters can be classified into groups, called classes, which are defined by particle size limits called class boundaries.  Statisticians often suggest the use of from 10 to 20 classes.  If less than 10 classes are used, considerable useful information in the unclassified data may be discarded and it may be difficult to visualize the size distribution of the sample—not to mention that of the infinite population.  When more than 20 classes are used, the classification process is tedious and the representation is not greatly improved.  Therefore, it is convenient to classify the hypothetical measurements into 10 classes, each having a class interval of 1 micron, as shown in Table 1-4.  For convenience, the midpoint of each class interval is called the class mark, $d_i$, and $i$ is the number of the interval.  The frequency, $f_i$, is the number of particles in each interval and for purposes of statistical analysis, the total number of particles measured is denoted by $n$.

TABLE 1-4. FREQUENCY DISTRIBUTION OF 250 PARTICLES

| Class Member | Class boundaries (microns) | Frequencies ($f$) | Class Marks ($di$) |
|---|---|---|---|
| 1 | 0–1 | 4 | 0.5 |
| 2 | 1–2 | 7 | 1.5 |
| 3 | 2–3 | 21 | 2.5 |
| 4 | 3–4 | 52 | 3.5 |
| 5 | 4–5 | 91 | 4.5 |
| 6 | 5–6 | 41 | 5.5 |
| 7 | 6–7 | 15 | 6.5 |
| 8 | 7–8 | 9 | 7.5 |
| 9 | 8–9 | 8 | 8.5 |
| 10 | 9–10 | 2 | 9.5 |

One of the more common types of graph for representing classified data is the histogram, which is particularly useful when the size range of the population is narrow or has a distribution which is essentially Gaussian (normal). Conventionally, the abscissa represents the variable quantity, the particle size, and the ordinate represents the frequency per class interval. Bars are erected over the class marks (between the class intervals) whose heights, and therefore areas, are proportional to the frequencies. The entire area of a histogram is proportional to the total number of observations. The bars may be replaced by vertical lines drawn from the class marks on the abscissa, and the histograms can be smoothed out by drawing curves through the mid-points of the tops of the bars to approximate size-frequency curves representing the infinite population. In fact, as the number of measurements approaches infinity and the class interval approaches zero, the top of the histogram approaches the frequency curve representing the entire population.

If the area (height) of each bar represents $\dfrac{f_i}{n}$ instead of $f_i$, the total area under the histogram is unity. Then as $n$ approaches infinity and the size of the class interval zero, areas under the resulting frequency curve represent the probability of occurrence of particles. Figure 1-5 is the histogram representing the data of Table 1-4.

When classifying data the class intervals need not be identical, but if not they should bear some simple relationship to each other. If the data are log normally distributed (see below) the class intervals can be equal differences between the logarithms of the diameters instead of equal differences between the diameters themselves. A logarithmic scale is also useful if

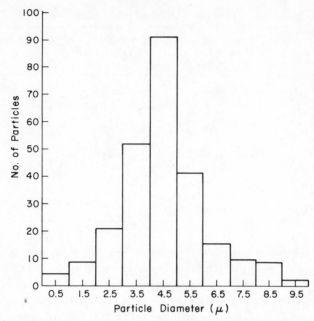

Figure 1-5. Histogram representing data of Table 1-4.

the particle size range is very large. Various progressions can of course be used, such as those employed for the globe and circle graticules. Histograms can be erected over such progressions. Furthermore, the ordinates can represent properties of the particles other than frequencies, for example, total surface or weight in the class intervals. Additional histograms, taken from the literature,[27] are shown in Figures 1-6 and 1-7. Figure 1-7 is interesting because it represents the highly skewed distribution so often encountered in fine particle work.

The histogram is one of the simplest and most useful methods for presenting size distribution data. It has the advantage of permitting one to observe at a glance the qualitative aspects of the distribution.

### Definition of "Mean Size"

When data have been classified and perhaps presented graphically it is often imperative that certain statistical properties of the distribution be estimated. Such properties can be used for describing the distribution and for comparing various populations of particles. Examples of such properties are the various means (arithmetic, geometric, etc.) and properties describing the spread (standard deviation, quartiles, etc.).

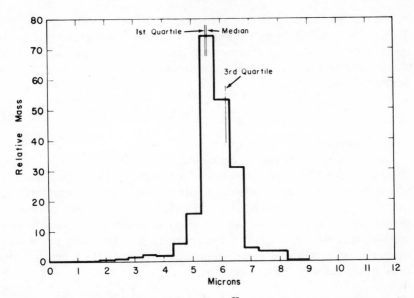

Figure 1-6. Zinc dust-microscope method.[27]   (*Courtesy of the American Society for Testing and Materials*)

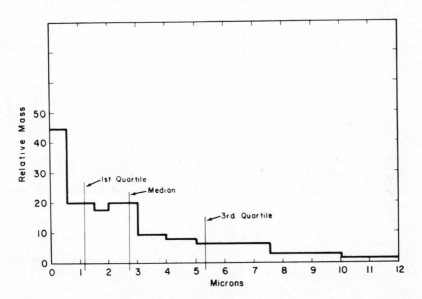

Figure 1-7. Zinc dust-sedimentation method.[27]   (*Courtesy of the American Society for Testing and Materials*)

The arithmetic mean or average value is defined as the sum of any group of values divided by the number of values in the group. It is the most common value for representing the central tendency of a set of measurements. For classified data the arithetic mean is defined by the equation

$$\bar{d} = \frac{1}{n} \sum_{i=1}^{i=h} d_i f_i \tag{1.3}$$

where $h$ is the number of class intervals.

The arithmetic mean can, of course, be calculated directly from unclassified or classified data, but such calculations, based directly on the definition of arithmetic means, are often extremely tedious. Several methods are available which considerably shorten the time required for calculating the arithmetic mean when there are many observations. The following method, described by Hoel,[24] is for classified data involving equal class intervals. The method is based on introducing a variable $u$ which is defined by the equation

$$d_i = cu_i + d_0 \tag{1.4}$$

where $c$ is the class interval and $d_0$ is a class mark chosen near the mean of the distribution. When this expression is substituted for $d_i$ in equation 1.3,

$$\bar{d} = \frac{1}{n} \sum_{i=1}^{h} (cu_i + d_0) f_i \tag{1.5}$$

$$= c \frac{1}{n} \sum_{i=1}^{h} u_i f_i + d_0 \frac{1}{n} \sum_{i=1}^{h} f_i \tag{1.6}$$

From equation 1.3 and the definition of $u$ it is seen that

$$\bar{d} = c\bar{u} + d_0$$

The $\bar{u}$'s are generally much smaller than the $d$'s, so this transformation considerably simplifies the calculation. From this relationship and Table 1-5

$$\bar{d} = \frac{1}{250} (9) + 4.5 = 4.53\mu$$

This method can also be used to calculate arithmetic means of surface and weight distributions, substituting surface or weight fractions of the total surface or weight of the sample for the frequencies.

Obviously, a knowledge of average particle size is highly inadequate for presenting an indication of the characteristics of the sizes of a particle

TABLE 1-5. TRANSFORMATION FOR CALCU-
LATING THE ARITHMETIC MEAN AND STAND-
ARD DEVIATION FROM DATA OF TABLE 1-4

| $d_i$ | $f$ | $u$ | $uf$ | $u^2f$ |
|-------|-----|-----|------|--------|
| 0.5 | 4 | −4 | −16 | 64 |
| 1.5 | 7 | −3 | −21 | 63 |
| 2.5 | 21 | −2 | −42 | 84 |
| 3.5 | 52 | −1 | −52 | 52 |
| 4.5 | 91 | 0 | 0 | 0 |
| 5.5 | 41 | 1 | 41 | 41 |
| 6.5 | 15 | 2 | 30 | 60 |
| 7.5 | 9 | 3 | 27 | 54 |
| 8.5 | 8 | 4 | 32 | 128 |
| 9.5 | 2 | 5 | 10 | 50 |
| Totals | 250 | | 9 | 596 |

population. An indication of the scatter about the mean is particularly valuable. There are a number of methods for supplying this, for example, the arithmetic average of the absolute values of the deviations of the individual values from the mean. However, a theoretically more attractive indication is the standard deviation. In order to define the standard deviation we first define "moments about the origin." The $k$th movement about the origin is defined by the equation

$$m'_k = \frac{1}{n} \sum_{i=1}^{h} d_i^k f_i \qquad (1.7)$$

Comparison with equation 1.3 shows that the arithmetic mean is the first moment about the origin. The second moment about the origin could be used as a measure of scatter, but since the arithmetic average is being used as a measure of central tendency, it is advantageous to define moments about this average and use the second moment about this average as a measure of variation:

$$m_k = \frac{1}{n} \sum_{i=1}^{h} (d_i - \bar{d})^k f_i \qquad (1.8)$$

The second moment, called the variance, has the dimension units of length squared, which is obviously inconvenient. In order that the measure of variation have the same dimensions as the mean, the square root of the variance, called the standard deviation, ($s$) is generally used. Examination of equation 1.8 shows that it is the square root of the average value of the squares of the deviations from the mean. When $n$ is small it should be replaced by $n - 1$.

The sizes of some powders have a normal distribution, as discussed below. An important property of the standard deviation is that the interval $(\bar{d} - s)$ to $(\bar{d} + s)$ for such powders usually includes about 68% of the measurements, and the interval $(\bar{d} - 2s)$ to $(\bar{d} + 2s)$ usually includes about 95% of the measurements.

When presenting the results of particle size determinations it is often advisable to state at least the number of observations, a value representing central tendency, and a value representing spread. The arithmetic mean and the standard deviation are often particularly appropriate for the latter values. The American Society for Testing Materials recommends that these properties always be reported.[28] However, for some types of data such values are rather meaningless. An example is the distribution of particles in the atmosphere, which is usually studied between rather artificially selected size limits. In such cases plots of the original data, or regression lines and curves and the standard errors of estimate, described below, may furnish the required information.

The standard deviation can be calculated using the transformation of equation 1.4. It is easily shown that

$$s = c \sqrt{\frac{1}{n} \sum_{i=1}^{h} u_i^2 f_i - \bar{u}^2} \tag{1.9}$$

for classified data, and for unclassified data,

$$s = c \sqrt{\frac{1}{n} \sum_{i=1}^{h} d_i^2 - \bar{d}^2} \tag{1.10}$$

From the values of $u^2 f$ in Table 1-5.

$$s = \sqrt{\frac{596}{250} - \left(\frac{9}{250}\right)^2} = \sqrt{2.38} = 1.54\mu$$

A problem often arises when two samples have been studied from two different batches of the same material, and it is desired to calculate the arithmetic mean and standard deviation of the resulting batch. Weighting by batch size, $B_1$ and $B_2$,

$$\bar{d}_{1,2} = \frac{B_1 \bar{d}_1 + B_2 \bar{d}_2}{B_1 + B_2} \tag{1.11}$$

and

$$s_{1,2} = \frac{B_1(s_1^2 + \bar{d}_1^2) + B_2(s_2^2 + \bar{d}_2^2) - \bar{d}_{1,2}^2}{B_1 + B_2} \tag{1.12}$$

Means of samples are usually useful only if they approximate the means of the very large ("infinite") populations from which the samples are obtained. A useful way of estimating the closeness of this approximation is to calculate the manner in which the means of the samples are distributed about the population means. Just as the standard deviation of individual measurements about the mean of the measurement is an indication of the scatter of the measurements, the standard deviations of the means of the samples about the population mean indicate the scatter of the means. The latter standard deviations are called the standard error of the means.

The standard deviation of the means ($\sigma_m$) can be obtained by determining the means of a number of samples containing the same number of particles and calculating the standard deviations by the methods suggested above. However, if the standard deviation of the individual measurements ($\sigma_d$) is known, $\sigma_m$ can be calculated from the equation

$$\sigma_m = \frac{\sigma_x}{\sqrt{n}} \tag{1.13}$$

where $n$ is the number of particles measured in the sample, or

$$\sigma_m = \frac{\Sigma d_i^2 - n\overline{d}^2}{n^2} \tag{1.14}$$

Equation 1.13 is particularly interesting since it shows that in general the accuracy of the estimation of the population mean increases as the square root of the number of measurements.

The third moment about the mean is an indication of the amount of skewness, or lack of symmetry:

$$m_3 = \Sigma(d_i - \overline{d})^3 f_i / n \tag{1.15}$$

Differing degrees of skewness actually observed for particle populations are demonstrated by Figures 1-6 and 1-7. A zero third moment corresponds to symmetry, while a positive third moment corresponds to a histogram with a large right "tail," and the histogram is said to be positively skewed or skewed to the right. While the third moment furnishes a qualitative indication of skewness it is not a satisfactory quantitative measure because it is highly sensitive to the units of measurement of the particle diameter. This difficulty can be overcome by dividing the third moment by the cube of the standard deviation ($m_3/m_2^{3/2}$) yielding a dimensionless number.

The fourth moment about the mean, divided by the fourth power of the standard deviation ($m_4/m_2^2$) is often used as a measure of peakedness. This value, often called the kurtosis, tends to be larger for more peaked distributions, but there are often exceptions. The peakedness of normal distributions, described below, is 3.

The third and fourth moments as well as the arithmetic mean and standard deviation are more easily calculated using a change of variable than directly from the definition. The general equation for the $k$th moment, using the transformation of equations 1-4 and 1-7, is[24]

$$m_k = c^k \left\{ \frac{\Sigma u_i k f_i}{n} - k\bar{u} \frac{\Sigma u_i k^{k-1} f_i}{n} \right.$$

$$\left. + \frac{k(k-1)}{2} \bar{u}^2 \frac{\Sigma u_i^{k-2} f_i}{n} - \cdots - (-1)^k \bar{u}^k \right. \quad (1.16)$$

Numerous other definitions of central tendency have been developed and are useful under various circumstances. The mode is the diameter with maximum frequency. Of course, there may be no maximum frequency, at least over the range that is of interest, or a distribution may have more than one mode (bimodal, etc.) The mode is often used when the distribution is highly skewed, and may be used with some other measure of central tendency, such as the arithmetic means, to indicate the degree of skewness. The mode, almost by definition, is readily visualized and this probably adds to its popularity. The mode has the disadvantage, however, that it is of questionable value in descriptive statistics, and for some distributions cannot be accurately determined.

Another indicator of central tendency is the median. The median is the middle measurement of a set of measurements arranged according to magnitude, or if there is no middle measurement, the interpolated middle value. For example, the median for the set of diameters 1, 1.5, 4, 15, 20, 30, 35, 51, 60, 62 is 25. The median, like the mode, is useful for data which are highly skewed and has the advantage over the latter of precision of definition. In fact, there is always a median for a distribution having finite size limits. The median is often much easier to estimate than the arithmetic mean, particularly where the data obtained by some method for determining size distribution are not readily classified into equidistant size intervals. The median is also a very useful form of central value when data are plotted as a cumulative percentage curve, since it is the value on the diameter-axis (conventionally the abscissa) corresponding to 50 percent of the percentage-axis (Figure 1-8).

Quartiles are often used in conjunction with the median to indicate degree of spread. These are defined in a manner similar to the median and represent the values which, with the median, divide the particles into four equal components. Thus there is a lower or first (smaller) and upper or third (larger) quartile. Quartiles and medians are shown in Figures 1-6, 1-7, and 1-8.

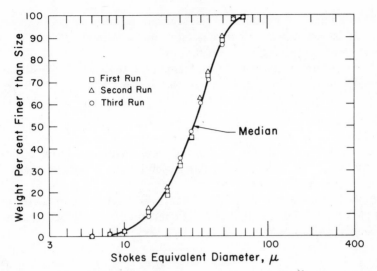

Figure 1-8. Sedimentation analysis of ammonium nitrate.[29] (*Courtesy of the American Society for Testing and Materials*)

Several other methods for describing the dispersion of particle size data are mentioned by Herdan.[1] However, they have found rather limited application.

Numerous definitions of mean in addition to that of the arithmetic mean are useful for various types of comparison. In general, the appropriate definition depends upon the intended application of the data. The following general equation, derived for a frequency distribution curve normalized so that the area under the curve is unity, can be used to define a number of these means.[30]

$$(\bar{d}_{qp})^{q-p} = \int_{d_0}^{d_m} d^q \frac{dn'}{d(d)} d(d) \Big/ \int_{d_0}^{d_m} d^p \frac{dn'}{d(d)} d(d) \qquad (1.17)$$

where $dn'$ is the fraction of the total count in the size interval $d(d)$, and $d_0$ and $d_m$ are the size limits of the size distribution. The individual definitions are determined by the values of $q$ and $p$. Thus the definition of the arithmetic mean is $p = 0$, $q = 1$, and the mean can be represented by the symbol $\bar{d}_{10}$.

The equivalent definition for classified, non-normalized data is

$$(\bar{d}_{qp})^{q-p} = \sum_{i=1}^{i=h} \frac{f_i}{n} d_i^q \sum_{i=1}^{i=h} \frac{f_i}{n} d_i^p \qquad (1.18)$$

which becomes equation 1-3 when $p = 0$ and $q = 1$. Note that the arithmetic mean diameter, when multiplied by the total count, gives the same result as adding the products of the separate frequencies and class numbers. It is sometimes called the linear mean diameter,[30] but we shall reserve this name for a different definition.

The mean surface diameter is the diameter of the particle whose surface is the arithmetic mean of the surfaces, that is, for which $q = 2$ and $p = 0$:

$$\bar{d}_{20} = \sqrt{\frac{1}{n}\Sigma f_i d_i^2} \tag{1.19}$$

Note that this is the square root of the second moment about the origin (see equation 1-8). It is a particularly useful mean when the surface behavior of powders is being considered.

Similarly, the mean volume (or weight) diameter is the diameter of the particle whose volume is the arithmetic mean of the volumes, that is, for which $q = 3$ and $p = 0$:

$$\bar{d}_{30} = \sqrt[3]{\frac{1}{n}\Sigma f_i d_i^3} \tag{1.20}$$

It is the cube root of the third movement about the origin and is particularly useful when one is interested in the contribution of particles of various sizes to the total mass of the particles in a given sample. It is not unusual to find that the diameter of the particle of average mass of a powder is one or two orders of magnitude larger than the arithmetic mean of the diameters, since a few large particles may account for most of the mass of a sample. In general, these averages are related to the arithmetic mean by the inequality $\bar{d}_{10} < \bar{d}_{20} < \bar{d}_{30}$. The magnitude of the differences among these diameters is another indication of the spread in particle size of the sample.

The averages described above have all been defined for $p = 0$; that is, they have been based on the total number of particles measured. However, sometimes it is appropriate to use means which are based, essentially, on total length, surface, or weight of the particles in the sample or the population which the sample represents. In these cases $p$ may be 1, 2, or 3.

We define the linear mean diameter by the equation

$$\bar{d}_{21} = \frac{\Sigma f_i d_i^2}{\Sigma f_i d_i} \tag{1.21}$$

This mean has been called the surface diameter by Mugele and Evans[30] and is useful where two functions of the powders are being compared which depend on surface and length, as in some adsorption studies.

The surface mean diameter, sometimes called the volume-surface mean diameter, is defined by the equation

$$\bar{d}_{32} = \frac{\Sigma f_i d_i^3}{\Sigma f_i d_i^2}$$ (1.22)

It is called the Sauter diameter by Mugele and Evans who point out that the efficiency of "atomizing" a liquid can be calculated from this diameter. Consider the efficiency of such an operation defined as the fraction of energy $E$ lost in pressure drop $\Delta p$ used in forming a new surface. Then

$$E\left(\frac{\pi d^3}{6} \Delta p\right) = \pi d^2 \gamma$$ (1.23)

for a single droplet, or

$$E\Delta p \Sigma d^3 = 6\gamma \Sigma d^2$$ (1.24)

for the entire spray. Then

$$E\Delta p d_{32} = 6\gamma$$ (1.25)

where $\gamma$ is the interfacial tension.

This mean is especially useful in connection with surface area determinations. Its reciprocal is proportional to the specific surface when expressed as area per unit volume instead of per unit weight. The proportionality factor for spheres and cubes is 6, and for other shapes is greater than 6.

The weight mean diameter, called the De Brouckere diameter by Mugele and Evans, is

$$\bar{d}_{43} = \frac{\Sigma f_i d_i^4}{\Sigma f_i d_i^3}$$ (1.26)

Another diameter, occasionally used in connection with studies of evaporation, is defined as

$$\bar{d}_{31} = \left(\frac{\Sigma f_i d_i^3}{\Sigma f_i d_i}\right)^{1/2}$$ (1.27)

These means are ratios of moments about the origin. For example, $\bar{d}_{43}$ is the ratio of the fourth to the third moment.

The family of "hypogeometric" mean values is defined by the equation

$$\ln \bar{d}_{qq} = \int_{d_0}^{d_m} d^q (\ln d) \frac{dn'}{d(d)} d(d) \int_{d_0}^{d_m} d^q \frac{dn'}{d(d)} d(d)$$ (1.28)

The geometric mean, $d_g$, is a member of this family and is defined by

$$\ln \overline{d}_g = \int_{d_0}^{d_m} (\ln d) \, \frac{dn'}{d(d)} \, d(d) \tag{1.29}$$

or in terms of classified data by

$$\overline{d}_g = (d_i^{f_i} d_2^{f_2} d_3^{f_3} \ldots d_n^{f_n})^{1/n} \tag{1.30}$$

When a population of particles is log-normally distributed (see below), a very common occurrence, the geometric mean represents the value with the greatest frequency of particles, so this mean is especially appropriate for such a population. The geometric mean is always less than or equal to the arithmetic mean, and the difference increases with increasing spread in the data.

The harmonic mean is also useful for certain applications, although it is less often used than most of those described above. For classified data it is

$$\overline{d}_h = \left[ \frac{1}{n} \sum \frac{f_i}{d_i} \right]^{-1} \tag{1.31}$$

It is less than or equal to the geometric mean.

Particle diameters can be defined having fractional and negative values of $p$ and $q$ and such definitions may apply to certain transfer problems.[30] However, the most generally useful definitions involve positive, integral values.

Numerous comparisons have been made of various mean diameters determined for the same material. One of the most interesting of these involved a set of four samples of zinc oxide prepared by the New Jersey Zinc Co. which were studied by several investigators using ten different methods. The results obtained were summarized by Arnell[31,32] and are reproduced in Table 1-6. The order: arithmetic mean diameter, less than the surface mean diameter, less than the weight mean diameter is the order of increasing statistical weight given to the larger particles, and was to be expected. Similarly, the arithmetic mean diameter was less than the mean weight diameter. Mean diameters obtained with the optical microscope were somewhat larger than those obtained with the electron microscope, as would be predicted for powders having diameters close to the limit of resolution of the light microscope. One reason is that particles smaller than the limit of resolution may be overlooked; another is that the diameters of the individual particles observed by a microscope appear to be larger than they are by an amount approximately equal to the resolving power of the microscope. Diameters determined with the ultra-

### TABLE 1-6. PARTICLE SIZE DATA FOR ZINC OXIDE PIGMENTS

| | Light Microscope | Electron Microscope | Liquid Adsorption | Sedimentation | Permeability: Liquid | Permeability: Air — Kozeny Equation | Permeability: Air — Arnell Equation | Gas Adsorption | Ultramicroscope Count | Turbidimeter | Infrared Transmission |
|---|---|---|---|---|---|---|---|---|---|---|---|
| **KADOX BLACK LABEL-15** | | | | | | | | | | | |
| **F-1601** | | | | | | | | | | | |
| $\bar{d}$[a] | 0.15 | 0.10 | ... | ... | ... | 0.26 | ... | 0.14 | 0.11 | ... | ... |
| $d_{vs}$[b] | 0.28 | 0.18 | 0.20 | 0.30 | 0.12 | 0.26 | ... | 0.14 | 0.11 | ... | ... |
| $S$,[c] sq m per g | 3.8 | 6.0 | 5.4 | 3.5 | 8.9 | 4.1 | ... | 7.8 | 9.5 | ... | ... |
| $d_w$[d] | 0.21 | 0.14 | ... | ... | ... | ... | ... | ... | 0.14 | ... | ... |
| $N$[e] $\times 10^{10}$ | 2042 | ... | ... | ... | ... | ... | ... | ... | 7257 | ... | ... |
| $d_{wm}$[f] | 0.37 | ... | ... | ... | ... | ... | ... | ... | ... | ... | 0.27 |
| | | | | | | | | | | | 0.34 |
| **XX RED-72** | | | | | | | | | | | |
| **K-1602** | | | | | | | | | | | |
| $\bar{d}$ | 0.19 | 0.12 | ... | ... | ... | ... | ... | ... | ... | 0.23 | ... |
| $d_{vs}$ | 0.34 | 0.23 | 0.25 | 0.37 | 0.15 | 0.32 | ... | 0.17 | 0.12 | ... | ... |
| $S$, sq m per g | 3.1 | 4.6 | 4.3 | 2.9 | 7.2 | 3.3 | ... | 6.2 | 8.8 | ... | ... |
| $d_w$ | 0.25 | 0.15 | ... | ... | ... | ... | ... | ... | 0.16 | ... | ... |
| $N \times 10^{10}$ | 1139 | ... | ... | ... | ... | ... | ... | ... | 4200 | ... | ... |
| $d_{wm}$ | 0.42 | ... | ... | ... | ... | ... | ... | ... | ... | ... | 0.44 |
| **XX RED-78** | | | | | | | | | | | |
| **G-1603** | | | | | | | | | | | |
| $\bar{d}$ | 0.30 | 0.25 | ... | ... | ... | ... | ... | ... | ... | 0.36 | ... |
| $d_{vs}$ | 0.79 | 0.48 | 0.56 | 0.76 | 0.25 | 0.62; 0.62 | ... | 0.38 | 0.27 | ... | ... |
| $S$, sq m per g | 1.3 | 2.2 | 1.9 | 1.4 | 4.3 | NBS[g] 1.7; NJZ[h] 1.7 | ... | 2.8 | 3.9 | ... | ... |
| $d_w$ | 0.49 | 0.35 | ... | ... | ... | ... | ... | ... | 0.26 | ... | ... |
| $N \times 10^{10}$ | 153 | ... | ... | ... | ... | ... | ... | ... | 1076 | ... | ... |
| $d_{wm}$ | 1.1 | ... | ... | ... | ... | ... | ... | ... | ... | ... | 0.54 |
| **REHEATED SUPERFINE** | | | | | | | | | | | |
| **KH-1604** | | | | | | | | | | | |
| $\bar{d}$ | 1.0 | ... | ... | ... | ... | ... | ... | ... | ... | ... | ... |
| $d_{vs}$ | 1.9 | ... | 5.3 | 2.1 | 1.25 | 1.63 | ... | 1.5 | 1.61 | ... | ... |
| $S$, sq m per g | 0.6 | ... | 0.2 | 0.5 | 0.85 | 0.65 | ... | 0.71 | 0.66 | ... | ... |
| $d_w$ | 1.4 | ... | ... | ... | ... | ... | ... | ... | 0.82 | ... | ... |
| $N \times 10^{10}$ | 6.6 | ... | ... | ... | ... | ... | ... | ... | 32 | ... | ... |
| $d_{wm}$ | 2.2 | ... | ... | ... | ... | ... | ... | ... | ... | ... | ... |

[a] $\bar{d}$ = arithmetic mean diameter $(\Sigma d/\Sigma n)$, $\mu$.
[b] $d_{vs}$ = surface mean diameter $(\Sigma d^3/\Sigma d^2)$, $\mu$.
[c] $S$ = surface area, sq m per g.
[d] $d_w$ = mean weight diameter $(\sqrt[3]{\Sigma d^3/\Sigma n})$, $\mu$.
[e] $N$ = number of particles per g and is given by $N = 1/\rho D^3$, where $\rho$ = density.
[f] $d_{wm}$ = weight mean diameter $(\Sigma n d^4/\Sigma n d^3)$, $\mu$.
[g] NBS = National Bureau of Standards.
[h] NJZ = New Jersey Zinc.

microscope agree well with those obtained with the electron microscope, which is not surprising since much smaller particles can be detected with the ultramicroscope than with the optical microscope. Smaller diameters were obtained with the gas adsorption technique than with the electron microscope, as is normal if the particles are highly irregular.

An excellent comparison of particle size distribution data obtained by various methods is given by Irani and Callis;[33] statistical methods for comparing data obtained by various methods of sampling and size determination are discussed by Herdan.[1]

A number of commonly used diameters are defined in Table 1-7.

TABLE 1-7. SOME DEFINITIONS OF MEANS

When appropriate, the symbols are those corresponding to equation 1.17:

| Name | Symbol | Definition |
|------|--------|------------|
| Arithmetic mean | $\bar{d}_{10}$ | $\dfrac{1}{n}\,\Sigma d_i f_i$ |
| Geometric mean | $\bar{d}_g$ | $(d_1^{f_1} d_2^{f_2} d_3^{f_3} \ldots \; d_n^{f_n})\,1/n$ |
| Harmonic mean | $\bar{d}_{ha}$ | $\left[\dfrac{1}{n}\,\Sigma\,\dfrac{f_i}{d_i}\right]^{-1}$ |
| Mean surface diameter | $\bar{d}_{20}$ | $\left(\dfrac{\Sigma f_i d_i^2}{n}\right)^{1/2}$ |
| Mean weight diameter | $\bar{d}_{30}$ | $\left(\dfrac{\Sigma f_i d_i^3}{n}\right)^{1/3}$ |
| Linear mean diameter | $\bar{d}_{21}$ | $\dfrac{\Sigma f_i d_i^2}{\Sigma f_i d_i}$ |
| Surface mean diameter | $\bar{d}_{32}$ | $\dfrac{\Sigma f_i d_i^3}{\Sigma f_i d_i^2}$ |
| Weight mean diameter | $\bar{d}_{43}$ | $\dfrac{\Sigma f_i d_i^4}{\Sigma f_i d_i^3}$ |

## Particle shape

Closely related to particle size is particle shape. In fact, particle size measurements can hardly be considered to be complete unless some indication of particle shape has been obtained, since a given definition of particle size does not have precisely the same significance for particles of different shape. Ways for expressing particle shape quantitatively have been developed along two lines. One of these involves defining geometric properties of the individual particles which are related to shape and can, if desired, be averaged over many particles. For example, Heywood[34] has suggested the following method for indicating particle shape.

The particle is assumed to rest on a plane surface in the position of greatest stability. The breadth ($B$) is defined as the smallest possible distance between two parallel lines tangent to the projection of the particle profile on the plane. Similarly, the length ($L$) is the distance between parallel lines tangent to the projection and perpendicular to the lines defining the breadth, and the thickness ($T$) is the distance between two planes parallel to the plane of greatest stability and tangent to the surface of the particle. Heywood defined flakiness as $B/T$ and elongation as $L/B$. Similar approaches have been suggested by numerous investigators. Another example is the ratio of the measured maximum diameter to the measured minimum diameter.[33,35]

The other general method for expressing particle shape depends on the finding that even for powders consisting of irregularly shaped particles, $\bar{v}/\bar{d}^3$ and $\bar{s}/\bar{d}^2$ remain essentially the same for various values of $\bar{d}$ for the same material, where $\bar{v}$ and $\bar{s}$ are the mean particle volumes and surfaces, respectively, and $\bar{d}$ is a mean particle size. Shape factors may be defined as the proportionality factors between $\bar{v}$ and $\bar{d}^3$ and between $\bar{s}$ and $\bar{d}^2$. This principle can be generalized be stating that the ratios between diameters (or powers of diameters) obtained by different methods are related to average particle shapes and are essentially constant for a given powder material; the shape factors are the proportionality factors. In practice, shape factors are usually defined as proportionality factors between averages of diameters determined for individual particles, as with a microscope, and those determined for the entire powder, as by sedimentation or permeability techniques. For example, Fries[36] defines "surface roughness" as the ratio of $\bar{d}_{32}$ determined with the electron microscope to the diameter determined by gas adsorption. Values of surface roughness for twelve samples of carbon black varied from 0.58 to 7.30.

## DISTRIBUTION FUNCTIONS

### The normal distribution

Consider a histogram which correctly represents an entire particle population and which is normalized so that the area under the histogram is unity. The area enclosed by any one bar is the probability that a single selection of a particle from the powder will produce a particle in the class interval represented by the bar. If the class intervals are made to approach zero (the number of class intervals to approach infinity) the top of the histogram becomes a smooth curve. The ordinate represents a function of particle size. The area under the curve and above any interval on the abscissa is the probability of occurance of diameters in that interval. The mathematical expression describing the curve is known as a distribution function. Distribution functions are not necessarily normalized to represent probabilities but they always represent relative frequencies.

Distribution functions have been developed, of course, to represent many different variables and their distributions. One of the best known is the normal distribution, which is produced when an infinite number of factors are introducing independent variations of equal magnitude. School teachers, for example, are often painfully aware of normal distributions when required to assume that grades of pupils in their classrooms should be normally distributed. A great many measurements made on manufactured items are essentially normally distributed, and the same is true of many biological measurements.[24] Often the means of some property of samples of a population are normally distributed although the individual values of the property are not. For particle diameters the normal distribution has the form

$$f(d) = \frac{1}{s\sqrt{2\pi}} \exp\left[-\frac{1}{2}\left(\frac{d - \bar{d}}{s}\right)^2\right] \tag{1.32}$$

where $s$ is the standard deviation (equation 1-10).

Since normal distributions are symmetrical about the arithmetic mean, the mode, median and arithmetic mean are identical and the third moment about the origin is zero. Normal distributions are completely determined by specifying the mean and standard deviation. Furthermore, they all possess the same peakedness as indicated by the fourth moment about the origin, namely 3. As mentioned earlier, the standard deviation for normally distributed particles is such that the interval $(\bar{d} - s)$ to $(\bar{d} + s)$ includes about 68% of the diameters and the interval $(\bar{d} - 2s)$ to $(\bar{d} + 2s)$ generally includes about 95% of the particles.

Because of these properties, determining whether or not a given distribution can be well represented by the normal distribution function is relatively simple, as is determining the precise function if the population is found to be normally distributed.

The application of the normal distribution function to physical measurements, which can have only positive values, has been criticized on the theoretical grounds that the function always predicts finite probabilities for negative values of the variable.[33,37] This has not detracted particularly from its practical application, since the predicted probabilities for negative numbers are generally very low. However, the normal distribution function is not often a satisfactory representation of particle size distributions since the distributions are often skewed.

## Normal distributions of functions of diameters

A function[38,39] which is often more satisfactory for representing particles size distributions than the normal distribution function is derived from the latter by substituting the logarithms of the diameters for the diameters themselves:

$$f(d) = \frac{1}{\log s_g \sqrt{2\pi}} \exp\left[-\frac{1}{2}\left(\frac{\log d - \log \bar{d}_q}{\log s_g}\right)^2\right] \tag{1.33}$$

Here $\bar{d}_g$, as usual is the geometric mean and $s_g$ is the geometric standard deviation.

For many years it was believed that the major reason why many size distributions were highly skewed, with the steeper slope on the side of the mode corresponding to small diameters, was the difficulty of measuring small particles, resulting in the fact that very small particles were overlooked. While such difficulties may sometimes be responsible for skewed distributions, much recent work indicates that populations of particles that are well represented by the log normal distribution are commonplace.

An interesting difference between a normal distribution and a log normal distribution is that if we have the former and choose particle diameters $d_1$ and $d_2$ which are on opposite sides of the arithmetic mean and equidistant from it, there is an equal probability that any randomly chosen particle will have the diameter $d_1$ or $d_2$, whereas if the particles are log normally distributed, the ratios $d_1/\bar{d}_{10}$ and $\bar{d}_{10}/d_2$ rather than the differences $d_1 - \bar{d}_{10}$ and $d_2 - \bar{d}_{10}$ must be equal in order to satisfy the condition of equal probability.

When reporting the results of particle size distribution determinations for particles whose diameters are log normally distributed, it is more significant to indicate the geometric mean and the geometric standard deviation than the arithmetic mean and the usual standard deviation.

It was pointed out earlier that particle size distributions having a very wide range could often be classified more simply by using class intervals defined in terms of the logarithms of diameters than in terms of the diameters themselves. Similarly, the log normal distribution function often is particularly useful for particles with a very wide size distribution.

Other variations of the normal distribution function have been suggested; a particularly interesting one is the "upper-limit equation."[30] This actually is a class of functions in which a new variable, $y$, instead of the diameter is considered to be normally distributed:

$$y = \ln \frac{ad^s}{d_m^s - d^s} \tag{1.34}$$

where $a$ is a dimensionless constant, $s$ is a positive number, and $d_m$ is the maximum diameter in a size distribution.

A major advantage of this function is that as $y$ goes from $-\infty$ to $+\infty$, $d$ goes from zero to the maximum diameter. The function is thus particularly useful for representing particle populations for which there is good reason to believe there is a maximum diameter. Mugele and Evans[30] applied this function to size distributions of spray droplets and obtained satisfactory representation for $s = 1, 2,$ or $3$. They found that the upper limit equation gave the proper trend and a good quantitative fit in all cases they studied, while the log probability, Rosin–Rammler, and Nuki-yama-Tanasawa equation (see below) were found to fit well in some cases and poorly in others (see Figure 1.9).

Krumbein[39] suggested the use of the transformation

$$\phi = \log_2 d$$

for describing the size distributions of sediments. The negative logarithm was suggested, since sediment particle sizes are measured in millimeters, and most particles are a fraction of a millimeter in size. The use of $\phi$ thus avoids negative numbers and converts the scale of frequency curves so that they increase to the right in the conventional manner. Krumbein pointed out that the various moments of $\phi$ could be used to obtain a series of measures corresponding to the mean size, the standard deviation, skewness, and kurtosis, and that the values obtained by the computations with $\phi$ would be logarithmic measures in terms of the log geometric mean, instead of arithmetic measures in terms of the arithmetic mean. He suggested substituting $\phi$ for $d$ in the normal distribution equation, producing another modification of the log normal distribution.

**Other functions**

Another function which is often used is the Rosin-Rammler relationship, which was developed for representing the size distributions of powdered coal.[41] It has been applied to various powdered materials and to suspensions of droplets.

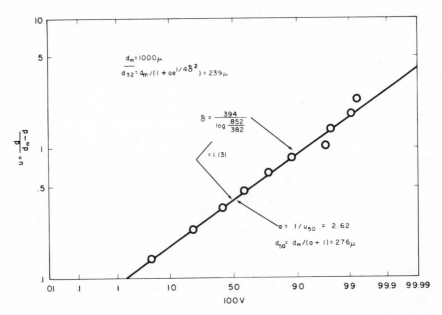

Figure 1-9.  Upper-limit analysis of Kolupaev data.      (*Courtesy of Industrial and Engineering Chemistry*)

The Rosin-Rammler function is often defined in the form

$$1 - v = \exp - (d/d')^b \tag{1.35}$$

where $1 - v$ is the volume fraction of particulate material occurring in particles having a diameter greater than $d$, $d'$ is a size parameter, and $b$ is a distribution parameter.  Equation 1.35 can be differentiated to obtain the volume distribution form:

$$\frac{dv}{d(d)} = b\,\frac{d^{b-1}}{(d')^b}\exp\left(-\frac{d}{d'}\right)^b \tag{1.36}$$

This can be converted[30] to the numerical-distribution form by dividing 1.36 by $d^3$ and inserting a factor to make

$$\int_0^\infty \frac{dN}{d(d)}\,d(d) = 1:$$

$$\frac{dN}{d(d)} = \frac{bd^{b-4}}{(d')^{b-3}\,\Gamma\!\left(1-\dfrac{3}{b}\right)}\exp(d/d') \tag{1.37}$$

The gamma function, defined as

$$\Gamma(c) = \int_0^\infty U^{c-1} c^{-u} dU \tag{1.38}$$

can be evaluated using tables of this function.

Mean diameters can be calculated from the equation

$$(\bar{d}_{qp})^{q-p} = (d')^{q-p} \Gamma\left(\frac{q-3}{b} + 1\right) \Big/ \Gamma\left(\frac{p-3}{b} + 1\right) \tag{1.39}$$

However, although equation 1.39 is theoretically sound, its use for calculating the mean diameters of powders which seem to be described by the Rosin-Rammler function may produce quite erroneous results.

Equation 1.35 is often applied in the form

$$\ln \ln \frac{1}{1-v} = b(\ln d - \ln d') \tag{1.40}$$

Thus if a plot of the values of a size distribution corresponding to the two sides of this equation produces a straight line, the Rosin-Rammler function can be assumed to furnish at least a fair representation of the size distribution. The slope of a plot on log log paper of $\log \frac{1}{1-v}$ vs $d$ is $b$ and $d'$ is the value of $d$ for which $1 - v = e^{-1}$.

The Rosin-Rammler relationship seems to be particularly appropriate for distributions which are more skewed than those obeying the log normal law and for distributions obtained by sieving.[1] For the latter distributions it is convenient to put the equation in the form

$$\log \log(R/100) = \log g + \log \log e + h \log d \tag{1.41}$$

where $R$ is the percentage by weight of particles larger than the sieve opening, and $g$ and $h$ are constants. Again, $g$ and $h$ can be evaluated by plotting log log $(R/100)$ against log $d$, and $R$ can be calculated for any value of $d$ using the equation

$$R = 100 \exp(-gd^h) \tag{1.42}$$

A number of completely empirical distribution functions are also in the form

$$\frac{dN}{d(d)} = U(d) \exp V(d) \tag{1.43}$$

For example, the Nukiyama-Tanasawa equation,[42] developed for spray droplets, is

$$\frac{dN}{d(d)} = Dd^2 d^{-bd^c} \tag{1.44}$$

This can be put in the form

$$\frac{dN}{d(d)} = \frac{\cdot cb^{3/c}}{\Gamma(3/c)} d^2 e^{-bd^c} \tag{1.45}$$

and for the volume distribution:

$$\frac{dv}{d(d)} = \frac{b^{6/c}}{\Gamma(6/c)} d^5 d^{-bd^c} \tag{1.46}$$

Mean diameters can be calculated from the equation[30]

$$\bar{d}_{qp}^{q-p} = b^{-\left(\frac{q-p}{c}\right)} \Gamma\left(\frac{q+3}{c}\right) \Big/ \Gamma\left(\frac{p+3}{c}\right) \tag{1.47}$$

Certain regions of some size distributions can be conveniently represented by equations of the form

$$\frac{dN}{d(d)} = ad^c \tag{1.48}$$

This type of function has been particularly useful in astrophysics and in atmospheric research. For example, Steffens and Rubin[43] obtained a value of $-4.5$ for $c$ for particles in Los Angeles smog. Junge[44,45] plotting $dN/d \log r$ against $r$ for particles in the natural atmosphere obtained a slope of about $-3$ on a logarithmic scale over much of the size range, corresponding to a value of about $-4$ for $c$. Of course, this distribution is limited with respect to the size region it represents, since when $c$ is negative, $dN/d(d)$ approaches infinity as $d$ approaches zero.

### Bimodal distributions

Not all particle size distributions are unimodal (or non-modal), and bimodal distributions are rather common, for example among coagulating aerosols.[46] Some multimodal size distributions can be represented as the sum of two or more unimodal functions. However, this is not always satisfactory.

Dalla Valle, Orr, and Blocher[47] have discussed a general equation for representing bimodal particle size distributions:

$$\frac{dN}{d(d)} = \exp[-(a_4 d^4 + a_3 d^3 + a_2 d^2 + a_1 d + a_0)] \tag{1.49}$$

If $g(d)$ represents the polynomial so that equation 1.49 takes the form

$$-\ln \frac{dN}{d(d)} = g(d) \tag{1.50}$$

the polynomial can be simplified so that

$$g(d) = a^2(d^4 + a'_3 d^3 + a'_2 d^2 + a'_1 d + a'_0) \qquad (1.51)$$

where

$$a'_3 = a_3/a^2, \quad a'_2 = a_2/a^2, \quad a'_1 = a_1/a^2 \quad \text{and} \quad a'_0 = a_0/a^2. \qquad (1.51)$$

Now $d$ is replaced by $d - a'_3/4$ and equation 1.51 becomes

$$q(d) = a^2(d^4 + td^2 + ud + w) \qquad (1.52)$$

where $t$, $u$, and $w$ are now constants. Then

$$\frac{d(N)}{d(d)} = \exp[-a^2 w]\exp[-a^2(d^4 + td^2 + ud)] \qquad (1.53)$$

If we differentiate equation 1.53 and set the result equal to zero we obtain

$$4d^3 + 2td + u = 0 \qquad (1.54)$$

The roots of 1.54, if real and distinct, correspond to the two modes and the minimum between the modes. The condition necessary for the roots to be real and distinct is that

$$-8t^3 > 27u^2 \qquad (1.55)$$

Orr *et al.* point out that:
(a) If $u$ is positive, the left peak is larger than the right, while if $u$ is negative the right peak is larger.
(b) For the distribution to be bimodal, $t$ must be negative.
(c) The curve is symmetrical about the minimum if $u = 0$.

Three methods are described for evaluating the constants in equations 1.49 or 1.53 so that the functions describe specific size distributions. These are a method of moments, a method of least squares, and a five-ordinate method. The latter method was found to be better than the former two for describing two bimodal distribution curves which occurred in studies of aerosol aggregation phenomena.

### Cumulative curves

So far the discussion of plots of distributions has emphasized frequency (or probability) vs. size plots, whereas for many applications cumulative plots are more informative. Cumulative curves are produced by plotting the percentage of particles (or weight, volume, or surface) having particle diameters greater than (or less than) a given particle size against the particle size. This method of plotting was mentioned earlier in connection with the use of the median and quartiles (Figure 1-7). Such curves have the advantage over histograms for plotting data that the class interval is eliminated, and they can be used to represent data which are obtained in classified form having unequal class intervals, such as data obtained by sieving or by cloud-chamber techniques.[48]

One of the reasons for the great popularity of cumulative curves is that they can often be plotted with ordinates chosen so that the plots are linear. Not only does this simplify curve fitting and extrapolation, but the linearity may be a test for the applicability of a particular distribution function.

One type of co-ordinate pair is used on the specially prepared graph paper commonly known as normal probability paper. Let the percentage of the particles less than $d$ in diameter, $Rn$, be represented by the equation

$$Rn = f_i(d) \tag{1.56}$$

so that a straight line is obtained by plotting $Rn$ against $f_i(d)$. Then, since probability paper is designed particularly for powders having particle diameters that are normally distributed, $f_i(d)$ in equation 1.56 is obtained by integrating the usual normal distribution function (equation 1.32):

$$Rn = \frac{100}{s\sqrt{2\pi}} \int_0^d \exp\left[-\frac{1}{2}\left(\frac{d - \bar{d}}{s}\right)^2\right] d(d) \tag{1.57}$$

This equation cannot be integrated directly, but the expression on the right can be evaluated from tables of probability integrals. Probability paper has one ordinate, usually the abscissa, which is a linear scale of $d$, whereas the other ordinate is $Rn$ on a probability scale such that a straight line is obtained when equation 1.57 is satisfied. The multiplier 100 enters equation 1.57 because cumulative curves are generally expressed in terms of percent instead of probability. Figure 1-4 is an example of size distributions plotted on normal probability paper. In this case the abscissa was chosen to represent percent finer than size. Apparently, the sizes of the particles of the two catalysts were not normally distributed. Even so, the plots on this paper provide an excellent representation of the size distribution.

For normal size distributions, the 50 per cent point represents both the median and the arithmetic mean. The difference in particle size between the arithmetic mean and the size corresponding to the 84 or the 16 percent point is approximately the standard deviation.

Just as functions of diameters can be substituted for diameters in the usual equation for normal distributions, so functions of diameters can be substituted for diameters on normal probability paper.

The most common of these substitutions is log $d$ for $d$, producing the so-called log-normal probability paper. When the diameters of particles are log-normally distributed, the distribution curve plotted on such paper is a straight line. The effect of changing from a plot on normal probability paper to one on log-normal probability paper for such a powder is demonstrated by comparing Figure 1-4 with Figure 1-10. The former was taken directly from the literature, and while plotting the data on normal probability paper was entirely appropriate, the fact that the data are essentially log-normally distributed is demonstrated by the linearity of the plots in Figure 1-10.

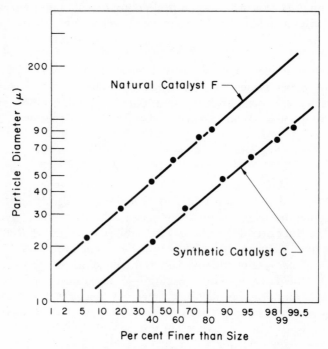

Figure 1-10. Size distributions from Figure 4 obtained with micromesh sieves replotted on log-normal probability paper.

When number-size distributions are log-normally distributed, surface and weight-size distributions are also log-normally distributed, and vice versa. Furthermore, all three distributions for a given population will have the same standard deviation and the straight line plots representing the three distributions will be parallel. When the plot for one distribution is given, a single point on the lines representing the other distributions is all that is needed to completely locate these lines. Thus given the mean diameter for one of these distributions and the standard deviation, diameters (number, surface, weight) can be calculated using the following equations:

$$\log \bar{d}_g = \log \bar{d}_{wg} - 6.908 \log^2 s_g \tag{1.58}$$

and

$$\log \bar{d}_{32} = \log \bar{d}_{wg} - 1.151 \log^2 s_g \tag{1.59}$$

where $\bar{d}_{wg}$ is the geometric mean of the weight distribution.[49]

The geometric standard deviations can be calculated from the equations

$$s_g = \frac{84.13\% \text{ size}}{50\% \text{ size}} = \frac{50\% \text{ size}}{15.87\% \text{ size}} \tag{1.60}$$

The Krumbein function,[39] $-\log_2 d$, can also be substituted for $d$ on the normal probability plot. In fact, this function was developed primarily to be used for plotting the size-frequency distributions of sediments.

The application of the upper-limit equation (equation 1.34) with $s = 1$, is shown in Figure 1-9. The maximum diameter can be found directly from a plot of $d$ against $100v$, drawing a smooth curve through the points. The 10th, 50th, and 90th percentiles $(d_1, d_2, d_3)$ are read directly from these curves. Then $d_m$ is calculated from the equation

$$\frac{d_m}{d_2} = \frac{d_2(d_3 + d_1) - 2d_1 d_3}{d_2^2 - d_1 d_3} \tag{1.61}$$

and $a$ can be calculated from the equation

$$a = \frac{d_m - d_2}{d_2} \tag{1.62}$$

If we use the normal distribution function in the form

$$\frac{dv}{dy} = \frac{c}{\sqrt{\pi}} \exp(-c^2 y^2) \tag{1.63}$$

we can determine $c$ from the slope of the line and therefore from any two points on it. Let $u$ designate the coordinate on the log scale:

$$u = \frac{d}{dm - d} \tag{1.64}$$

Then by reading the values $u_{90}$ and $u_{50}$ at the 90th and 50th percentiles,

$$c = \frac{0.394}{\log (u_{90}/u_{50})} \tag{1.65}$$

When the parameters of the upper limit equation have been established various means can be calculated:

$$\bar{d}_{32} = d_m/\{1 + a \exp(1/4c^2\}  \tag{1.66}$$

$$\bar{d}_{31} = d_m/\{1 + 2a \exp(1/4c^2) + a^2 \exp(1/c^2)\}^{\frac{1}{2}}  \tag{1.67}$$

$$\bar{d}_{30} = d_m/\{1 + 3a \exp(1/4c^2) + 3a^2\exp(1/c^2) + a^3 \exp(9/4c^2)\}^{\frac{1}{3}}  \tag{1.68}$$

Values of $\bar{d}_{21}$, $\bar{d}_{20}$, and $\bar{d}_{10}$ can be calculated from these using the following equation

$$\bar{d}_{qp}^{q-p} = \bar{d}_{qc}^{q-c}/\bar{d}_{pc}^{p-c}  \tag{1.69}$$

Mugele and Evans[30] calculated mean diameters for various values of $a$ and $c$, showing that the upper-limit distribution predicts $\bar{d}_{21}$ slightly larger than $\bar{d}_{30}$. This prediction was borne out by the data they analyzed, suggesting that at least for sprays the upper limit function has a slight advantage over the log normal function, which predicts $\bar{d}_{21}$ exactly equal to $\bar{d}_{30}$.

A method for plotting size distributions which is particularly useful when the distribution is very wide but the distribution is not necessarily normal or log normal involves plotting log $d$ against $dN/d(\log d)$, or the mathematically equivalent $d \cdot dN/d(d)$. This has the advantage over plotting $dN/d(d)$ against log $d$ in that the former plot is essentially a smoothed histogram using equal class intervals of log $d$, whereas the latter method involves the use of unequal class intervals of $d$.

This type of plot has recently been used extensively in connection with determinations of particle size distributions in the natural atmosphere.[44,45,50] Usually $dN/d(\log r)$ per cm$^3$ has been plotted against log $r$. Straight lines are obtained over much of the distribution and can be represented by the distribution function equation 1.48.

## ASCERTAINING THE IMPORTANCE OF PARTICLE SIZE

### Regression lines

The effect of the sizes of particles on the properties of a powder or suspension can often be predicted, at least semi-quantitatively. However, such a prediction is not always possible without an empirical determination of the relationship. Once data designed to test this relationship have been acquired, questions arise as to the degree of correlation between particle size and the property of interest and also as to the scatter of the data. An example of a relationship which might have to be determined is that between the size distribution of dust particles in the air of a room in which equipment is being manufactured and the reliability of the equipment.

Usually the property which is influenced by particle size is also affected by other factors. In the case just mentioned, the nature of the material comprising the particles (soft, gummy, abrasive, etc.) may be at least as important as particle size over a wide size range, and of course when dealing with suspensions the concentrations of suspended particles may be especially important.

When data obtained by various methods for determining particle size distributions are compared with data concerning some other property of the powder or suspensions, scatter in both sets of data resulting from experimental error will prevent a functional relationship between the two. This is true even in the absence of other disturbing factors such as those mentioned in the preceding paragraph.

The usual first steps in studying the relationship of one property of a material to another property of the same material after data representing the two properties have been obtained is to plot one set of data against the other and observe whether there is any relationship. The data will generally be scattered to some extent on the plot, and may be highly scattered so that the extent of the dependence of one property on the other is far from obvious. Fortunately, such data can be compared by statistical methods to yield a "best" curve through the data (a regression line or curve) and a mathematical indication of the extent to which the values of one property are determined by those of the other. In fact, a large percentage of the problems in statistical work involve the relationships among two or more variables; several variables can be studied simultaneously as well as in pairs.

A thorough treatment of statistical methods for determining relationships among variables is beyond the scope of this book, and the investigator desiring to apply these powerful mathematical methods is referred to works on mathematical statistics.[1,24,25,26] Nonetheless, this subject is so fundamental to a discussion of the importance of particle size that some of the basic concepts will be described.

Consider two variables, the relationship between which we wish to examine. Since our interest here is in particle size, the independent variable is diameter or a mean diameter, which we will simply call $d$; the variable whose relationship to $d$ we wish to determine we will call $y$. The problem is to determine the relationship between $d$ and $y$ in some convenient mathematical form.

The simplest situation is that in which a plot of $d$ vs. $y$ (the so-called scatter diagram) appears to be linear.[24,51] The problem is really one of fitting a straight line to the set of points, and although there are a number of ways for doing this, one of the most satisfactory, and most generally used is the method of least squares. The philosophy of this method is to generate a line which is located in such a position that deviations of the points about the line are minimized. One way to do this would be to minimize the deviations themselves or, since they may be positive or negative, the absolute values of the deviations. However, this usually is not convenient, so the squares of the deviations are minimized.

The equation of any straight line can be written in the form

$$y' = a + m(d - \bar{d}) \tag{1.70}$$

where $m$ is its slope, $a - m\bar{d}$ is the $y$ intercept, and $d$ is the arithmetic mean. Note that $\bar{d}$ as used here is the average of the average diameters of a number of powders each of which has (or contributes) a value $y$ for the property which presumably is affected by the average diameter. The desired equation (and line) is obtained by selecting $a$ and $m$ so as to make the sum of the squares of the deviations a minimum. Let the coordinates of the $i$th point be $d_i$ and $y_i$ so that the sum of the squares of the deviations is

$$\sum_{i=1}^{i=u} (y_i - y_i')^2$$

Calling this sum $F$ and substituting the expression for $y_i'$ from equation 1.70 we obtain

$$F = \sum_{1}^{n} [y_i - a - m(d_i - \bar{d})]^2 \tag{1.71}$$

The partial derivatives of $F$ with respect to $a$ and $m$ must be zero for $F$ to have a minimum value:

$$\left(\frac{\partial F}{\partial a}\right)_m = \Sigma 2[y - a - m(d - \bar{d})][-1] = 0 \tag{1.72}$$

$$F = \left(\frac{\partial F}{\partial m}\right)_a = \Sigma 2[y - a - m(d - \bar{d})][-(d - \bar{d})] = 0 \tag{1.73}$$

The solution of these simultaneous equations, taking advantage of the fact that $\Sigma(d - \bar{d}) = 0$, is

$$a = \bar{y} \quad \text{and} \quad m = \frac{\Sigma(d - \bar{d})y}{\Sigma(d - \bar{d})^2}$$

where $\bar{y}$ is the arithmetic mean of $y$. The desired line is thus described by the equation

$$y' - \bar{y} = m(d - \bar{d}) \tag{1.74}$$

which is often called the regression line.

The reader is warned that the two parameters determining the regression line (here $a$ and $m$) are defined slightly differently by different authors depending on the form used for equation 1.70. This does not, however, affect the final expression for the regression line with the symbols for the parameters eliminated.

Various methods have been suggested for making the calculation of the parameters less arduous. Hoel[24] has suggested changing the form of $m$ as follows:

$$m = \frac{\Sigma dy - \bar{d}\Sigma y}{\Sigma d^2 - 2\bar{d}\Sigma d + \Sigma \bar{d}^2} = \frac{\Sigma dy - n\overline{dy}}{\Sigma d^2 - n\bar{d}^2} \qquad (1.75)$$

Herdan[1] has suggested grouping (classifying) the data and making use of what he calls the grouped correlation table for calculating correlation coefficients (described below) and the parameters of the regression line. A useful work sheet is demonstrated in the ASTM Manual on Fitting Straight Lines.[51]

## The correlation coefficient

Another important statistic that can be calculated for such data is the correlation coefficient, which gives a quantitative indication of the extent to which some property of the powder or aerosol ($y$) depends on the particle size. Thus it indicates the usefulness of the regression line for predicting $y$ from size distribution data. The correlation coefficient, sometimes called the product moment correlation, is derived by most textbooks of statistical methods and will not be derived here. It is defined by the equation

$$c = \left(1 - \frac{\Sigma(y - y')^2}{\Sigma(y - \bar{y})^2}\right)^{\frac{1}{2}} = \left(1 - \frac{s_c^2}{s_y^2}\right)^{\frac{1}{2}} \qquad (1.76)$$

where $s_c$ is the standard deviation of the scatter about the regression line and $s_y$ is the standard deviation of the scatter about the arithmetic mean. It has a value equal to or close to zero for a regression line incapable of prediction, and close to $+1$ or $-1$ for a line capable of nearly perfect prediction. The greater the absolute value of the correlation coefficient, the more completely is $y$ determined by the particle size. The positive sign is generally used if $y$ increases with increasing particle size, that is, if the slope of the regression line is positive. The correlation coefficient can be interpreted quantitatively from the fact that the coefficient squared equals the percentage of the variance of $y$ ($s_y^2$) that is accounted for by the relationship with $d$.[24] The remainder of the variance of $y$ is produced by variables other than particle size.

Equation 1.76 is not convenient for calculating the correlation coefficient. A much better form of the equation for this purpose is

$$c = \frac{n\Sigma dy - \Sigma d\Sigma y}{\sqrt{[n\Sigma d^2 - (\Sigma d)^2][n\Sigma y^2 - (\Sigma y)^2]}} \qquad (1.77)$$

When large amounts of data are to be analyzed, it is helpful to classify the data and apply transformations of the type used for computing moments:

$$d_i = q_d u_i + d_0 \qquad (1.78)$$

and

$$y_i = q_y v_i + y_0 \qquad (1.79)$$

where the $q$'s are class intervals and $u$ and $v$ are the new variables. Then it is readily shown that

$$c = \frac{(u - \bar{u})(v - \bar{v})}{n s_u s_v} \qquad (1.80)$$

where $\bar{u}$ and $\bar{v}$ are the arithmetic means.

Perhaps another word of caution is appropriate here. A strong correlation between two variables by no means proves that a cause and effect relationship exists between them. For example, as a powder is progressively more finely ground it may become more highly contaminated with a metal oxide from the mill. The oxide could be an excellent catalyst, so that a positive correlation might exist between powder fineness and catalytic action, although there is no direct cause and effect relationship between the two.

It is also important to realize that the calculated value of the correlation coefficient is precisely correct only for the actual numbers analyzed and may only roughly represent the total populations of $y$'s and $d$'s. Thus if the value of the calculated correlation coefficient is small, it is often important to determine whether the apparent correlation is significant or is merely the result of scatter about the coefficient for the entire population. Methods for estimating the reliability of calculated correlation coefficients are presented in books on statistics.

### The standard error of estimate

Another useful statistic is the standard error of estimate. The intensity of the correlation of $y$ and $d$ depends on the scatter of the $y$'s about the regression line. The standard deviation of the $y$'s from the regression line serves as an indication of the extent of lack of correlation. The deviations from the regression line are called errors of estimate and if they are called $z$, their standard deviation is given by the equation

$$s_z = s_y \sqrt{1 - c^2} \tag{1.81}$$

This quantity is the standard error of estimate. It can be used to determine the likelihood that a measured value of $y$ will fall within a given distance from the value $y$ predicted by the regression line. This is possible since the absolute values of $z$ are approximately normally distributed. Thus about 95% of the deviation on both sides of the regression line will be within a range of $\pm 2s_z$ and about 99.7% will be within a range of $\pm 3s_z$.

### Curvilinear regression lines

Often it is obvious from the scatter diagram or from some previous knowledge of the probable type of dependence of $y$ on $d$ that a straight line will not fit the diagram because the relationship is non-linear. In such a case, where the mathematical form of the relationship may be known or suspected, it may be possible to obtain a linear relationship by considering functions of the variables as new variables. For example, the light extinction coefficient, $E$, for suspensions of particles having a fairly wide particle size distribution, can be represented over a limited range of particle sizes by an equation of the form

$$E = a\bar{d}^b \tag{1.82}$$

where $a$ and $b$ are constants. Taking the logarithms of both sides,

$$\log E = \log a + b \log \bar{d} \tag{1.83}$$

and $\log E$ is a linear function of $\log \bar{d}$. The new variables would then be $\log E$ and $\log \bar{d}$, and the statistics described above would refer to the logarithms rather than to $E$ and $\bar{d}$.

Often however, such a relationship cannot be predicted, but it still may be possible to find a simple curve that will fit the data satisfactorily. Polynominals are usually used and the proper degree can generally be judged by examination of the scatter diagram. For example, suppose the equation is a polynomial of the third degree:

$$y' = a + a'd + a''d^2 + a'''d^3 \tag{1.84}$$

The treatment is similar to that for a linear equation and one obtains a set of simultaneous equations which is solved to obtain the $a$-constants:

$$an + a'\Sigma d + a''\Sigma d^2 + a''' = \Sigma y \tag{1.85}$$

$$a\Sigma d + a'\Sigma d^2 + a''\Sigma d^3 + a'''\Sigma d^4 = \Sigma dy \tag{1.86}$$

$$a\Sigma d^2 + a'\Sigma d^3 + a''\Sigma d^4 + a'''\Sigma d^5 = \Sigma d^2 y \qquad (1.87)$$

$$a\Sigma d^3 + a'\Sigma d^4 + a''\Sigma d^5 + a'''\Sigma d^6 = \Sigma d^3 y \qquad (1.88)$$

The correlation coefficient as defined in equation 1.76 can be applied to curvilinear regression lines if the variance $s_c^2$ is based on the least-squares polynomial; it is then called the correlation index. Another method for measuring non-linear correlation, which has the advantage that curve fitting is not required, is the correlation ratio.[1]

As mentioned before, a particular property of a powder or suspension is almost never completely determined by the nature of the size distribution. Therefore, if a regression curve is constructed from data which were obtained without consideration of other pertinent variables it may not be particularly useful for prediction. An example is the effect of particle density as well as size on settling velocity. Of course, it is conventional for experimentalists to attempt to control all important independent variables except the one of interest and for field workers, who may have less control of conditions, to select what they hope are comparable situations. Correlation coefficients determined under controlled or selected conditions are called partial correlation coefficients.

A major accomplishment of mathematical statistics is that it permits the simultaneous treatment of several variables both in the design of experiments and the analysis of the data. It is often possible to construct regression lines and planes which permit the prediction of a dependent variable from a knowledge of powder particle size distributions and of the other pertinent variables. Similarly, multiple correlation coefficients can be determined.[24]

The importance of the use of statistical methods in the study of particle size distributions and of the effects of particle size can hardly be overemphasized. In this brief chapter only a few of the most commonly used applications of statistics to the study of fine particles have been mentioned, and such important topics as the design of experiments, Student's $t$ distribution, analysis of variance, and sequential analysis have had to be omitted from this discussion.

### REFERENCES

1. Herdan, G., "Small Particle Statistics," 2nd ed., Academic Press, New York, 1960.
2. Kuhn, W. E., ed., "Ultrafine Particles," Wiley, New York, 1963.
3. Martin, G., C. E. Blythe, and H. Tongue, *Trans. Ceram. Soc. (Eng.)*, **23,** 61 (1924).
4. Tomkeieff, S. L., *Nature*, **155,** 24 (1945).

5. Moran, P. A. P., *Nature*, **154**, 490 (1944).
6. Feret, L. R., Assoc. Int. pour l'Essai des Mat. 2, group D, Zürich (1931).
7. Patterson, H. S., and W. Cawood, *Trans Faraday Soc.*, **32**, 1084 (1936).
8. Fairs, G. L., *Chemistry and Industry*, **62**, 374 (1943).
9. May, K. R., *J. Sci. Inst.*, **22**, 187 (1945).
10. Sharpe, J. W., *J. Sci. Inst.*, **26**, 308 (1949).
11. Fairs, G. L., *Roy Micros. Soc. J.*, **31**, 209 (1951).
12. Watson, H. H., *Brit. J. Industr. Med.*, **9**, 80 (1952).
13. Hamilton, R. J., J. F. Holdsworth, and W. H. Walton, *Brit. J. Appl. Phys. Suppl.* 3 (1954).
14. Watson, H. H., and D. F. Mulford, *Brit. J. Appl. Phys. Suppl.* 3 (1954).
15. Bovey, D., *J. Sci. Inst.*, **39**, 405 (1962).
16. Cadle, R. D., and W. C. Thuman, *Ind. Eng. Chem.*, **52**, 315 (1960).
17. Roberts, F., and J. Z. Young, *Nature*, **169**, 962 (1952).
18. Dell, H. A., *Brit. J. Appl. Phys., Suppl.* 3, 156 (1954).
19. Taylor, W. K., *Brit. J. Appl. Phys. Suppl.*, 3, 173 (1954).
20. Orr, Jr., Clyde, and J. M. Dalla Valle, "Fine Particle Measurement," Macmillan, New York, 1960.
21. Shergold, F. A., *Trans. Soc. Chem. Ind.*, **65**, 245 (1946).
22. Cadle, R. D., "Particle Size Determination," Interscience, New York, 1955.
23. Daeschner, H. W., E. E. Seibert, and E. D. Peters, in ASTM special technical publication 234, "Symposium on Particle Size Measurement," Am. Soc. for Testing Materials, Philadelphia, 1958.
24. Hoel, P. G., "Introduction to Mathematical Statistics," Wiley, New York, 1947.
25. Gore, W. L., "Statistical Methods for Chemical Experimentation," Interscience, New York, 1952.
26. Fisher, R. A., "Statistical Methods for Research Workers," 13th ed., Hafner, New York, 1958.
27. Calbeck, J. H., in ASTM special technical publication 234, "Symposium on Particle Size Measurement," Am. Soc. for Testing Materials, Philadelphia, 1958.
28. American Society for Testing Materials, "ASTM Manual on the Presentation of Data," Philadelphia, 1945.
29. Cartwright, L. M., and R. I. Gregg, in ASTM special technical publication 234," Symposium on Particle Size Measurement," Am. Soc. for Testing Materials, Philadelphia, 1958.
30. Mugele, R. A., and H. D. Evans, *Ind. Eng., Chem.*, **43**, 1317 (1951).
31. Arnell, J. C., *Can. J. Res.*, **27A**, 207 (1949).
32. Cadle, R. D., and W. C. Thuman, in ASTM special technical publication 234, "Symposium on Particle Size Measurement," Am. Soc., for Testing Materials, Philadelphia, 1958.
33. Irani, R. R., and C. F. Callis, "Particle Size: Measurement, Interpretation, and Application," Wiley, New York, 1963.
34. Heywood, H., in "Symposium on Particle Size Analysis," Institution of Chemical Engineers, London, Feb. 4, 1947.
35. Irani, R. R., and D. P. Ames, *Mater. Res. Std.*, **1**, 637 (1961).
36. Fries, R. J., in ASTM special technical publication 234, "Symposium on Particle Size Measurement," Am. Soc. For Testing Materials, Philadelphia, 1958.

37. Kottler, F., *J. Franklin Inst.*, **250**, 339 (1950).
38. Galton, F,, and D. Mac Alister, *Proc. Roy. Soc.*, **29**, 365, 367 (1879).
39. Krumbein, W. C., *J. Sedim. Petrol.*, **6**, 35 (1936).
40. Kolupaev, P. G., "Atomization of Heavy Fuel Oil," Sc.D. thesis in chemical engineering, Mass. Inst. Tech., 1941.
41. Rosin, P., and E. Rammler, *J. Inst. Fuel,* **7**, 29 (1933).
42. Nukiyama, S., and Y. Tanasawa, *Trans. Soc. Mech. Engrs. (Japan)*, **4**, No. 14, 86 (1938).
43. Steffens, C., and Sylvan Rubin, in "Proceedings of the First National Air Pollution Symposium," Stanford Research Institute, Menlo Park, Calif., 1949.
44. Junge, C. E., *Tellus*, **5**, 1 (1953).
45. Junge, C. E., *J. Meteorol.*, **12**, 13 (1955).
46. Sinclair, D., Measurement of particle size and size distribution, in "Handbook on Aerosols," Atomic Energy Commission, Washington, D. C., 1950.
47. Dalla Valle, J. M., C. Orr, Jr., and H. G. Blocker, *Ind. Eng. Chem.*, **43**, 1377 (1951).
48. Rich, T. A., *Geofisica,* **31**, 60 (1955).
49. Hatch, T., J. Franklin Inst., **215**, 27 (1933).
50. Junge, C. E., Atmospheric chemistry, Chapt. 7, in "Advances in Geophysics," Vol. IV, Academic Press, New York, 1957.
51. Am. Soc. for Testing and Materials, "ASTM Manual on Fitting Straight Lines," ASTM Special Technical Publication No. 313., Philadelphia, 1962.

# Chapter 2 General Principles

Before considering the effects of particle size in applied or derived situations it is essential to consider the effect of size on the basic physical properties of finely divided materials. The fundamental equations relating size to physical properties have been applied to such diverse subjects as sediments on the ocean floors, the effectiveness of paint pigments, the nature of the atmosphere of Venus, and the design of dust-free rooms. Throughout the discussion it is important to keep in mind the distinction between the behavior of individual particles, of a group of particles, of a group of particles all of one size, and of a group of particles having a distribution of sizes and various mean diameters. As mentioned before in a different context, sometimes a definition of mean diameter can be chosen that can be used to predict a particular property of a group of particles using an equation derived for individual particles.

## LIGHT SCATTERING

Most observable light is scattered, either by particles or by irregularities on surfaces. Particles in the size range considered in this book are for the most part very effective for scattering visible radiation. Although general equations for predicting scattering throughout this size range have been derived, it is convenient to consider scattering in terms of size range relative to the wavelength of the light.

The general equation, usually referred to as the Mie equation, was derived from Maxwell. It is quite complicated, but for particles small relative to the wavelength of light it becomes much simpler, assuming a form originally derived by Lord Rayleigh. Particles that are large relative to the wavelength of light scatter on the basis of Kirchhoff diffraction, external reflection, and transmission with refraction.

The scattering equations were derived for scattering from single particles, but unless the number concentration of particles in a suspension is very high, the scattering from a suspension can be considered to be the sum of the scattering by the individual particles. When the concentrations are high, secondary scattering of the scattered radiation must be taken into account.

## Rayleigh Scattering

First we shall consider particles with diameters which are small relative to the wavelength $\lambda$ or more properly relative to $\lambda/2\pi$. One of the earliest equations to describe light scattering quantitatively was derived by Lord Rayleigh[1] to account for the blue color of the sky. It is usually presented in the form

$$s = 24\pi^3 \left(\frac{m^2 - 1}{m^2 + 2}\right) \frac{V^2}{\lambda^4} \tag{2.1}$$

where $s$ is the total amount of light of wave length $\lambda$ scattered by a sphere of volume $V$ and refractive index $m$ (relative to air) per unit intensity of illumination. This equation holds for spherical transparent particles when $r \leq 0.1\lambda$. The total energy scattered varies directly with the sixth power of the radius and inversely with the fourth power of the wavelength. Since very small particles, such as molecules, need not be spherical for the equation to apply, blue light is scattered much more than red by air molecules, which accounts for the blue color of the sky. If the air contains dust particles larger than $0.1\lambda$ the relative scattering, as discussed below, may be radically changed.

Sinclair[2] points out that when a particle is illuminated with unpolarized light, the intensity scattered at an angle $\gamma$ to the incident light is

$$I_\gamma = \frac{9\pi^2}{2R^2} \left(\frac{m^2 - 1}{m^2 + 2}\right) \frac{V^2}{\lambda^4} (1 + \cos^2 \gamma) \tag{2.2}$$

where $R$ is the distance from the particle to the point of observation and must be very large relative to the radius of the particle. The angle $\gamma$ is that between the direction of propagation of the scattered light and the reversed direction of propagation of the incident light. The right-hand side of this equation actually is the sum of two terms[3]; the multiplier of one is unity and the other $\cos^2 \gamma$. The former refers to the intensity of the vertical ($i_1$) and the latter to the horizontal ($i_2$) polarized component of the scattered radiation. Thus the scattered light normal to the incident beam is plane-polarized with the direction of vibration at right angles to the plane of observation.

If, on the other hand, the particle is illuminated by polarized light, the intensity of the scattered light is given by the equation[2]

$$I_\psi = \frac{9\pi^2}{R^2} \left(\frac{m^2 - 1}{m^2 + 2}\right) \frac{V^2}{\lambda^4} \sin^2 \psi \tag{2.3}$$

where $\psi$ is the angle between the direction of observation and the direction of the electric vibrations in the incident polarized light. When the particle is illuminated by plane-polarized light, the scattered light is polarized regardless of the direction of observation.

The angular distribution of intensity for Rayleigh scattering by small particles is symmetrical about a plane normal to the illuminating beam, as shown in Figure 2-1. Rayleigh's derivation is based on the idea that

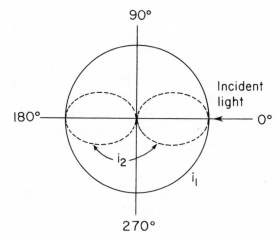

Figure 2-1. Angular distribution of intensity of light scattered by very small particles.

the oscillating electric field of the radiation induces a corresponding electric moment in the particle, which then acts as a linear electrical oscillator. It radiates light in all directions except that of the vibrations. The Rayleigh equation is derived for optically isotropic particles, that is, particles composed of a material whose index of refraction is independent of direction through the particle. When the particles are anisotropic, the direction of the electric field of the incident radiation may not coincide with the direction of the induced moment. As a result, the radiation scattered at 90° will not be completely plane-polarized with vertical vibrations, but will have a weak horizontal component. Methods for determining the degree of depolarization have been reviewed by Oster.[3]

The application of the Rayleigh equation is not restricted to visible light. A very important application is the use of radar to detect and study rainstorms.[4] The radar used for this purpose may produce radiation in the S-band ($\lambda$ = 10 cm), the X-band ($\lambda$ = 3 cm) or the K-band

($\lambda$ = 1 cm). Thus generally the raindrops are very much smaller than the wavelength of the radiation and the Rayleigh equation is applicable. Since the intensity of Rayleigh scattering is inversely proportional to the sixth power of the particle diameter, cloud droplets scatter the radiation much less effectively than raindrops and the radar radiation penetrates fog and clouds. This enables aircraft radar, for example, to penetrate clouds and locate the raining heart of a storm.   Impressive and very useful time-lapse movies of hurricanes have been made in this manner (Figure 2-2). By using radar of millimeter wavelength it is possible to study clouds.

Figure 2-2a is of a hurricane observed by the VW4 Naval Hurricane Hunters at Jacksonville, Florida.   Figure 2-2b is a radar photograph of a mid-western squall line which was approaching a mid-western radar station in 1956.   This picture is something of a curiosity since three kinds of meterological echoes are displayed.   The long, narrow echo close to the station just ahead of the main body of the storm is believed to have been caused by the gradient of index of refraction between cool dry air brought down from aloft and flowing out in front of the storm, and the warm moist low level air into which the storm is advancing.   The main body of the storm is next, the scattering being Rayleigh scattering from rain, snow, and hail.   The branched echoes behind the storm are from the ionized columns of gas produced by lightning.   These photographs were furnished by Dr. Myron Ligda, who also supplied the above interpretation.

Actually, the Rayleigh equation does not predict the scattering of radar by water droplets as accurately as the scattering of visible radiation by very small isotropic spheres.   In fact, the radar cross section may become more than twice the value predicted by the Rayleigh equation because of magnetic resonance.[5]   However, the Rayleigh equation is sufficiently accurate for most practical purposes.

### Mie Theory

When a particle is comparable in size or large relative to the wavelength of the incident radiation, the scattered light will be the resultant of light waves originating from various parts of the particle. The phase and intensity of such waves are related in a highly complicated way. The Mie equation predicts the nature of the light scattered from such spheres.[4] This equation is a series expression in terms of spherical harmonics. The coefficients of the terms are $m$ and $x$, where $x$ is $2\pi r/\lambda$. When $x \geq 1$ and the index of refraction differs somewhat from unity the summation of the series is very tedious.   Fortunately, numerous tables of solutions to the

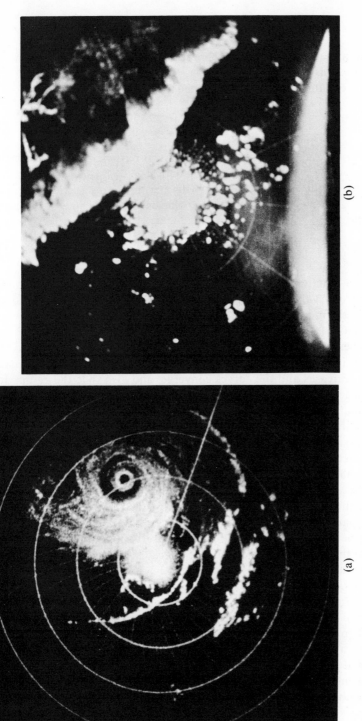

(a)

(b)

Figure 2-2. (a) Hurricane presented on a radar screen. (b) Radar photograph of a Mid-Western squall line. The branched echoes behind the storm are from the ionized columns of gas produced by lightning. The echo in front of the main body of the storm is believed to have been caused by the gradient of index of refraction between cool dry air brought down from aloft and the warm moist low level air into which the storm is advancing. (*Photographs by Dr. Myron Liqda*)

Mie series are available. A bibliography of numerical computations by the Mie theory is given by van de Hulst.[5]

The Mie equation can be written in the form[2]

$$s = \frac{\lambda^2}{2\pi} \sum_{v=1}^{\infty} \left( \frac{a_v^2 + p_v^2}{2v + 1} \right) \tag{2.4}$$

where $s$ is the total scattering by one spherical particle per unit intensity, and the $a_v$'s and $p_v$'s are functions of $x$ and of $\beta = 2\pi rm/\lambda$.

When $s$ is divided by $\pi r^2$, the scattering per unit cross sectional area of the particle, known as the scattering coefficient $K$, is obtained. Equation 2.4 then becomes

$$K = \frac{2}{x^2} \sum_{v=1}^{\infty} \left( \frac{a_v^2 + p_v^2}{2v + 1} \right) \tag{2.5}$$

Thus $K$ is a function of $r/\lambda$, and when the scattering coefficient is known for a particular value of $r$ and $\lambda$, its value is established for the ratio regardless of the individual values.

The complexity of the variation of scattering coefficient for single isotropic spherical particles is demonstrated by the graph prepared by Sinclair[2] (Figure 2-3). Note the approach to Rayleigh scattering as the ratio $r/\lambda$ decreases and the curves converge, and also that the radius for maximum scattering decreases with increasing refractive index.

The angular distribution of intensity also varies with $r/\lambda$, and the symmetrical pattern shown in Figure 2-1 becomes increasingly asymmetric with increasing $r/\lambda$ as shown in Figure 2-4. The most marked effect of the asymmetry is that as the ratio $r/\lambda$ increases, the forward scattering increases markedly relative to the backward scattering, and for very large values of $r/\lambda$ the backward scattering is negligible.

Light scattered by particles that are almost the same size as the wavelength is partially polarized into two plane-polarized components, one vibrating perpendicular to the plane of observation ($i_1$) and the other parallel to the plane of observation ($i_2$). Sinclair[2] has suggested the use of this polarization as the basis for a method for determining the size of aerosol particles from the Rayleigh region up to about $0.4\mu$ diameter. The particles in any given aerosol must be nearly the same size ("monodispersed"). The relative intensity of $i_2$ to $i_1$ varies from a low value up to greater than 1, but above $0.4\mu$ diameter the polarization varies rapidly and is not a single-valued function of the radius. The polarization is measured at a scattering angle of $90°$ with a polarization photometer.

When a monodispersed aerosol (as defined above) is illuminated with a beam of white light, the variation of scattering with wavelength at various

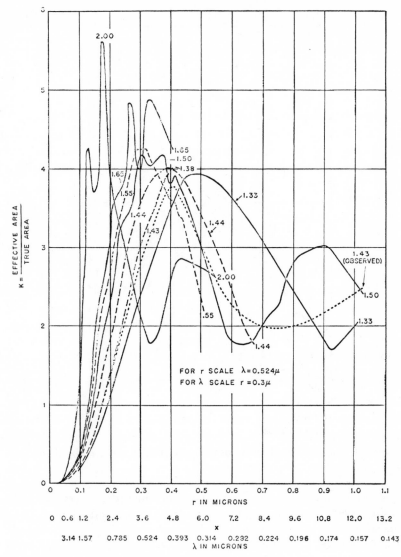

Figure 2-3. Scattering coefficient for spherical particles. $K$ vs $x$, $r$ and $\lambda^2$.

angles relative to the incident beam results in a succession of spectra as the angle is increased. These are known as higher order Tyndall spectra. As the angle of observation is varied from the forward to the backward direction, the order of colors is violet, blue, green, yellow, orange, and red

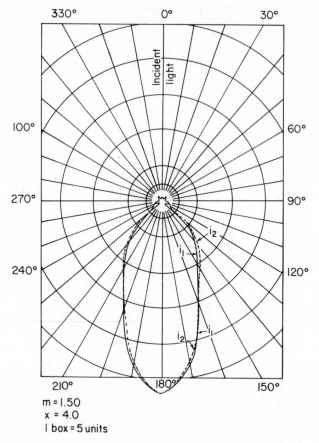

m = 1.50
x = 4.0
I box = 5 units

Figure 2-4. Angular distribution[2] of intensity of light scattered by a spherical particle. $i_1$ and $i_2$ vs $v$.

for the polarized component $i_1$. At about 90° the order reverses and the opposite series is repeated until the backward direction is reached.

Sinclair studied these phenomena using oleic acid fogs, stearic acid fogs, and sulfur smokes of uniform particle size. The angular distribution of color agreed closely with Mie theory. Calculations by Sinclair showed that the number of times that red is observed when the scattering angle is varied through a fixed number of degrees is independent of refractive index for values up to 2.0 and for radii up to 0.5 micron. Figure 2-5 shows the positions of the reds for the vertically polarized scattered light from stearic acid aerosols producing one to seven spectra. These same curves apply to other aerosols composed of materials of various refractive

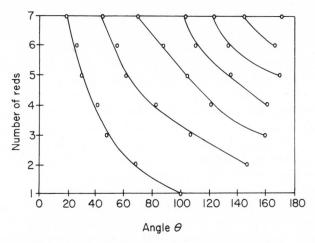

Figure 2-5. Angular position vs number of reds.[2]

indices. Sinclair and La Mer[6] developed an instrument for determining the particle size of monodispersed aerosols which uses the polarization of the scattered ($i_1$) light for particles 0.1 to 0.4 micron diameter and the angular distribution of color for particles between about 0.4 and 2 microns in diameter. A commercial version of this instrument has been used successfully for a number of investigations in the author's laboratory.

Numerous experimental investigations of light scattering by individual particles have demonstrated the validity of the Mie equation.[7,8] A confirming curve obtained by Sinclair is shown as the dotted line in Figure 2-3. The angular variation of light scattered by dioctyl phthalate aerosol droplets was determined by Gucker and Rowell.[9] They charged individual droplets, suspended them in an electric field, illuminated them with monochromatic light, and measured the light scattered into a photometer placed at angles of 40 to 140° with respect to the direction of the incident light. The particle radius was determined from the rate of fall of the droplets. The results obtained agreed very well with Mie theory. They also undertook detailed calculations of the intensity of scattered light over the range of $x(= \pi r/\lambda)$ from 0.1 to 30 for a refractive index of 1.486 and at several values of $x$ for a refractive index of 1.50. They found that the number of maxima in the scattering diagrams increases with increasing $x$.

Most particles, of course, are not transparent, isotropic spheres. Absorbing particles have a complex refractive index consisting of a real and an imaginary part which can be written

$$m = n - in'$$ (2.6)

The Mie equation has been solved for spheres of a number of substances, such as iron, nickel, zinc, copper, and carbon in air; and gold, silver, and mercury in water.[5] Totally reflecting spheres, for which $m = \infty$, constitute a special case, and for these even the Rayleigh equation does not apply. The Mie equation has also been partially solved for a number of special shapes, such as cylinders.

An interesting and often important type of light scattering is produced by particles consisting of a core encased in a shell of a second material. The theory of scattering by such particles was worked out by Aden and Kerker[10] and has been applied to a number of problems such as the scattering of microwaves by dielectric coated spheres.

Another type of light scattering often encountered is that by a highly concentrated suspension. Churchill, Clark, and Sliepcevich[11] studied the effect of particle separation distance on the light-scattering properties of dispersions of closely sized spheres as the concentration was decreased by dilution. The data were correlated in terms of a two-flux model, that is, a model in which the angular distribution of radiation scattered by a single sphere is represented by forward and backward components. The scattering coefficient was found to be nearly constant down to a distance between centers of about 1.7 particle diameters, and varied by less than 10% to a distance of about 1.4 diameters, which corresponded to 28% solids by volume. The dispersions were prepared from very uniformly sized polystyrene spheres. Two batches were used, one with a mean diameter (presumably $\bar{d}_{10}$) of $0.814\mu$ and a standard deviation of $0.011\mu$ and the other with a mean diameter of $1.171\mu$ and a standard deviation of $0.013\mu$. The authors suggest that the direct simulation of dilute aerosols having dimensions of the order of kilometers is feasible with very dense hydrosols having dimensions of the order of millimeters.

However, Sinclair[2] has pointed out what seems to be an interesting effect of multiple scattering. The color of a cloud of colored smoke becomes paler upon dilution. A dense cloud of orange particles is orange by scattered light and deep red or orange by transmitted light. The cloud transmits red or orange because of absorption of other wavelengths and the color pales with dilution just as the transmitted light from a solution pales with dilution.

The cloud of small orange dye particles appears orange because of multiple scattering and absorption, since the primary scattering is almost colorless. Each rescattering removes slightly more green than red by selective absorption. In a dilute cloud, according to Sinclair, the multiple scatter is greatly decreased and a great deal of primary scattering is seen. In a cloud of large particles, according to this concept, the color decreases less rapidly with dilution, since larger particles abstract a greater proportion of green at each scattering process. Thus less multiple scattering is required to produce a strong orange color. If the particles are sufficiently large (somewhat larger than about $0.2\mu$ radius for orange dye in oil of real refractive index 1.5) the transmitted light may appear green due to selective scattering.

As mentioned above, equation 2.4 applies to single particles and to suspensions of particles which are the same size and are sufficiently dilute that secondary scattering is not important. However, in practice, fine particles usually have a range of size as well as being of irregular shape. The total scattering is the sum of the scattering by the individual particles, but the scattering coefficient may vary greatly from one particle to another. Hodkinson[12] has pointed out that, although the diffraction patterns of individual non-spherical objects vary greatly with their shape, the resultant forward diffraction lobe for an assembly of non-spherical particles in random orientation would not be expected to differ much from that for an assembly of spheres equal in projected area to the irregular particles. Similarly, the angular distribution of the light scattered by external reflection would be the same for an assembly of irregular particles as for spheres, since the surface of a sphere offers equal probabilities of reflection for all angles of incidence, as does a random assembly of particle surfaces.

The effect of adding the scattering from a number of particles of varying size would be expected to damp out the wide fluctuations in scattering coefficient with varying size that occur for single particles, so that the change in mean coefficient with mean particle size would be expected to be monotonic over wide ranges of $2\pi r/\lambda$. Similarly, the variation of scattering intensity with angle relative to the incident beam would be expected to fluctuate much less for a polydispersed suspension than for one which is monodispersed or for a single particle (Figure 2-4).

Hodkinson made measurements of the angular scattering distribution over the range 0.5 to 90° using suspensions of powdered flint, diamond, anthracite, and bituminous coal. Smooth curves were obtained which were quite unlike those for single particles or monodispersed spheres.

This effect of polydispersion has also been observed by Neuberger, Panofsky, and Sekera.[13] They suggest that from this effect it is obvious that it is impossible to express the scattering properties of an aerosol with a mean size. To a large extent this is correct, but there are important exceptions. A mean size can never determine all the scattering properties of a polydisperse aerosol; but for a given type of powder, and a properly selected definition of mean there may be an important correlation between the value of the mean and some particular aspect of the scattering. Examples of such aspects are the hiding properties of a smoke screen, the covering properties of certain pigments, and any property or properties of scattered light which are effectively used to determine a mean size.

Polydisperse aerosols do not exhibit higher order Tyndall spectra, since the orders overlap, although they may appear colored by transmitted or scattered light as a result of preferential scattering of light of long or short wavelength. The polarization is also a mixture, the effect of the larger particles predominating because of the increase of intensity with size.

### Scattering by large particles

The Mie theory applies to large particles, and as $d$ becomes very large relative to the wavelength of light, the scattering coefficient $K$ approaches 2 (Figure 2-1). Since the scattering coefficient is defined as the ratio of the effective area for scattering to the actual area, this implies that a large sphere scatters twice as much light as falls on it. This interpretation has caused considerable confusion, but the explanation is relatively simple. The amount of light intercepted by the sphere for unit intensity of illumination is $\pi r^2$, and the sphere will also diffract an amount of light $\pi r^2$. Thus the total amount of light intercepted and diffracted is $2\pi r^2$, corresponding to a scattering coefficient of 2. The diffracted light is scattered in a direction almost parallel to the incident beam and in the same direction as that beam, so that the light-sensing device such as a photocell in a turbidimeter will often receive this light and the apparent value of $K$ will be unity.

Sinclair[2,14] undertook an interesting experiment which demonstrated this effect. He chose lycopodeum spores as the particles since they are very uniform in diameter (his were $30.0 \pm 2\mu$) and are easy to disperse in air. A cloud of lycopodeum spores was allowed to settle on a glass plate and the plate was placed in a parallel beam of light in front of a photocell. The transmitted intensity was measured at different distances between the plate and the photocell. When the distance from the plate to the photocell was decreased from 18 ft to 6 in., the reading of the photocell increased by a factor of 2.1. Calculations showed that at 18 ft the observed scattering cross section was $2\pi r^2$ and at 6 in. it was $\pi r^2$. At 6 in. the light scattered in a nearly forward direction was received by the photocell, but at the greater distance none of the scattered light reached the cell.

Gumprecht and Sliepcevich[15] studied this effect and agreed with Sinclair that the limiting value of $K = 2$ could be satisfactorily explained on the basis of Babinet's principle, which shows that a circular opaque disc diffracts an amount of light around the edges of the disc equal to the amount of light which actually strikes the disk. They also point out that no known type of light-measuring device can measure the intensity of only the undisturbed part of the parallel beam, with complete exclusion of light scattered in a forward direction.

## Light transmission

When a measure of total scattering is desired it is much more convenient to measure the percent transmission than to attempt to integrate the intensity of the scattered light. Transmission methods have been used in many fundamental studies of light scattering and are the basis of a number of methods of particle size determination.

When a beam of light is passed through a suspension of particles, the intensity of the beam is attenuated as a result of the scattering, and the decrease in intensity obeys the exponential law

$$I/I_0 = \exp(-\tau l) \tag{2.7}$$

The initial intensity is $I_0$, the intensity after the light has traversed the distance $l$ is $I$, and $\tau$ is the extinction coefficient. The term $\tau l$ is called the optical density. The equation can also be written in the form

$$I/I_0 = \exp(-K\pi r^2 nl) \tag{2.8}$$

where $n$ is the number of particles per unit volume of suspension and $K$ is the total scattering coefficient as previously defined. Equation 2.7 is applicable to polydispersions, but 2.8 is strictly applicable only to monodispersed systems.

For very small particles, which obey the Rayleigh relationship, equation 2.8 can be written

$$\frac{I}{I_0} = \exp\left[-\frac{128\pi^5 r^6}{3\lambda^4}\left(\frac{m^2 - 1}{m^2 + 2}\right)^2\right]nl \tag{2.9}$$

On the other hand, when the diameter is large, $K$ becomes 2, as explained above, and one-half of the light is scattered in a nearly forward direction. This causes considerable difficulty when interpreting the results of transmissivity (turbidity) measurements made on suspensions of particles which are about 2 to 50 microns in diameter. The apparent scattering coefficient $K_a$ will vary from 2 to 1 with increasing particle size, since the relative amount of forward scattered light reaching the photocell or other sensor increases with increasing particle size.

An equation which may be used to correct for this effect has been derived by Gumprecht and Sliepcevich.[15] $K$ is based on the total amount of light scattered by a particle in all directions and $K_a$ is also based on this amount of light except within a cone of half-angle $\theta$ in the forward direction. Therefore, $K$ may be defined in terms of the Mie theory as

$$K_a = K - \frac{1}{x^2} \int_{\pi-\theta}^{\pi} (i_1 + i_2) \sin \gamma \, d\gamma \qquad (2.10)$$

Then $R$, the correction factor, can be defined as

$$R = \frac{K_a}{K} = 1 - \frac{1}{Kx^2} \int_{\pi-\theta}^{\pi} (i_1 + i_2) \sin \gamma \, d\gamma \qquad (2.11)$$

Thus for large spherical particles and any real equipment, equation 2.8 becomes

$$I/I_0 = \exp(-RK \pi r^2 nl) \qquad (2.12)$$

According to diffraction theory the fraction ($f$) of the light-diffracted by an opaque circular disc and falling outside of a cone of half-angle $\theta$ in the forward direction is

$$f = [J_0(x\theta)]^2 + [J_1(x\theta)]^2 \qquad (2.13)$$

where $J_0$ and $J_1$ are Bessel functions of order 0 and 1, respectively; $x$ as usual is $2\pi r/\lambda$; $\theta$ is in radians and must be small enough so that $\theta \simeq \sin \theta$. A value of $K = 2$ was assigned the disc and $R$ redefined as

$$R = \frac{1 + [J_0(x\theta)]^2 + [J_1(x\theta)]^2}{2} \qquad (2.14)$$

Gumprecht and Sliepcevich compared values of $R$ computed by both the Mie theory and the diffraction theory. The values computed by the two methods showed very good agreement, which was best for small values of $\theta$. Thus for small values of $\theta$ (preferably less than 1.5°) $R$ can be calculated from the relatively simple equation 2.14. They developed a lens-pinhole transmitted light detector for experimentally determining $R$ which provides a constant value of $\theta$ regardless of the position of a particle in the light beam. Using this apparatus and small glass beads, they obtained very good agreement between computed and experimental values of $R$.

Based on the results just described Gumprecht and Sliepcevich[15] developed a method for the measurement of particle sizes in polydispersed systems using light transmission measurements combined with differential settling. The apparatus consisted of a settling chamber, chopped-light source, light filter, a lens-pinhole optical system, a phototube, amplifiers, and a strip chart recorder. This of course, is just one of a very large number of techniques that have been suggested for determining particle sizes and particle size distributions using light scattering or transmission.

### Coronae

When particles larger than a few microns, suspended in a fluid, are illuminated by a beam of light directed toward an observer, diffraction rings (coronae) may occur around the light beam. Coronae are often seen around the sun or moon when the atmosphere contains water droplets, ice crystals, or dust particles in the proper size range. The angular position of the individual rings produced by a single opaque sphere which is considerably larger than the wavelength of light is given by the classical theory for Fraunhofer diffraction. For the first bright ring[2] this is $\sin \theta = 0.819\lambda/r$, for the second it is $\sin \theta = 1.346\lambda/r$, for the third $\sin \theta = 1.858\lambda/r$, and for the fourth $\sin \theta = 2.362\lambda/r$. The positions of the dark rings are given by the equation

$$\sin \theta = (n + 0.22\lambda)/d \tag{2.15}$$

where $n$ is the order of the ring.

These relationships were developed for opaque particles but they apply to transparent particles for which $\pi d/\lambda$ is greater than about 30. Although the rings are observed most clearly in a suspension of uniform particle size, the particles need not be as nearly monodispersed as is necessary to observe higher order Tyndall spectra. For example, Sinclair has observed several colored rings in water fogs which contained droplets varying in diameter from 8 to 32 microns.

Sinclair used coronae to measure the size of lycopodium spores whose radii were found with a microscope to vary from 13.6 to 16.0 microns. The spores were dispersed in air and allowed to settle on a glass plate placed in a beam of light. The angular positions of two orders of light and dark diffraction rings were measured and the particle size was calculated from the above relationships to be $15.5 \pm 0.2$ microns.

Van de Hulst[5] points out that in quantitative interpretation of the coronae anomalous diffraction can cause difficulties, and the intensity of the first bright ring and the position of the first minimum are subject to strong fluctuation for $x < 50$ ($d < 8\mu$).

Coronae have been used extensively for particle size determination. They were used by Kohler[16] to determine the size of droplets in fogs and by several investigators to determine the size of blood cells.[17,18,19]

Humphries[20] has suggested that the sizes of particles as small as one micron can be determined using coronae if the technique is calibrated against particles of known size.

An interesting related phenomenon has several names, the more common of which are the "glory" and the "Brocken spectre." It is generally observed when a person is located between a very extensive, uniform cloud or fog bank and the sun. It may take the form of a shadow of the observer, surrounded by a large, well-defined halo. It is most commonly observed from aircraft, where it appears to be a shadow of the plane surrounded by a large halo. As observed by the author, the halo has symmetrically surrounded the entire aircraft. According to van de Hulst,[5] as the position of the observer in the plane changes, the center of the rings shifts from the shadow of the head of the plane to the shadow of its tail.

The Brocken spectre has often been seen at the Grand Canyon of the Colorado River when an observer has stood on the rim and observed his shadow on the clouds below.

Van de Hulst developed the main features of the theory of the glory on the basis of Huygens' principle, which states that each point of a wave front may be considered as a center of secondary waves, so that the envelope of secondary waves forms a new wave front.

## BROWNIAN MOTION

### Diffusion

Brownian motion can be defined as the irregular movement of particles suspended in a fluid as a result of bombardment by atoms and molecules. When the particles are very small, as are atoms and molecules or small clusters of atoms and molecules, they move in a zig-zag path with sharp changes in direction. However, a particle suspended in a gas must be bombarded by many atoms or molecules before it changes direction and the path is a tortuous curve rather than an intercepting succession of straight lines.

The average square of a particle displacement in time $t$ is given by the equation derived by Einstein

$$\overline{\Delta}_x^2 = 2Dt \tag{2.16}$$

where $D$ is the diffusion coefficient. Substituting for the value of the diffusion coefficient, $RT/N'K$, we obtain

$$\overline{\Delta}_x^2 = 2RTt/N'K \tag{2.17}$$

where $K$ is the resistance factor, $R$ the gas constant, $T$ the absolute temperature, and $N'$ Avogadro's number[3]. For particles sufficiently large that Stokes' law applies,

$$\overline{\Delta_x^2} = 2RTt/N'3\pi Nd \tag{2.18}$$

When the particles are small relative to the mean free path of the gas, Stokes' law must be corrected for "slippage" (the Cunningham correction[22]) and the equation becomes

$$\overline{\Delta_x^2} = \frac{2RT(1 + 2A\lambda/d)t}{N'3\pi\eta d} \tag{2.19}$$

where $A$ is a constant, usually with a value of about 0.9, $\lambda$ is the mean free path, and $\eta$ is the viscosity of the gas.

The root mean square Brownian displacement per second in air at 760mm Hg pressure and 20°C is about $3.7 \times 10^{-3}$ cm for particles $0.1\mu$ in diameter and about $7.4 \times 10^{-4}$ cm for particles $1.0\mu$ in diameter. The settling rate and Brownian displacement for such particles become equal for $d$ about $0.6\mu$.

The Einstein equation has been verified by a number of workers. De Broglie[23] in 1909 used Brownian movement of particles produced by electric arc volatilization and particles of tobacco smoke to determine the value of the charge on the electron. Millikan[24] made an extensive study of Brownian motion in connection with his studies of the charge on the electron and again verified the Einstein equation.

The Brownian movement of particles has been used for measuring their size by means of photographic records. The method is not very accurate but it does permit the measurement of the size of individual particles which are small relative to the mean free path of the gas in which they are suspended without having to remove them from the gas.

A Brownian rotational movement occurs in addition to the translational motion. Although it is difficult to observe, it has an important randomizing function in that it often prevents or hinders particles from becoming oriented in a fluid with respect to shape or polarity. An equation for the rotational motion was derived by Einstein.[21]

$$\overline{\Delta_r^2} = 2RT/N'\pi d^3\eta \tag{2.20}$$

This equation, along with that for translational motion, has been verified experimentally by Jean Perrin.[25,26]

The diffusion coefficient can be defined as the quantity of matter which traverses unit surface in unit time when the concentration gradient is unity. Thus it has the dimensions length squared per unit time. Consider a surface of area $S$ in a suspension of particles of varying concentration with position. If $dc/dx$ is the concentration gradient at right angles to the surface, the rate of flow of mass of particles through $S$ is given by the differential equation

$$dm/dt = SDdc/dx \qquad (2.21)$$

Table 2-1 shows a few values for the diffusion coefficient, as calculated by Fuks,[27] for particles in air at atmospheric pressure and 23°C. Diffusion constants in a liquid are of course very much smaller.

TABLE 2-1.  DIFFUSION CONSTANTS[27] OF SPHERICAL PARTICLES IN AIR AT ATMOSPHERIC PRESSURE, 23°C

| $r$ (microns) | $D$ (cm² sec⁻¹) |
|---|---|
| $10^{-3}$ | $1.28 \times 10^{-2}$ |
| $10^{-2}$ | $1.35 \times 10^{-4}$ |
| $10^{-1}$ | $2.21 \times 10^{-6}$ |
| $1$ | $1.27 \times 10^{-7}$ |
| $10$ | $1.38 \times 10^{-8}$ |

Brownian motion diffusion (as contrasted with eddy diffusion, discussed later) is very slow, even in a gas. However, it is important in a few situations. When an aerosol is drawn through a filter made from fine fibers, relatively large particles are collected mainly by impaction on, and interception by, the fibers. However, when the particles are quite small (for example, $<0.1\mu r$) the particles are collected mainly as a result of diffusion of the particles to the fibers. For intermediate sizes none of these mechanisms may be very effective and there may be a size corresponding to maximum penetration of the filter. This effect has been observed several times, for example by Cadle and Thuman[28] during a study of a method for the preparation of organic fiber filters, as shown by Table 2-2. Collection efficiencies are expressed in two ways, namely, as percent of particles collected, and by means of a parameter $F$ defined by the equation

$$\frac{C_1}{C_0} = \exp \frac{-F\Delta p}{100} \qquad (2.22)$$

where $C_1$ is the number concentration of particles leaving the filter and $p$ is the pressure drop across the filter. The parameter $F$ is particularly useful for comparing various filters at a given face velocity.

Diffusion is an important mechanism for the collection of particles in the lungs, and is discussed in a later chapter.

The variation of diffusion constant with particle size is the basis of a number of techniques for determining the size of particles. The particles may be suspended in either a liquid or a gas, but techniques developed for suspensions in liquids are for the most part designed to determine the sizes of particles much smaller than those considered in this book. However, diffusion of particles suspended in gases is the basis of several methods for particles up to about 0.3 micron diameter.

These methods all depend on passing the suspension through a narrow channel and determining the fraction of the particles that has diffused to the walls. They are most effective for suspensions that are nearly monodispersed.[29,30,31,32] The best known of these is probably the diffusion battery[29] which consists essentially of a pile of plates in which the individual plates are held apart to produce uniform channels of equal thickness.

TABLE 2-2. COLLECTION EFFICIENCY AS A FUNCTION OF FIBER AND PARTICLE SIZE

| Median Fiber Diameter, $\mu$ | Filter Density, Grams/ Sq. Cm. | $\Delta p$, Mm. $H_2O$ | Efficiency for Indicated Diameter, % | | | $F$ for Indicated Diameter, Mm.$^{-1}$ | | |
|---|---|---|---|---|---|---|---|---|
| | | | $0.01\,\mu^a$ | $0.1\,\mu^b$ | $1.0\,\mu^b$ | $0.01\,\mu^a$ | $0.1\,\mu^b$ | $1.0\,\mu^b$ |
| 2.0 | 0.0022 | 10 | 68 | 8 | 90 | 11 | 0.83 | 23 |
| 2.0 | 0.0105 | 17 | 97.2 | 57 | 99.0 | 21 | 5.0 | 27 |
| 0.4 | 0.0027 | 120 | 97.2 | 85.7 | >99.99 | 3.0 | 1.6 | ... |
| 0.4 | 0.0050 | 408 | 99.9 | 98.3 | >99.99 | 1.7 | 1.0 | ... |
| 0.3 | 0.0032 | 680 | 99.2 | 99.2 | >99.99 | 0.71 | 0.71 | ... |

$^a$LiF aerosols. $^b$(NH$_1$)$_2$SO$_1$ aerosols.

Sinclair[33] has made an interesting calculation concerning the effect of Brownian motion diffusion on the upper boundary of a cloud of uniform particles. For a 0.2 micron radius particle, at 293°K, the displacement $\bar{x}$ in one hour will be $6.4 \times 10^{-2}$ cm, or slightly more than 0.5 mm. During this time some particles will have moved upward and others downward by this amount so that the top of a cloud of uniform particles falling in still air will be spread vertically over a distance of about 1.25 mm. The entire cloud would have settled during this time through a distance of 2.5 cm, as calculated from the Stokes-Cunningham equation. Sinclair points out that the spread of 1.25 mm in 2.5 cm corresponds to a particle size spread of 2.5%, which is considerably less than the spread of particle size even in very uniform aerosols.

### Coagulation

Another property of particles suspended in a fluid which results at least in part from Brownian motion is coagulation. Here again size plays a very important role, as would be expected for any property related to Brownian motion. The movement of particles toward one another may be brought about solely by Brownian motion, but usually other influences play a major role, e.g., turbulence of the fluid, gravitational forces, electrostatic forces, and photophoresis. For particles in the size range we are considering, Brownian motion and electrostatic forces usually play the major role in effecting coagulation.

The theory of the coagulation of particles suspended in a fluid is based on the assumption that the particles adhere upon every contact. A large amount of experimental evidence indicates that this assumption is generally valid. Smoluchowski[34,35] derived the following equation for monodispersed spheres which are large relative to the mean free path of the fluid in which they are suspended:

$$-\frac{dn}{dt} = HN^2 \qquad (2.23)$$

where $H$ is $4kT/3\eta$ or in terms of the gas constant $4RT/3N'\eta$ and $N$ is the concentration of particles. For air at 20°C, $H = 3.0 \times 10^{-10}$ cc per second. This equation applies only to the early stages in the life of a suspension, since coagulation causes a suspension to become polydisperse. It is of interest that when the particles are all one size—large relative to the mean free path—and coagulation results from Brownian motion alone, this theory predicts that the coagulation rate is independent of particle size. Upon integration equation 2.23 becomes

$$\frac{1}{N} - \frac{1}{N_0} = HT \qquad (2.24)$$

where $N_0$ is the initial particle concentration.

The validity of an equation of the form of 2.24 was first established by experiments described by Whytlaw-Gray and Patterson.[36] They developed a method for following the course of the coagulation that was essentially an ultramicroscope snap-count technique. They found, as predicted by equation 2.24, that if $1/N$ for a smoke is plotted against time, a straight line generally results. The reciprocal $1/N$ is the average volume occupied by a particle and is sometimes called the particulate volume.

According to equation 2.23 the coagulation rate is independent of size. However, when the particles are small relative to the mean free path, account must be taken of slippage and the Cunningham correction applied as before. Equation 2.23 then becomes

$$-\frac{dn}{dt} = \frac{4}{3} \frac{kT}{\eta} \left(1 + \frac{A\lambda}{r}\right) N^2 \qquad (2.25)$$

Thus under these circumstances size becomes important to the coagulation rate.

Surprisingly little evidence is available concerning the effect of particle size on the coagulation rate. Quon[37] has studied the coagulation of particles in air where size ranged from $6 \times 10^{-3}$ to $3 \times 10^{-2}$ microns. He determined the relationship between the coagulation rate constant $K'$ and an "equivalent" radius $(r_0)$. He defined $K'$ to include the Cunningham correction and defined the equivalent radius in terms of the fraction of charged nuclei and Boltzmann's law of charge distribution. The equivalent radius is intended to be a single size characteristic of a polydispersed aerosol. He found the experimental value of $K'$ to be proportional to $r_0^{-1.3}$ and an order of magnitude greater than values predicted by the Smoluchowski expression.

Quon also found that the distance which particles must approach each other $(2r_0 - \delta)$ for coagulation is a function of the ratio of the particle mean free path $(l_p)$ to the equivalent radius:

$$\delta = r_0 \left[2 + 11.3 \left(\frac{l_p}{r_0}\right)^{0.43}\right] \qquad (2.26)$$

Other results which rather indirectly substantiate the effect of particle size on coagulation rate have been reviewed by Green and Lane.[38]

Most aerosols, of course, are polydispersed and there is a large amount of evidence to the effect that the more nearly an aerosol approaches monodispersity, the more slowly it coagulates. Here, again, is an example of a property of a particle population which cannot be accurately predicted from mean particle size alone. Some measure of the polydispersity is also required.

The general equation[27,36] for the coagulation of a polydispersed aerosol is

$$-\frac{dN}{dt} = \frac{kT}{3\eta} \frac{(r_1 + r_2)^2}{r_1 r_2} \left(1 + \frac{A\lambda}{r}\right) N^2 \qquad (2.27)$$

where $r$ is the arithmetic mean of $r_1$ and $r_2$. When $r_1 = r_2$ the term $(r_1 - r_2)^2/r_1 r_2$ has the minimum value of 4 and the coagulation rate is also a minimum. The effect of polydispersity on coagulation rate is usually relatively small. In an aerosol made up of equal numbers of large and small particles with a range of radius of 8 to 1, the ratio of coagulation rate to that of a monodispersed aerosol is given by the expression $(r_1 - r_2)^2/4r_1 r_2$, or in this case 1.27. However, a polydispersed aerosol with a size range of 8 to 1 would coagulate somewhat more slowly, since many particles would collide with others of nearly the same size.

Whytlaw-Gray and Patterson pointed out that it is easier to control the conditions during the dispersal of a smoke and produce a relatively homogeneous aerosol when the substance is volatilized in a constant current of air than when it is produced by other methods, such as heating the same substance in the relatively still air of the chamber in which coagulation is to be studied. This principle was later made the basis for the method for preparing monodispersed aerosols developed by Sinclair and La Mer,[6] although they went one step farther and controlled the nuclei concentration. The difference in heterogeneity is explained by considering that the freshly formed smoke has a high particulate concentration which results in very rapid coagulation unless the smoke is diluted almost immediately. In the case of the Sinclair-La Mer method, very high concentrations are prevented by maintaining the temperature of the bulk aerosol material considerably below the boiling point. Whytlaw-Gray and Patterson compared coagulation rates of resin smokes prepared by the two methods and found that the more polydispersed system coagulated at the greater rate, as theory predicts. They also observed that the experimentally determined values of $H$ calculated from equation 2.24 for magnesium oxide smoke and for smokes produced in electric arcs are much higher than those for more homogeneous smokes. However, the interpretation of this latter observation is confused by the differences in electrical charge among the different aerosols.

Fuks[27] points out an interesting experimental discrepancy. Many experiments have demonstrated a linear relationship between $1/N$ and time, in accordance with equation 2.24, even when there is a large change in $N$ (as much as 10 to 30 times) during the time of the experiment. He reviews the work of Deryagin and Vlasenko[39] undertaken with particles of initial average radii of 0.1 to 0.3 micron and points out that the particles must change in size by 2 to 3 times during the experiments. This might be expected to produce curvature, and the fact that it does not suggests that the effect of the increase in the average particle size is compensated by the simultaneous increase in polydispersion. According to Fuks, the smaller the initial radius of the particles the more important becomes the effect of the change in particle size and a linear relationship might not be expected for very small particles. The behavior of ammonium chloride aerosols studied by Whytlaw-Gray and Patterson, shown by Figure 2-6, may be an example of this effect of size. Both weight and number concentrations are

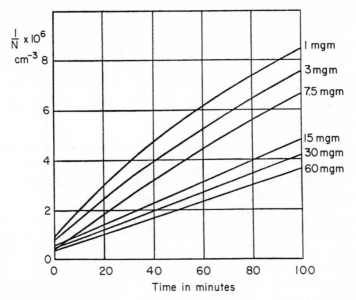

Figure 2-6. The coagulation of ammonium chloride aerosols.[36] (*Courtesy of Edward Arnold (Publishers) Ltd.*)

given, and decreasing weight concentrations in general correspond to decreasing particle size. The top curve corresponds to a particle size of about 0.08 micron. The increasing curvature with decreasing size is very marked.

Fuks also discusses the problem of determining a coagulation constant, $H'$, for a polydispersed aerosol. $H'$ can be expressed by the equation

$$H' = \int_0^\infty \int_0^\infty H(r_1, r_2)\, f(r_1, t)\, f(r_2, t)\, dr_1\, dr_2 \qquad (2.28)$$

where $f(r, t)$ is a function of the particle size distribution at time $t$ and $H(r_1, r_2)$ is the coagulation constant of particles with radii $r_1$ and $r_2$. $H(r_1, r_2)$ is the entire factor of $N^2$ in equation 2.27, although Fuks uses the slightly more precise definition

$$H(r_1, r_2) = 8\pi\, \frac{r_1 + r_2}{2}\, \frac{D_1 + D_2}{2}$$

$$= \frac{kT}{3\eta}\, (r_1 + r_2) \left[ \frac{1 + A\, \dfrac{\lambda}{r_1}}{r_1} + \frac{1 + A\, \dfrac{\lambda}{r_2}}{r_2} \right] \qquad (2.29)$$

Substituting this expression into 2.28 and integrating one obtains

$$H' = \frac{2kT}{3\eta}\left[1 + \bar{r}\left(\frac{\bar{1}}{r}\right) + A\lambda\left(\frac{\bar{1}}{r}\right) + A\lambda\bar{r}\left(\frac{\bar{1}}{r^2}\right)\right] \qquad (2.30)$$

Thus all that is needed to obtain $H'$ for a polydispersed aerosol which can be used in place of $H$ in equations 2.23 and 2.24 is a knowledge of the average values $\bar{r}$, $\left(\dfrac{\bar{1}}{r}\right)$, and $\left(\dfrac{\bar{1}}{r^2}\right)$.

A much more difficult problem is, given a particle size distribution at zero time and an initial particle concentration, to determine the size distribution at any time $t$. Zebel[40] developed the following equation which enables one to undertake such a calculation:

$$\frac{\partial N(r,t)}{\partial t} = \frac{W_0}{4} \int_{Q=0}^{Q=\frac{r}{\sqrt[3]{2}}} H(\sqrt[3]{r^3 - Q^3}, Q)$$

$$\cdot N(Q,t)N(\sqrt[3]{r^3 - Q^3}, t)\ \frac{r^2}{\sqrt[3]{r^3 - Q^3}}\ dQ$$

$$- N(r,t) \int_{Q=0}^{Q=\infty} H(r,Q)N(Q,t)\,dQ \qquad (2.31)$$

where $W_0 = 8kT/3\eta$, $Q$ is a particle radius at zero time, $r$ is the radius produced by the collision of two particles of radii $Q$ and $Q_1$ and the $H$'s are esentially those defined by equation 2.29. Zebel illustrated the application of this equation starting with a highly-peaked particle size distribution and calculating the distribution at various times from equation 2.31 using an IBM 650 computer. The results are shown in Figure 2-7. As expected, the mode shifted to larger diameters and the peakedness decreased with increasing time.

Yaffe and Cadle[41] studied the kinetic behavior of submicron size, polydispersed sodium chloride and titanium dioxide aerosols. A condensation-nuclei counter was used which permits determination of the concentrations of submicron-size aerosol particles in various size ranges.[42] Aerosols were formed by the condensation of vapors produced by heating crystalline $TiO_2$ or NaCl supported on a bare, coiled heating filament of 1 ohm resistance. The vapors were introduced into clean, filtered air at room temperature until a reproducible steady-state aerosol condition was obtained. The aerosol was then allowed to age either in a 5-liter flask or a 250-liter plastic bag and concentrations were determined at various times during the aging process by withdrawing aliquots into the previously evacuated viewing chamber of the counter.

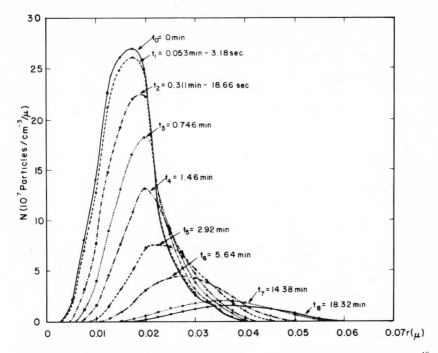

Figure 2-7. Calculated change in particle size distribution with time.[40] (*Courtesy of Dr. Dietrich Steinkopff Verlag*)

Some of the results are shown in Figure 2-8. These are smoothed curves which were averaged over several replications of each determination. The average deviation of the experimental points from each smoothed curve was ±10%. The significant features of each curve, e.g., positions of maxima, inflection points, and slopes, were reproducible from run to run. Perhaps the most interesting aspect of these curves is the linearity of the terminal slopes for each size range on the semi-log plots. This suggests that a first-order or pseudo-first-order process governs this portion of the coagulation, the rate being directly proportional to the first power of the particle concentration. Thus for the linear portions of the decay, the rates may be controlled by the collision of the particles in the size range considered with much larger particles whose concentration remains nearly constant and with the walls of the flask. The fact that the slopes in general increase with decreasing particle size agrees with this interpretation.

Values for the coagulation constants for a number of aerosols, all of them more or less polydispersed, are shown in Table 2-3. The deviation

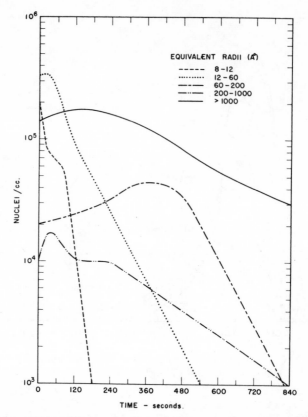

Figure 2-8. NaCl aerosol in 5-liter glass flask. Concentration of various size ranges as a function of time.[41]

from the theoretical value probably results largely from a combination of polydispersity and electrical charging.

Not much is known about the effect of particle shape on the coagulation constant. What is known suggests that shape is not very important except for great differences such as those between long rods or chains and spherical particles. Fuks computes that the coagulation coefficient of an ellipsoid with a 10–1 proportion of axes coagulating with spherical particles would be 1.1 times the coagulation coefficient of spherical particles coagulating with each other; for oblately shaped particles the factor would be 1.04. However, Fuks emphasizes that his calculation ignores the Brownian rotation of the particles which would considerably increase the factor, especially for ellipsoidal particles coagulating with each other.

TABLE 2-3. COAGULATION CONSTANTS $(H)$ FOR SEVERAL AEROSOLS

| Dispersed Material | $H \times 10^8$ (cm$^3$ min$^{-1}$) | Reference |
|---|---|---|
| Theoretical value | 1.8 | — |
| Stearic acid | 3.1 | 44 |
| Ammonium chloride | 3.3–4.7 | 43 |
| Ammonium chloride | 3.0–4.7 | 36 |
| Cadmium oxide | 4.0–5.3 | 36 |
| Magnesium oxide | 8.5–10.9 | 43 |
| Copal resin | 9.3 | 43 |
| Carbon | 14.1 | 43 |
| Zinc oxide | 18.9–19.6 | 43 |
| Silica powder | 26.0–28.0 | 43 |

The pertinent work by Artemov[45,46,47] showed that the size of the coagulation constant of ammonium chloride smoke produced under controlled conditions varies greatly with the water-vapor content of the gas. $H$ decreased from 5 to $3 \times 10^{-10}$ cm$^3$ sec$^{-1}$ as the moisture content increased from 30 to 40%, but with continued increase in moisture content, $H$ increased to $8 \times 10^{-10}$ at 75% relative humidity. Microscopic examination of the aggregates showed that they became increasingly rounded with increasing humidity. This explains the decrease in $H$ for low relative humidities but not the increase at higher humidities.

Whytlaw-Gray and Patterson[36] compared the coagulation rates of stearic acid aerosols, consisting of essentially spherical particles, with that of aerosols of benzene-azo-$\beta$-naphthol, consisting largely of acicular particles. The two aerosols were prepared under essentially the same conditions. The latter aerosol coagulated much more rapidly than the former, presumably because of the difference in particle shape. On the other hand, $p$-xylene-azo-$\beta$-naphthol, which formed particles shaped like those of stearic acid, coagulated only slightly faster than the stearic acid. Beischer and Winkel[48] undertook an interesting study of the coagulation of dimethylamino-azobenzol aerosols. These were prepared much like the Whytlaw-Gray and Patterson "blown" aerosols in that they were prepared by heating the dye in a stream of air. The plots of time vs $1/N$ were convex with respect to the time axis, indicating an increase of $H$ with time. When first formed, the particles were supercooled droplets but they crystallized into acicular form, presumably producing an increase in the coagulation coefficient.

The possibility of influencing the coagulation rate of particles suspended in air by introducing a second gas or vapor has intrigued many workers, probably largely because of the hope that in this manner an aerosol could be stabilized. It has often been suggested that a thin layer absorbed on aerosol particles might affect the surfaces so that the particles would not so readily cohere. A large number of experiments have been performed with these possibilities in mind. The only clean-cut results seem to be those in which the added vapor in some way affects the shape of the particles, as mentioned above, or in which vapor is actually being transferred between the vapor phase and the particles so that appreciable gaseous diffusion occurs.

So far we have been discussing particles as though they were uncharged, although electrical charges have been mentioned as possibly producing some of the deviations from the theoretical value of $H$. In principle, an aerosol could be stabilized by unipolar charging of the particles; indeed, unipolar aerosols have been prepared for which the coagulation coefficient is essentially zero. However, the number concentration in such aerosols decreases with time because of the mutual repulsion of the charged particles. For this reason the coagulation of homopolar aerosols cannot be studied by measuring $1/N$ vs $t$. Instead, it is necessary to collect and examine the individual aggregates. On the other hand, the coagulation constant of a homopolar electrically charged aerosol is not necessarily zero, even if all the particles are charged, since the close approach of the particles may induce charges of opposite sign. This is particularly likely if the particles are highly polydispersed.

When an aerosol is charged in a bipolar, symmetrical manner, that is, when for every positively charged particle there is a particle having a negative charge of equal magnitude, the charging may have little effect on the coagulation rate. On the other hand, where the charging is unsymmetrical it may have a definite effect on the coagulation rate.

Studies of the effects of electrical charges on particles are complicated by the fact that the charging influences the collection of the particles on the walls of any containing vessel.[49]

One of the most thorough discussions of the effects of electrical charging on the coagulation of aerosols is that by Gunter Zebel.[50] He proposed an equation similar to the one he developed for uncharged particles (equation 2.31) which includes the effect of the charge on the particles. Again, using an electronic computer, he calculated the variation with time of the particle size distribution of the same aerosol when uncharged, when mildly charged (unipolar), and when strongly charged (unipolar). It is of interest that the effect of charge varies with particle size both in the theory of Zebel and of Fuks.[27]

## Sonic coagulation

The coagulation rate of particles suspended in fluids can be considerably increased by several methods. One which has received considerable attention is sonic coagulation. The suspending fluid may be either liquid or gas. It is interesting that ultrasonic radiation has been used for dispersing materials in fluids, particularly in liquids, as well as causing them to agglomerate. When mixing two liquids by ultrasonic methods the maximum concentration of the dispersed phase is often less than that which can be achieved by other methods. If the concentrations exceed this maximum, ultrasonic radiation may produce agglomeration. Appreciable mixing of liquids seems to require cavitation, but agglomeration may occur in the absence of of cavitation. Carlin[51] points out that the widespread use of ultrasonic radiation for agglomeration in liquids will probably not occur until more economical means are available for producing large amounts of ultrasonic energy.

The rapid agglomeration of aerosol particles by high-intensity supersonic radiation has often been observed and studied.[52,53,54] Smokes of various kinds have been coagulated using frequencies as low as 4000 cps, and aerosols of large particles such as water fogs of droplet radii from 4 to 16 microns can be coagulated by sound of 250 to 1000 cps if sufficient energy is provided. Sinclair[33] states that available theory indicates that sound of 350 cps should cause nearly as rapid coagulation of natural water fog as any higher frequency.

A number of experimental studies have been made of the influence of aerosol characteristics (particle size, concentration) and sound characteristics (power, frequency) on the coagulation. Podoshevnikov[55] has investigated the dependence of such coagulation on the magnitude of the sound exposure, particularly the effect of sound pressure, $P$, and the duration of exposure. A light-scattering method was used to determine the effect of sound on the particle concentration. For a given change in light scattering, and thus in concentration, the time $t$ required to produce the change increased linearly with a decrease in the sound pressure $P$. The product $Pt$, called the sound exposure, determined both the coagulation progress and the threshold for the start of coagulation. Both dioctyl phthalate and zinc oxide aerosols were studied. The threshold for the start of coagulation decreased with increasing concentration.

The theory of coagulation by sonic and supersonic vibrations has been reviewed by several authors.[27,33,38] It seems to be due to several causes. When a polydispersed aerosol is subjected to radiation in the proper frequency range, particles of different size will vibrate with different amplitudes. These differences considerably increase the probability of collision. The ratio of the amplitude of the particle vibration to that of the sound wave, $(x_0)$ is a function of particle size and is obtained from Stokes' equation corrected for slip:

$$\frac{x}{x_0} = \left\{ \left[ \frac{4\pi r^2 \rho N_1}{9\eta} - \left( 1 + \frac{A\lambda}{r} \right) \right] + 1 \right\}^{-1/2} \tag{2.32}$$

This has been made the basis of methods of particle size determination.[56,57] However, the coagulation rates are often so high that they cannot be accounted for by the differences in particle vibration frequencies.

A second and probably more important effect of the vibrations is to produce hydrodynamic forces of attraction between the particles resulting from the flow of air among them. This is the attractive force between two bodies when air is blown between them. The theory of this action suggests that for a given mass concentration the time required to halve the number of particles in a monodispersed aerosol is independent of particle size, is inversely proportional to the sound intensity, and also to the five-thirds power of the mass concentration. However, experiments with fog[33] have shown that the time for the visibility through the fog to double was only one-hundredth of the time predicted by the theory. At least part of the discrepancy results from the fact that the fog was polydispersed.

A third mechanism promoting acoustic coagulation is radiation pressure. King[58] has shown that when stationary sonic waves are generated in gas, a small sphere suspended in the gas is subjected to a periodic force which pushes it toward the position of maximum amplitude, the antinode. The maximum value of this force is given by the equation

$$F_m = \frac{10\pi^2 r^3 E}{3\lambda} \tag{2.33}$$

where $E$ is the energy density of the sound field. Thus standing waves in an aerosol should cause an accumulation of the particles at the antinodes. It might be expected that ultrasonic pressure contributes appreciably to the coagulation of aerosols by moving the particles toward the antinodes where the hydrodynamic forces between the particles are particularly strong.

Fuks[59] suggests that two mechanisms, acting together, are mainly responsible for sonic coagulation: turbulent displacement of particles and hydrodynamic forces between them. The pulsating turbulent action can bring two particles close together quickly, but not to the point of actual contact. The hydrodynamic forces are effective only at small distances, but effect the actual contact. Fuks suggests that if this hypothesis is correct it may be possible to increase the efficiency of sonic coagulation by causing small sound-produced eddies to appear, for example by means of a turbulizing grid.

Earlier it was mentioned that ultrasonic radiation has been rarely used for agglomeration in liquids. For similar reasons it has not been much used for agglomeration in gases, as in the prevention of air pollution. However, Fuks[27] states that industrial installations are available for the agglomeration of sulfuric acid smoke and other aerosols, and that they can handle 1000 $m^3$/min. Varlamov and co-workers[60] have described the acoustical agglomeration of suspensions of coal dust, sulfuric acid, and solutions of $NH_4NO_2$, $NH_4NO_3$ and $H_2SiF_6$ on a pilot-plant scale. Best results were obtained at frequencies of 16 and 22 kc.

## Coagulation with stirring

Coagulation can also be increased by stirring. This produces turbulence, which increases the motion of particles relative to one another. However, the extent of this increase is very difficult to determine experimentally because the stirring increases the rate of deposition on the walls of any containing vessel as well as increasing the rate of coagulation.

Some of the most extensive studies of the effect of turbulence have been conducted by Langstroth and Gillespie.[61,62] They introduced an aerosol of ammonium chloride into a 1 cu in. chamber equipped with a motor-driven paddle. Number concentration was determined as a function of time for both still and stirred aerosols. An attempt was made to differentiate between coagulation and deposition on the walls using the equation

$$\frac{dN}{dt} = -(HN^2 + \beta N) \tag{2.34}$$

where $\beta$ is the rate constant for deposition. Of course, both $H$ and $\beta$ are functions of the speed of stirring, and because of the change in particle size with time, both are functions of time. However, for short periods of time both $H$ and $\beta$ should be nearly constant and the integrated form of equation 2.34 can be used

$$\ln\left(\frac{1}{N} + \frac{H}{\beta}\right) = \ln\left(\frac{1}{N_0} + \frac{H}{\beta}\right) + \beta t \tag{2.35}$$

$H$ and $\beta$ were evaluated for a number of conditions. For example, as the air velocity increased from 0 to 50 m/min, $H$ increased from $4.5 \times 10^{-8}$ $cm^3$/min to $6.9 \times 10^{-8}$ $cm^3$/min.

Most of the experimental work on coagulation has been undertaken with polydispersed aerosols. Much highly useful information has been obtained with such aerosols, but it is unfortunate that more experimental work has not been done with nearly monodispersed aerosols, such as those prepared by the method of Sinclair and La Mer.[6]

## SEDIMENTATION

### Stokes' equation

When particles in a given size range are suspended in a liquid or gas of lower density than that of the particles, they settle through the fluid, and if the particles are sufficiently far apart the settling velocity increases until a constant rate is attained. This constant rate is known as the terminal velocity. For a given fluid the terminal velocity depends on particle size, shape, and density. If the particle density is less than that of the fluid it will rise, although the principles governing rate are not appreciably changed. Particles small relative to the mean free path of the fluid undergo Brownian motion and diffusion which is superposed on the sedimentation.

The basic equation for the motion of a spherical particle suspended in a fluid and subjected to a constant force $f$ was obtained by Stokes. He equated that force to the opposite viscous force exerted by the fluid when the particle attains a steady velocity $u$:

$$f = 6\pi r\eta u \tag{2.36}$$

For a sphere falling under the influence of gravity, the constant downward force is $(4/3)\pi r^3(\rho - \rho')g$, where $\rho$ and $\rho'$ are the densities of the particle and the medium, respectively. The opposing force of viscosity increases with increasing rate of fall of the sphere until the terminal velocity is reached. Then

$$(4/3)\pi r^3(\rho - \rho')g = 6\pi r\eta u \tag{2.37}$$

and

$$u = \frac{2gr^2(\rho - \rho')}{9\eta} \tag{2.38}$$

The Stokes equation assumes that the fluid is continuous and that viscous drag is the only restraining force on a particle. These assumptions can no longer be made when the particles are so large that a turbulent wake forms, or so small that the diameters are approximately equal to or less than the mean free path of the fluid in which they are suspended. When the latter situation exists, the particles can be considered to slip between the atoms or molecules of the fluid and thus achieve a higher terminal velocity than the Stokes equation predicts.

The problem of correcting for slippage has challenged a number of early investigators, notably Millikan[63,64], Knudson and Weber[65], and Mattauch.[66] However, for most purposes the correction introduced by Cunningham,[22] mentioned previously, is satisfactory:

$$u = \frac{2gr^2(\rho - \rho')}{9\eta}\left(1 + \frac{A\lambda}{r}\right) \tag{2.39}$$

Here $A$ is a constant close to unity (0.9 is often used) and $\lambda$ is the mean free path of the fluid. Sinclair[33] points out that the settling rate for particles having radii between 2 and 0.1 microns can be calculated quite accurately by adding 0.04 micron to the radius. The terminal velocity of particles smaller than about 0.1 micron radius is so low that it is very difficult to observe or determine.

As mentioned above, when particles are sufficiently large that turbulence develops behind the particle, Stokes' law no longer applies, that is, when the inertia of the fluid has an effect. The Reynolds number can be used as a measure of the ratio of inertial forces to the viscous forces. It is a dimensionless quantity which for spherical particles falling through a fluid is defined as $ud/v$, where $v$ is the kinematic viscosity of the fluid. The kinematic viscosity is the viscosity divided by the density. Arnold[67] found experimentally that the effect of the inertia of the fluid on $u$ is negligible for Reynolds numbers less than 1.2. On the other hand Davies[68] has estimated that the Reynolds numbers corresponding to errors of 1, 5, and 10% in the velocities of settling particles are 0.074, 0.38, and 0.82, respectively. The particle diameter corresponding to a Reynolds number of 0.82 is about 120 microns and that corresponding to a Reynolds number of 0.074 is about 50 microns for particles of about 2g/ml density settling in water. Davies has developed a semi-empirical equation which yields accurate results when the Reynolds number is as high as 4:

$$Re = \psi Re^2/24 - 2.3363 \times 10^{-4}(\psi Re^2)^2 + 2.0154$$
$$\times 10^{-6}(\psi Re^2)^3 - 6.9105 \times 10^{-9}(\psi Re^2)^4 \tag{2.40}$$

where Re is the Reynolds number, and

$$\psi = \text{drag coefficient} = \frac{(m - m')g}{\pi \dfrac{d^2}{4} \cdot \dfrac{1}{2}\rho u^2} \quad , \tag{2.41}$$

and $m$ and $m'$ are the mass of the spherical particle and of the fluid displaced by the particle, respectively.

These equations apply only to terminal velocity, and a certain time must elapse before this velocity is reached. However, this time is generally negligible for particles in the size range being considered. The equations are based on the assumption that the particles are rigid. The effect of circulation within bubbles rising in a liquid and within drops rising or falling in a liquid or gas has been discussed by Davies.[68] Throughout the particle size range where Stokes' law applies, for drops of high viscosity falling through a medium of low viscosity, circulation effects can be neglected. Obviously most solid particles can be considered to be rigid, but there seem to be exceptions. For example, Martin[69] suggests that clay, which swells when suspended in water, is such an exception.

Stokes' equation was developed for small solid spheres and does not necessarily apply to particles of other shapes. Numerous investigations have been made of the effect of particle shape on sedimentation velocity. When the departure from spherical shape is rather small, the variation of settling velocities from those calculated using Stokes' equation is likewise small. Whytlaw-Gray and Patterson[36] calculate that for an ellipsoid having a ratio of axes of 2 to 1, or even 3 to 1, the average value that would have to be assigned to the radius so that the Stokes' equation would predict correct velocities differs only slightly from the radius of the sphere having the same volume. However, where the ratio is as large as 5 or 6 to 1, the correction is very large. Irani and Callis[70] suggest that if the ratio of maximum to minimum diameter does not exceed 4, the uncorrected Stokes' law applies.

Highly irregular particles are often the result of coagulation. If the extent of coagulation is such that fluid is trapped, even imperfectly, within the aggregates, the effective density of the aggregates is very much less than that of the bulk material. Even if the aggregates are nearly spherical this decrease in effective density may greatly change the rate of sedimentation.

The theory of the sedimentation of non-spherical particles is discussed by Fuks.[27] He points out that for a given volume of material a sphere has a greater mobility in a fluid than any other shape, at least when the mobility is averaged over a large number of particles which have been permitted to orient themselves within the fluid.

Sedimentation of particles in a liquid or gas is often used for determining particle sizes or size distributions. When the particles are very small, centrifugal force may be substituted for gravitational force. Centrifuges are often used in industry for separating particles from a supernatant liquid and sometimes for classification according to size. Svedberg[71,72] derived a modification of Stokes' equation which is applicable to the motion of particles subjected to centrifugal force:

$$d = \frac{6}{\omega} \sqrt{\frac{\eta \ln \frac{x_2}{x_1}}{2(\rho - \rho')t}} \tag{2.42}$$

where $x_1$ is the distance from the axis of rotation to the bottom of the centrifuge tube, $x_2$ is the distance from the axis of rotation to the meniscus of the suspension, and $\omega$ is the angular velocity.

### Particle interaction

So far we have treated sedimentation from the standpoint of the individual particles. However, when the particle concentrations become sufficiently great, the drag which a particle exerts on the liquid around it in turn affects other particles. When these effects are small they take the form of small variations in settling velocities from those predicted by Stokes' equation. When they became large, a cloud may begin to behave as a unit in which the particles drag the liquid or gas along with them, or vice versa. One of the most startling examples of this is the "base surge" accompanying the surface, underwater, or underground explosions of nuclear devices. Tremendous quantities of the soil or water which are thrown into the air in finely divided form settle back to the surface as a great turbulent cloud surrounding the stem of the main explosion cloud.

A related phenomenon is "fluidization," an industrial process in which very high concentrations of particles suspended in gases or liquids behave much like fluids. Fluidization has been used extensively in the petroleum industry for handling catalysts. To initiate fluidization a gas or liquid is passed upward through a bed of particles until the bed or layer begins to expand. When fluidization has been achieved, the expanded layer of particles is in a very turbulent state and appears to boil. Contact between the particles is maintained, but the friction between them is very slight, which explains the high fluidity. If the rate of flow of fluids is increased sufficiently, the particles are transported by the fluid.

There appear to be optimum sizes for fluidization, perhaps near 25 microns radius for many powders, although the powders used in industrial fluidization are usually larger. The formation of aggregates in fine powders and hydrodynamic forces between individual particles in coarse powders may prevent uniform fluidization.

### Stirred settling

Most of the preceding discussion of sedimentation has assumed that the suspension is tranquil. However, sedimentation is often accompanied by stirring. This of course produces turbulence which superposes a random motion on the downward movement of the particles. Since upward movement of cells of air is generally compensated by downward movements, the stirring does not affect the average rate of fall, but tends to maintain a uniform concentration throughout the stirred volume. The result[33] is a gradual decrease in the concentration accompanied by a decrease in the amount of aerosol settling out per unit time. The basic equation for the stirred settling of particles in a monodispersed aerosol in a box of height $h$ is

$$\frac{u}{h} dt = -\frac{dN}{N} \tag{2.43}$$

or in integrated form,

$$N = N_0 \exp - (ut/h) \tag{2.44}$$

When the aerosol is polydispersed the behavior is more complicated, although various groups of particles having nearly the same diameters will settle at the rate predicted by equation 2.44. Sinclair[33] has analyzed stirred settling in air of a polydispersed aerosol having a log normal size distribution. He obtains the equation

$$-\frac{d}{dt} \log C_t = 1.3 \times 10^5 \frac{\rho}{h} d_m^2 \tag{2.45}$$

where $C_t$ is the cross sectional area per $cm^3$ of the particles, and $d_m$ is the median weight diameter. This is the same as $\overline{d}_{60}$ defined by equation 1.17 and can be converted to other means for this type of distribution using the equation

$$\log d_{q,0}^n = n \log dg - 2.303 \frac{nq}{2} \log^2 s_g \tag{2.46}$$

Similarly,

$$-\frac{d}{dt} \log M_t = 1.3 \times 10^5 \frac{\rho}{h} \overline{d}_{80}^2 \tag{2.47}$$

This has been made the basis of a method of particle size determination.

## INERTIAL EFFECTS

### Theory of inertial impaction

A particle moving through a fluid possesses momentum, which is responsible for many properties of the particle. The requirements of conservation of momentum and inertial behavior in general play a major role in the laws governing many methods for the collection of particles, such as filtration and impaction of aerosol jets on slides.

The following discussion of the theory of inertial impaction is based on the development by Ranz.[73,74]

First consider the case of an aerosol which is forced to make a turn of large radius either because it is in a duct making such a turn or because it is undergoing a swirling motion. Our aim is to apply terminal velocity relationships to calculating the impaction efficiencies of the outside walls. Assume that the gas flow takes a circular motion with a constant diameter $2R$ and a characteristic velocity $v_0$. Then, if impaction is considered to take place only from the aerosol close to the outside wall, the acceleration $a$ toward the wall can be considered to be constant and equal to $v_0^2/R$. The particles will be subjected to this acceleration for a time $t = 2\pi Rn/v_0$ where $n$ is the number of revolutions the gas undergoes during the impaction process. The depth of the gas next to the wall from which particles of diameter $d$ have been removed will be $2u\pi Rn/v_0$, where $u$ is the terminal velocity of these particles when subjected to the acceleration $a$. It is assumed that the particle attains this velocity very rapidly at the start of the process.

The impaction efficiency $N_I$ is now defined as the depth of the gas layer from which particles of size $d$ are removed, divided by the total thickness of the layer subjected to rotation:

$$N_I = 2u\pi Rn/v_0 D_c \qquad (2.48)$$

where $D_c$ is the thickness of the gas stream and $D_c \gg R$.

For the Reynolds number region where Stokes' law applies, the Stokes equation, 2.38, with $a$ substituted for $g$ and $\rho$ assumed to be $\gg \rho'$ can be substituted in equation 2.48:

$$N_{Is} = 2\pi n\rho v_0 d^2/18\eta D_c \qquad (2.49)$$

Figure 2-9 can be used to predict the maximum possible collection efficiencies of particle collectors such as cyclone separators, mechanical-centrifugal separators, and screw separators. The figure includes curves for the parameter $N_{\rho'}/(2\pi n)^2(R/D_c)^2$ where $N_{\rho'}$ is $9(\rho')2v_0 D_c/\rho\eta$ which accounts for air inertia and is independent of particle size. When Stokes' law applies, the value of this parameter is essentially zero. Ranz points out that all particles above a certain size hit the collecting surface and that the impaction efficiencies decrease rapidly for smaller sizes. Figure 2-9 is for a highly idealized system. It does not apply when $D_c$ is nearly as large as $R$, for in this case $v_0$ cannot be considered to be constant and extensive calculations of limiting particle trajectories are required.

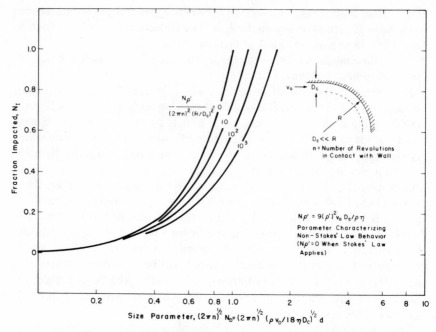

Figure 2-9. Impaction on the outside walls of a sweeping bend or Vortex.[74]

Next we consider the mechanics of a single particle. The general equation of motion of a single particle in a flowing gas when the fluid resistance force is the only force acting on the particle is given by the equation

$$-\frac{(\vec{u} - \vec{v})\,|\vec{u} - \vec{v}|}{2g_c}\,(\rho'\pi d^2 \psi/4) = (\rho'\pi d^3/6g_c)\,d\vec{u}\,dt \qquad (2.50)$$

where $\vec{u}$ and $\vec{v}$ are the velocities of the particle and the gas relative to a fixed coordinate system and $g_c$ is a dimensional conversion factor = 32.2 (lb mass/lb force)(ft/sec$^2$) = 1(gm mass/dyne)(cm/sec$^2$). This equation applies only when the fluid resistance opposing the relative movement of the particle through the gas, represented by the left side of the equation, is very much larger than the force of gravity.

When a particle is given an impulse velocity $u_0$ in a still gas at zero time $t$, the position and velocity of the particle relative to the gas are functions of time and can be calculated using equation 2.50 and the appropriate boundary conditions.

Equation 2.50 for one-dimension and zero gas velocity reduces to

$$-(3\rho'\psi/4\rho d)u_x^2 = du_x/dt \qquad (2.51)$$

and can be written in terms of the variable Reynolds number, a dimensionless time, $t^* = (18\eta/d^2\rho)t$, or a dimensionless distance, $x^* = (18\rho'/d\rho)x$:

$$\int_{Re}^{Re_0} 24d\text{Re}/\psi\text{Re}^2 = t^* \qquad (2.52)$$

or, since $dx/u_x = dt$

$$\int_{Re}^{Re_0} 24d\text{Re}/\psi\text{Re} = x^* \qquad (2.53)$$

where $Re_0$ is the Reynolds number for the impulse velocity $u_0$ of the particle at zero time. When Stokes' law applies, equation 2.52 can be integrated to give

$$\ln(u_0/u_x) = (18\eta/d^2\rho)t \qquad (2.54)$$

and 2.53 can be integrated to give

$$dp'/\eta(u_0 - u_x) = (18\rho'/d\rho)x \qquad (2.55)$$

The value of $x$ that is reached by the time the particle comes to a stop is called the stopping distance, $Ss$, and is reached for infinite time where $u_x$ becomes zero:

$$Ss = d^2\rho u_0/18\eta \qquad (2.56)$$

Ranz has plotted $t^*$, $x^*$, and the stopping distance $S$ when Stokes' law may or may not apply as shown in Figure 2-10, where

$$S = (Ss/Re_0)\int_0^{Re_0} 24d\text{Re}/\psi\text{Re} \qquad (2.57)$$

The time required and the distance traversed between any two instantaneous velocities (that is, between any two Reynolds numbers) can be obtained from the two ordinates.

We now are in a position to consider the impaction of particles on surfaces. When an aerosol is directed against a surface, the larger, heavier particles hit the surface, but smaller and lighter particles may not reach it, being dragged around by the deflected air before contact with the surface can be made. The trajectory of a particle which just reaches the surface is called the limiting trajectory. The problem of limiting trajectories and impact efficiencies can be generalized by writing equation 2.50 in dimensionless terms:

$$-(\tilde{u}_x - \tilde{v}_x)f(\text{Re}) = 2N_D^2 d\tilde{u}_x/d\tilde{t}$$
$$-(\tilde{u}_y - \tilde{v}_y)f(\text{Re}) = 2N_D^2 d\tilde{u}_y/d\tilde{t}$$
$$-(\tilde{u}_z - \tilde{v}_z)f(\text{Re}) = 2N_D^2 d\tilde{u}_z/d\tilde{t} \qquad (2.58)$$

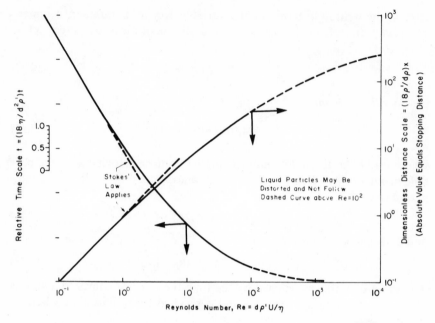

Figure 2-10. Acceleration and deceleration of a single particle.[74]

where $N_D$ is a parameter representing a dimensionless particle size, $(\rho v_0 / 18 \eta D_c)^{1/2} d$, $D_c$ is a characteristic linear dimension of the impaction system, such as the diameter of an orifice, $v_0$ is the characteristic velocity in the impaction process, and a function of the Reynolds number, defined by $\psi = 24 f(\mathrm{Re})/\mathrm{Re}$, has been substituted for $\psi$. This function is such that $f(\mathrm{Re}) = 1$ where Stokes' law applies. The dimensionless variables $\tilde{u}_x$, $\tilde{u}_y$, $\tilde{v}_x$, $\tilde{v}_y$, etc. have the form $\tilde{u}_x = u_x/v_0$, $\tilde{v}_x = \tilde{v}_x/v_0$, etc.

The variable Reynolds number Re, which is changing with changing particle velocity, is related to a known Reynolds number, $\mathrm{Re}_0 = dp'v_0/\rho$, as follows:

$$(\mathrm{Re}/\mathrm{Re}_0)^2 = (\tilde{u}_x - \tilde{v}_x)^2 + (\tilde{u}_y - \tilde{v}_y)^2 + (\tilde{u}_z - \tilde{v}_z)^2 \qquad (2.59)$$

The trajectories of the particles are fully described by equations 2.58 and 2.59 for proper sets of initial and boundary conditions. Of course, a knowledge of the flow field, $\vec{v} = \vec{v}(s,y,z)$ is necessary to obtain a solution.

Ranz points out that the usual boundary and initial condition chosen is that the particle velocity, $\vec{u}$, equals the gas velocity, $\vec{v}$, at the entrance to the impaction zone.

Equations 2.58 and 2.59 also describe limiting trajectories as defined above. The limiting trajectories form the boundaries of cross-sectional areas through which pass the trajectories of particles which impact.

The fractional efficiency of impaction, $N_I$, is defined for the impaction of particles on surfaces as the cross-sectional area of the original aerosol flow from which particles of a given size are impacted, because their trajectories intersect the surface, divided by the total cross-sectional area or by the area of a body collector projected in the flow direction.

For ideal gas flow, that is, for flow for which the velocity is a function of $x$, $y$, and $z$ and is not a function of the Reynolds number of the gas flow, the limiting trajectories and $N_I$ are a function only of $N_D$ and Re. According to Ranz, the relationship is usually given as

$$N_I = N_I(N_D, N_{\rho'}) \tag{2.60}$$

where $N_{\rho'} = \mathrm{Re}_0^2/2N_D^2 = 9\rho'^2 v_0 D_c/\rho\eta$. $N_{\rho'}$ is equivalent to the Reynolds number of the gas flow multiplied by $9\rho'/\rho$.

An unrestricted dimensional analysis of the variables $N_I$, $\rho$, $v_0$, $N$, $D_c$, $d$, and $\rho'$ indicates the need for four independent dimensionless groups to describe the impaction process. These might be $N_I$, $N_D$, $N_{\rho'}$ and $D_c\rho v_0/\eta$.

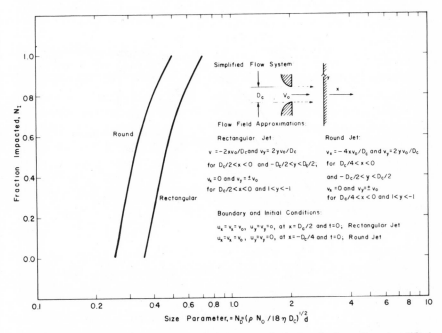

Figure 2-11. Impaction from aerosol jets; analytical solutions for simplified flow systems.[74]

If the gas flow is ideal one of these is eliminated, and if the particle motion obeys Stokes' law, one is eliminated. If both restrictions hold, the relationship becomes a single function of $N_I$ and $N_D$.

Solutions of equations 2.58, 2.59, and 2.60 for simplified flow systems are shown in Figures 2-11 and 2-12. Ranz states that the form of the solution is characteristic of more complex systems, and that analytical solutions represented by Figures 2-9, 2-11 and 2-12 are inter-related, and for practical purposes can be applied to nearly all impaction systems. In fact, additional refinements may not be justified if they must be based on the assumption of conditions, such as ideal flow, which may not be realized in practice.

The region in the figures by Ranz where Stokes' law does not apply are based on experimental results by Hughes and Gilliland.[75]

The report by Ranz[74] includes the results of calculations of the impaction efficiencies in graphical form of a number of basic flow systems. The figures are measures of the ideal impaction efficiencies of simple systems.

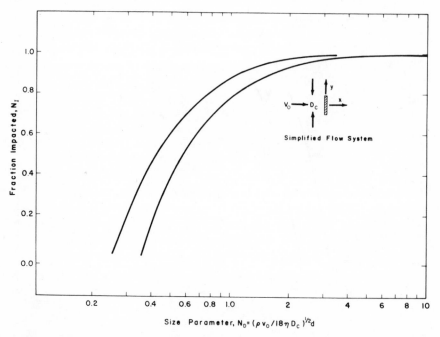

Figure 2-12. Impaction on body collectors; analytical solutions for simplified flow systems.[74]

## Re-entrainment

Impaction efficiencies, whether calculated or experimentally determined, usually do not consider the possibility of re-entrainment of the particles. This is likely to be especially severe when the aerosol velocities are high and the particles are solids.[76] For example, Schadt and Cadle showed that the experimentally determined slope for apparent collection efficiency vs. aerosol velocity curves may be the reverse of that predicted by theory as a result of re-entrainment. These experiments were undertaken using an impactor similar to the May impactor described in Chapter 1. This severe re-entrainment was obtained using sodium chloride and stearic acid aerosols. On the other hand, when glycerine aerosols were impacted, the curves were relatively close to those predicted by theory.

The entrainment described by Schadt and Cadle[76] resulted largely from the sloughing off of aggregates of impacted material which had been allowed to build up on surfaces. Gillespie[76] describes the re-entrainment of liquid and solid particles impacted directly on the surfaces of cylinders. The experiments consisted in directing a stream of aerosol particles toward a single grounded cylinder, and then making counts to determine the number densities of the particles of a given size on various parts of the cylinder. The densities were compared with those expected from theory. The results indicated that an intermediate range of velocities exist within which permanent capture of a particle is relatively low. Velocities on both sides of this range were more conducive to retention once contact was made.

Gillespie and Rideal continued this work with an investigation of the oblique impaction of liquid and solid drops on plane surfaces. The actual impaction process was studied with high-speed photography. The results again indicated that there is a range of velocities of impact in which adhesion on contact is not certain and that drops leave the surface at or near the point of contact. The photographic study revealed that there is an elastic reaction on impact and that the area of contact may be relatively small for a considerable time. Lack of adhesion was attributed to air drag throughout the impaction process, aided by the tendency to bounce. Drops were removed by a "necking out" process and solid particles by a "peeling" action. Air drag is too small at low velocities to remove the particles, and at large velocities the area of contact is large enough to ensure adhesion. This accounts for the range of velocities of low adhesion.

## Impaction and sedimentation

Another factor which can modify the applicability of the above equations is settling of the larger particles during the impaction process. Generally, settling is important only for the relatively large particles in the size range considered in this book, and in any particular case relatively simple calculations based on Stokes' law will show whether settling must be taken into account.

For relatively large particles interception is of importance. This is because the trajectories of the particles need to come only close enough to the collecting surfaces so that the surface of the particle comes in contact with the collector.

### Drag coefficients of evaporating droplets

An aspect of the mechanics of gas-borne particles which has received little attention is the effect of evaporation or burning on the drag coefficients, and thus on the dynamic behavior of drops. A knowledge of this effect is important for several practical applications of sprays, for example, as fuels for jet engines.

Rabin, Schallenmuller, and Lawhead[77] have studied the drag coefficients and shattering of droplets of liquid rocket propellents in a blast of air. Two rather conventional shock tubes were used, one for low and one for high pressures. Shocks were produced by rupturing a cellophane diaphragm, separating the pressure- and expansion-test sections, with a solenoid-activated plunger. The duration of the flow, that is, of the constant-velocity region following the shock front to which the droplets were subjected, was varied by using different lengths of tubing. Quartz windows were provided for visual and photographic observation of the droplet breakup processes.

A hypodermic syringe was used to suspend test droplets on a 0.020 in. stainless steel wire in the test section. Because of the possibility of interference of the wire with the test, the wire was rapidly retracted with a solenoid. The retraction and the diaphragm-puncturing operations were programmed so that the drop was free of the wire and relatively motionless before the shock reached the test section. The retraction of the wire produced several small satellite drops in addition to the primary drops, so that there were always at least two droplets per test. The primary drops ranged from 500 to 1600 microns and the satellite drops from 50 to 300 microns in diameter.

In order to study burning drops, those at atmospheric pressure were ignited with a match during part of the program and with a hydrogen jet igniter the rest of the time. Drops at high pressures were ignited with a high-voltage spark of short duration. High-speed motion pictures were used to determine drop diameters and whether or not a drop shattered.

Part of the testing was carried out with RP-1 (a mixed hydrocarbon) and the rest with diethylcyclohexane.

Drag coefficients, $2F/\rho u^2 A$, where $F$ is the force and $A$ the surface area were plotted against the Reynolds number of the drop. The drag coefficients for LP-1 at one atmosphere increased slightly with increasing Reynolds number between Re = $10^2$ and $10^4$. Throughout most of this range they were much higher than the coefficients for solid spheres and had an average value of about 1.8. The burning droplets had somewhat lower drag coefficients averaging about unity. However, the drag coefficients for the diethylcyclohexane droplets at 34 atmospheres were about unity for both the burning and non-burning droplets.

The studies showed that the flow field following the shock causes the drop break-up rather than any impulsive action of the front itself. For a given duration of flow there is a critical flow velocity above which a drop will shatter.

Two distinct types of breakup were observed: a bag type in which the drop is first blown into the form of a bag, and a shear type. Near the critical flow rate both types may occur. At much greater velocities and at high pressures only the shear type was observed. The critical conditions for breakup of the nonburning drop were well represented by the equation

$$\text{We Re}^{-\frac{1}{2}} = \frac{1}{2} \qquad (2.61)$$

where We is the Weber number, $= ru^2\rho/\sigma$, and $\sigma$ is the surface tension of the liquid.

Drag coefficients and vaporization rates of isooctane sprays in turbulent air streams were determined by Ingebo.[78] Air at 82°F and 16 percent relative humidity flowed along an 8-inch inside-diameter plastic tube, after being metered with a variable-area orifice and passed through a screen to minimize approach stream turbulence. Two transparent optically flat windows were installed in the test section to permit photographing the spray.

Isooctane (2,2,4-trimethyl pentane) was injected into the test section through a 0.041-inch diameter orifice which was pointed into the air stream at the test-section center line. Drop-size and drop velocity data were obtained by photographing the spray at distances of 1, 5.5, 14, and 18 inches from the injector center line.

The camera was a device for obtaining *in situ* photomicrographs of the droplets so that size distributions of the droplets could be obtained without having to collect them. It also provided information concerning droplet velocity. The rapidly moving droplets were optically "stopped" by a combination of two techniques. Images of the particles produced with a lens system were focused on a rapidly rotating mirror and again onto film in the camera. The rotation was at such a speed (3000 to 11,000 rpm) and direction as to largely compensate for the droplet velocity. However, exact compensation was not necessary since illumination was achieved with a short (4 microsecond) duration flash produced by discharging two 1.0-microfarad capacitors across a pair of magnesium ribbon electrodes. Droplet diameters were determined from the photomicrographs with an accuracy of ±3 microns. Droplet velocities were obtained from the mirror rotation speeds required to obtain sharp photomicrographs of the drops.

The size distributions were found to be well represented by the log-probability and the Nukiyama-Tanasawa relationships, described in Chapter 1, and $\bar{d}_{20}$ obtained from these functions was very close to that calculated directly from the data.

An empirical equation was obtained for the drop drag coefficient:

$$\psi = 444 \, \frac{\rho}{\rho'} \, \frac{d}{\Delta u} + \frac{8 k_g \Delta \tau \, \mathrm{Nu}}{H_v \rho' d \Delta u} \tag{2.62}$$

where $k_g$ is the thermal conductivity of the gas, $H_v$ is the heat of vaporization of the liquid, and Nu is the heat transfer Nusselt number. Nu is defined as $hd/k_g$ where $h$ is the heat transfer coefficient in g-cal/sec cm$^2$ °C. The coefficient 444 contains the dimensions sec$^{-1}$. This equation of course applies only to isooctane, and the generality of its application is unknown. The drag-coefficient values are plotted in Figure 2-13. It shows that the drag coefficient of evaporating liquids is not a single-valued function of the drop Reynolds number, but that the relationship varies with relative air velocity with respect to the drop, $\Delta u$. The drag coefficient for solid spheres is included for comparison.

### Filtration

A very large literature has accumulated concerning both the theoretical and the applied aspects of inertial effects on particles.* Nonetheless, three specific aspects of inertial impaction will be discussed because of their practical importance and because they involve several complicating effects. These aspects are filtration, the impaction of small suspended particles by larger particles, and "isokinetic" sampling.

The filtration of particles suspended in a fluid, either liquid or gas, is

---

*No attempt is made here to review this literature and for such a review the reader is referred to books such as Fuks' "The Mechanics of Aerosols"[59] and Richardson's "Aerodynamic Capture of Particles."[79]

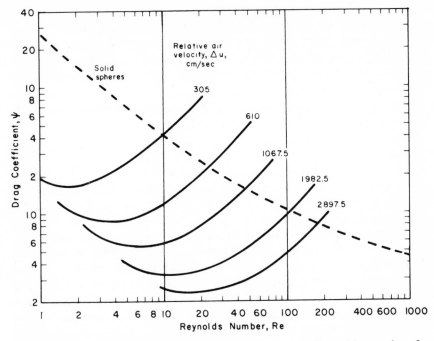

Figure 2-13. Relation between drag coefficient and Reynolds number for isoctane droplets and solid spheres.[74]

generally accomplished by one of two types of filters. One is essentially a sieve, removing particles larger than the openings and allowing smaller ones to pass through. This is the basis of most filters for suspensions in liquids and of membrane filters for both liquids and gases. The other type involves the use of filters consisting of fibers which may be woven or in the form of a mat. The spaces between the fibers are much larger than the diameters of the particles to be removed and the removal is effected by diffusion, interception, and impaction. This discussion will be restricted to the latter type of filtration. The literature concerning this type of filtration has been reviewed by Chen[80] and more recently by Dorman.[81]

As was pointed out in the section on diffusion, the larger particles are captured by fiber filters by impaction and interception, while particles which have diameters about equal to or smaller than the mean free path of the gas are captured largely as a result of diffusion of the particles to the fiber surfaces. Fibers of intermediate size are collected very inefficiently, as shown by Table 2-2, because none of these mechanisms operates very efficiently.

No equation based on filtration theory has been very successful in predicting the filtration efficiency of fiber filters. One probable reason is that the fibers are never all the same size and the "effective mean diameter" may differ for the different mechanisms of collection. Another is the fact that the paths of flow through the filters are tortuous, so that the flow field is very difficult to define.

Langmuir[82] developed equations based on the assumption that only diffusion and interception effect the collection:

$$\frac{P}{\alpha \beta b} = \frac{2.24 \eta D}{(\epsilon_0 + \epsilon_\lambda)(\epsilon_0 - \epsilon_s)^2 r_F^3} \tag{2.63}$$

and

$$\gamma = \frac{\epsilon_0 r_F A R (\epsilon_0 + 2\epsilon_\lambda)}{\pi \eta} \tag{2.64}$$

where $P$ is the pressure drop, $\alpha$ is a constant near unity to correct for inaccuracies in the theory, $\beta$ is the ratio fiber volume/filter volume, $b$ is the filter thickness, $r_F$ is the fiber radius, $r_s$ the particle radius, $\epsilon_s = r_s/r_F$, $\epsilon_\lambda = 0.68 \lambda / r_F$, $A$ is the filter area, $R$ is the resistance per unit area and is equal to $P$/volume flow rate of air, and $\epsilon_0 r_F$ is the minimum distance from the fiber of the layer of the aerosol from which particles diffuse to within a distance $r_s$ of the cylinder. The filtering action, $\gamma$, is defined by the equation

$$N/N_0 = \exp(-\gamma) \tag{2.65}$$

The value of $\epsilon_0$ can be evaluated from equation 2.61 or it can be calculated from experimentally determined values of $\gamma$ and $AR$ using the equation

$$\gamma = \epsilon_0^2 r_F A R / \pi \eta \tag{2.66}$$

Langmuir suggested that $r_F$ could be calculated from the equation

$$r_F^2 = \frac{4M\phi b \beta L(1 - \beta)v_0 \eta}{P} \tag{2.67}$$

where $M$ is a numerical factor usually lying between 0.5 and 1.5 which must be determined for individual cases, $L$ is the total length of fibers per unit volume, and $\phi = [\ln(1/\beta) + 2\beta - \beta^2/2 - \frac{3}{2}]^{-1}$. $M$ depends on the degree of dispersion and the orientation of the fibers.

Langmuir's equation predicts the existence of a particle size for maximum penetration (minimum $N/N_0$) as discussed above.

Several attempts have been made to include the effect of inertia in the expression for $\gamma$. One of these is due to Davies.[83] He defined a distance $x$ from the axis of the fiber outside which particles are not collected by the fiber. He then derived the approximate equation

$$x/r_f = [r_s/r_F + (0.25 + 0.4r_s/r_F)P_F - 0.0263r_sP_F^2/r_F]$$
$$\cdot (0.16 + 10.9\beta - 17\beta^2) \qquad (2.68)$$

Then

$$\gamma = \left(\frac{\beta}{1 - \beta} \cdot \frac{2}{\pi r_F} \cdot \frac{x}{r_F}\right)b \qquad (2.69)$$

This expression shifts the particle size for maximum penetration to smaller values than those predicted by the Langmuir equation. According to Green and Thomas,[84] the Langmuir equations tend to overestimate the filtration efficiency and the Davies equations tend to underestimate it.

Dorman approached the problem of including inertial effects using a combination of dimensional analysis and the experimental results of Ramskill and Anderson.[85] He found that an equation of the form

$$N = N_0 \exp[-A'v_0^2 + B'v_0^{-\frac{1}{2}} + I)^b] \qquad (2.70)$$

fitted the experimental data in a satisfactory manner. $A'$, $B'$, and $I$ are inertial, diffusion, and interception parameters.

Dorman concluded that there is reasonable agreement between the Langmuir and experimental values for the interception parameter when $M$ is chosen to be 0.5. However, then the diffusion parameter from experiment does not agree with that calculated from Langmuir's equations, the divergence increasing with decreasing radius. At relatively high velocities the inertial parameter becomes important and depends on $v_0^2$.

A number of aspects of aerosol filtration by fiber-filters have been neglected in the above discussion. The particles, particularly solids, are not always retained by the fibers following contact. Large particles may settle onto fibers within the filter, increasing the collection efficiency. Electrical charges on the filters, on the particles, or both may considerably increase the collection efficiency.[86,87,88]

### Collection of small particles by large ones

The collection of droplets by falling drops was investigated by Langmuir[89] who introduced a dimensionless parameter $K$ defined as

$$K = L/R = \tfrac{2}{9}r^2\rho U/R\eta \qquad (2.71)$$

where $L$ is the range which the droplet of radius $r$ would have if projected into air at the velocity $U$. $R$ is the radius of the collecting drop. The collision efficiency $E$ was defined by Langmuir as the ratio of the capture cross section to the cross-sectional area of the drop. When the Reynolds number of the drop is high,

$$E_h = K^2/(K + \tfrac{1}{2})^2 \qquad (2.72)$$

and when it is much smaller than 1000,

$$E_e = [1 + (\tfrac{3}{4}) \ln 2K/(K - 1.214)]^{-2} \qquad (2.73)$$

Langmuir proposed an empirical equation for intermediate Reynolds numbers which combined $E_h$ and $E_i$:

$$E = [E_e + E_h(\mathrm{Re}/60)][1 + (\mathrm{Re}/60)] \qquad (2.74)$$

The Langmuir equations led to calculated efficiencies which agree rather closely with experimental results when there is a large size difference between drops and droplets. However, both theoretical considerations and comparison of the equations with experimental results show that Langmuir's equations are much less satisfactory when the drops and droplets are nearly the same size.

The latter situation has been considered theoretically by Hocking[90] for drops small enough for Stokes' equation to apply. His definition of $E$ was essentially that of Langmuir, and his method of approach was to determine the forces on the spheres from the solution of Stokes' equation for two moving spheres, making allowance for their mutual interaction.

This approach led to a series of differential equations of motion which were solved by a Runge-Kutta method of step-by-step integration using an electronic computer. The results are shown in Figure 2-14. They indicate that no collisions occur if the radius of a drop of unit density is less than 18 microns. The inertia for smaller drops is so small as to make collisions impossible.

An experimental study of the collection efficiencies of water drops in air was undertaken by Picknett,[99] who confirmed the idea that there is a critical drop size below which coalescence does not occur. When the drop size was 40 microns, droplets smaller than 2 microns were not collected; when the drop size was 30 microns, droplets smaller than 4 microns were not collected.

These studies somewhat underestimate the effectiveness of rain clouds for scrubbing fine wettable particles from the atmosphere. If the particles are actually suspended in the clouds, coagulation with the cloud droplets may occur which in turn are swept up by raindrops. In this way, even submicron-size particles can be removed.[92]

When the smaller particles are solid and non-wettable rather than liquid, the efficiency $E$ is markedly reduced, as has been shown by several investigators.[93,94] Pemberton[95] has investigated this situation theoretically

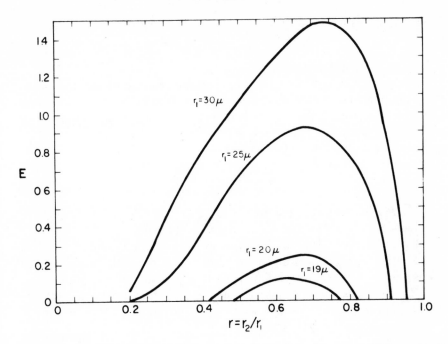

Figure 2-14. The collision efficiency for drops of radius $r_2 \mu$ colliding with droplets of radius $r_1 \mu$.[90]

and has proposed a mechanism of capture of a non-wettable particle by a liquid drop, in which capture is opposed by the surface tension of the drop. He derived a non-dimensional number called the penetration factor, which is used in a mathematical formula for the condition for the retention of the particle by the drop. He also derived the equations of motion of a particle moving according to Stokes' law in the velocity field due to the potential flow around a sphere.

According to this theory capture can be achieved only by penetration of the drop by the solid particle, which is accomplished by doing work against the surface tension force at the expense of kinetic energy.

The penetration factor is defined as

$$Z = \left(\frac{2W}{m}\right)^{\frac{1}{2}} \Big/ u \qquad (2.75)$$

where $u$ as usual is the terminal velocity of the drop, $m$ is the mass of the particle, and $W$ is the total amount of work done by the particle against the surface tension of the drop. The incident kinetic energy of the particle must be at least equal to $W$, which can be calculated from the equation

$$W = \tfrac{8}{3}\pi r^2 \gamma \tag{2.76}$$

where $\gamma$ is the surface tension.

The particle is assumed to be captured and retained by the drop when the component of the velocity of impact normal to the surface of the drop exceeds $V_{PN}$, and, if the impact is oblique, the tangential component of velocity is destroyed before the particle leaves the surface again. This further condition leads to the inequality

$$\frac{v^2 - V_{PN}^2}{v^2 \cos^2 a - V_{PN}^2} \leq \frac{4R^2 C^2}{m^2} \tag{2.77}$$

where $R$ is the radius of the drop, $v$ is the impact velocity at an angle of incidence $a$, $c = 6\pi\eta r$, and $\eta$ is the viscosity of the liquid.

The differential equations of motion were solved for a number of values of $Z$ using an electronic digital computer, and the collection efficiency was plotted against a dimensionless particle parameter for various values of $Z$. Pemberton also prepared a nomograph for calculating the percentage of particles of various diameters removed by rainfall of various intensities and duration (Figure 2-15).

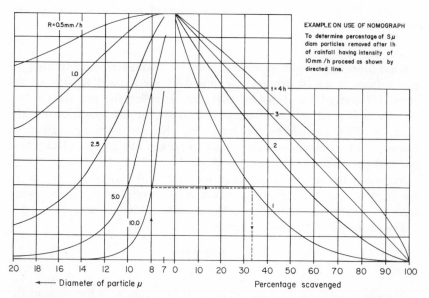

Figure 2-15. Nomograph for rain-scavenging of non-wettable particles. (Rainfall intensity, Rmm/hr duration of rainfall, t hr).[95] (*Courtesy of Pergamon Press*)

Unfortunately, no experimental results have been obtained which can be used to directly test the quantitative aspects of Pemberton's equations, although an attempt to do this was made by Oakes.[94]

### Isokinetic sampling

One other important aspect of inertial effects will be mentioned before leaving the subject. When an aerosol is sampled with a probe, drawing the sample into a duct, if a difference in velocity exists between the aerosol being sampled and that in the probe, the momentum of the larger particles may prevent their being sampled in a representative manner. For example, if the velocity of the aerosol being sampled is directed toward the probe, a probe velocity lower than the external velocity will cause large particles to be impacted into the probe orifice, and the sample will contain a disproportionately large number of particles; a larger than external velocity will have the opposite effect. Sampling in which a serious attempt is made to match the internal and external velocities is known as isokinetic sampling. Strictly speaking, this is achieved only when the aerosol enters the orifice of the sampling device without disturbance or acceleration of any kind. There should be no eddy formation near the orifice and no change of direction as the suspension enters the orifice. Thus the flow should be laminar. Anisokinetic sampling produces significant errors for particles of unit density only when the diameters are larger than about two microns.

Watson[96] has developed a semi-empirical equation which predicts the errors which result from deviations from isokinetic sampling:

$$\frac{C}{C_0} = \frac{U_0}{U}\left[1 + f(p)\left\{\left(\frac{U}{U_0}\right)^{\frac{1}{2}} - 1\right\}^2\right] \tag{2.78}$$

where $C$ is the concentration measured, $C_0$ is the true concentration, $U_0$ is the stream velocity, and $U$ is the mean air velocity at the sampling orifice. The parameter $p$ is the same size parameter that is used in Figures 2-9,

TABLE 2-4. RELATIONSHIP[96] BETWEEN
$f(p)$ AND $p$

| $p$ (Dimensionless) | $f(p)$ (Dimensionless) |
|---|---|
| 3.2 | 0.10 |
| 1.3 | 0.50 |
| 0.5 | 0.72 |
| 0 | 1.0 |

2-11, and 2-12 and here takes the form $d^2 p_p U_0/18nD$, where $D$ is the diameter of the orifice. Values of $f(p)$ were determined experimentally using two varieties of spores. A few values of $f(p)$ are shown in Table 2-4. Equation 2.76 suffers from the fact that it cannot be used when either $U$ or $U_0$ approaches zero, which is a serious drawback since sampling from nearly still aerosols is commonplace.

## PACKING, COHESION, HEAT CONDUCTION

### Packing

A number of properties of powders are related to their closeness of packing: bulk density, heat conduction, compressibility, and even adhesion. For the sake of simplicity, consider first a powder consisting of spheres of equal size, spheres of which are piled on top of each other according to one of several patterns. Actually, there are only six discrete, regular, and stable ways in which such particles can be packed. These have been given the names rhombohedral (two orientations), tetragonal-spheroidal, orthorhombic (two orientations), and cubic, and are arranged in order of increasing porosity, that is, size of the voids. Thus the rhombohedral orientations produce the closest packings. Suppose that the spheres are lined up in rows and the rows combined to form a single layer. If the rows are arranged so that the spheres of one fit into the grooves of the other, combining the layers into regular packings produces so-called hexagonal packings. If these layers are arranged so that the centers of the spheres are directly above each other, the packing is known as orthorhombic. If the rows of the first layer are arranged so that the centers of the spheres are opposite each other, additional layers can still be arranged in either of the two ways first described, giving rise to tetragonal-spheroidal or the cubic orientation, respectively.

The term voids is defined[97] as the ratio of open space volume to the combined open-space and solid material volume; porosity is this same ratio expressed as percentage. The unit cell is defined as the smallest portion of a packing which gives complete information concerning the packing.

The voids and porosity are independent of particle size, as long as the particles are all of one size. However, the volume of a unit cell and the pore volume per unit cell depend on particle size, as shown in Table 2-6. In fact, rather obviously, any property (ratio) of such an array which is dimensionless will be independent of particle size, but any property which includes dimensions (length, area, or volume) will vary with size.

TABLE 2-5. THE EFFECT OF PARTICLE SIZE ON THE CO-HESIVE FORCE $(F_a)$ OF SILICON CARBIDE IN NITROGEN[105]

| Average Diameter (microns) | $F_a$ (dynes/cm²) | Coefficient of Friction |
|---|---|---|
| 25 | 120 | 0.62 |
| 35 | 90 | 1.00 |
| 56 | 17 | 0.93 |
| 63 | 10 | 1.00 |
| 73 | 13 | 0.80 |
| 95 | 10 | 0.78 |
| 111 | 12 | 0.68 |
| 135 | 0 | 0.70 |

Of course, an infinite variety of irregular or unstable arrangements is possible, which will give porosities between 26.95 and 47.64 percent (the values for rhombehedral and cubic packings).

When a powder consists of particles having a distribution of sizes the situation is, of course, quite different. Almost any degree of porosity is possible, although most powders have a porosity between 30 and 50 percent.[99]

A number of attempts have been made to generalize the relationships for uniform powders to powders with a size distribution. One of these was undertaken by Furnas.[100] Mixtures of particles of different sizes will have voids formed by the larger particles that are partially filled by the smaller ones. Furnas first considered a binary system and demonstrated that the voids change with the ratio of the particle size and with the percentage composition of the two components. The results were then extended to a multicomponent system.

TABLE 2-6. CHARACTERISTICS OF PACKINGS OF UNIFORM SPHERES[97,98]

| Packing | No. of Points of Contact | Vol. of Unit Cell | Porosity | No. of Spheres per Unit Volume | Pore Volume per Unit Cell |
|---|---|---|---|---|---|
| Cubic | 6 | $d^3$ | 47.64 | $1.00/d^3$ | $0.48d^3$ |
| Orthorhombic (two orientations) | 8 | $0.87d^3$ | 39.54 | $1.15/d^3$ | $0.34d^3$ |
| Tetragonal-spheroidal | 10 | $0.75d^3$ | 30.19 | $1.34/d^3$ | $0.23d^3$ |
| Rhombohedral (two orientations) | 12 | $0.71d^3$ | 25.95 | $1.41/d^3$ | $0.18d^3$ |

Consider the voids (the fractional void volumes), $V$, to be the same for the different sizes in a powder, if they could be separated out to form powders consisting of single-sized particles. Then the condition for maximum packing density is given by the series

$$\frac{1}{1+V}, \quad \frac{V}{1+V}, \quad \frac{V^2}{1+V} \cdots \tag{2.79}$$

The terms correspond to the volumes of the different component sizes, and the proportion by volume of each of the component sizes is the ratio of the corresponding term to the sum of the terms. Furnas plotted curves of porosity vs. ratio of largest to smallest size. The results demonstrate, as would be expected, that the porosity decreases and the bulk density increases with increasing size range, and that the porosity decreases with an increasing number of components. In practice, the number of components, that is, the number of different sizes, is usually infinite. This approach permits one to make up a mixture of maximum bulk density from powders of various sizes.

Functional relationships between particle size or size distribution and properties such as porosity, number of spheres per unit volume, total surface per $cm^3$, etc. are possible only for regular packing of particles of regular shape. In actual practice it is almost always necessary to determine such effects of particle size experimentally for any given type of material, and to determine correlation coefficients as indications of the usefulness of size for predicting such properties. Herdan[101] states that the dependence of porosity on particle size is much less than the 100 percent implied by a functional relationship. He presents data for 68 surface soils which show that the correlation coefficient between porosity and the weight percent of aggregates greater than 0.22 mm is 0.57 rather than unity.

Heywood[102] has made some interesting generalizations concerning the porosities of real powders. He points out that although smaller particles can fit in the voids between larger ones, decreasing the voidage, fine particles tend to cohere, forming loose chains with a high voidage, and thus nullifying the expected voidage decrease. Hence the porosity for mixed sizes may be greater than for closely packed uniform spheres. In fact, a rough proportionality exists between specific surface and porosity in a dry powder.

Heywood suggests that increased packing densities may be obtained by mixing powders when wet in order to disperse aggregates. Minimum porosity with dry powders is probably attained when a fine powder is mixed with a relatively coarse powder that is nearly uniform in size. He states there should be a gap between the powder sizes which will yield a ratio of 6:1.

When a powder consists entirely of relatively large particles for which cohesion is negligible, the porosity is decreased when the particle size distribution is large.

Graton and Fraser[97] studied the effect of wet and dry conditions on the porosity of powders consisting of powders of different shapes. All the samples were rather coarse, passing an 18-mesh and being retained on a 35-mesh screen. The variation among most of the powders was rather small, varying from about 35 to 43 percent for material compacted by tapping, but the porosity for crushed mica was about 87 percent. Materials which were compacted when wet and then dried were slightly more porous than those which were packed dry, which seems to be contrary to Heywood's experience. However, Heywood may have been working with small particles which form aggregates.

### Cohesion and adhesion

The term "cohesion" is applied to particles of the same composition; "adhesion" refers to particles of different composition. The cohesion of particles is of considerable practical importance and has already been mentioned in several places, for instance, in connection with coagulation.

Cohesion between two solid particles results from the fact that when they approach each other closely enough, a force appears which opposes their separation. If one considers only thermodynamically reversible processes, the repulsive and attractive forces between the two bodies as they approach each other or move apart depend only on the distance between them. Such forces have been studied both theoretically and experimentally by Derjaguin and his co-workers.[103] If the particles are in a gas or vacuum, molecular attraction increases with decreasing distance and Born repulsion forces occur on direct contact. Thus the attractive force passes through a maximum when the particles are separated by a distance of the order of molecular diameters. The molecular attraction is a van der Waals attraction which in turn results from polarization of the molecules and the resulting electrostatic forces. Derjaguin developed a balance for experimentally studying such forces and demonstrated the existence of molecular forces at distances between particles of about $10^{-5}$ to $10^{-4}$ cm. The force of cohesion is the height of the maximum $F$ (on a conventional force diagram it is the depth of the minimum), and is given by the equation

$$F = 2\pi r \sigma \qquad (2.80)$$

where $\sigma$ is the surface tension of the particles.

Similar considerations can be applied to the cohesion of spherical particles in a liquid. However, two complicating features of this situation must be taken into consideration. The first is that concentrations of dissolved ions and molecules near the particles differ from the bulk value. Derjaguin points out that this is particularly important in the presence of ions, since at moderate ionic strength they are capable of forming ionic atmospheres of considerable thickness. If this occurs, account must be taken of forces of repulsion, the magnitudes of which depend on the composition of the electrolyte and on the surface potential of the particles. The second complicating feature is that the structure of the liquid near the surface of a particle may differ considerably from the structure of the bulk liquid. This may explain the fact that unexpected repulsion forces often seem to exist, judging from experimental results.

The existence of such "iono-electrostatic" forces produce two minima instead of one in the distance-force diagrams. If the force bringing the two particles together does not exceed the height of the force barrier between the two minima, the cohesion force will correspond to the first minimum and will be rather small; if it exceeds this height, stronger cohesion will be achieved. For particles which are very hydrophilic, attraction forces predominate only at large distances and cohesive forces are always small. When particles are hydrophobic and weakly charged there is no force barrier and cohesion is always rather strong.

When the particles are dissimilar the situation becomes even more complicated.

The situation is also more complicated when the particles are separated by a liquid film. This is a common occurrence however, an example being soils beneath humid air. The radius of the liquid film and the capillary pressure and surface tension of its menisci must be taken into account. The theory of cohesion under these conditions has also been considered by Derjaguin.[103] For example, when spherical particles come into direct contact and the distance between them is essentially the intermolecular distance and $\delta$, the molecular attraction is

$$N = 2\pi\sigma_{1,2}r \tag{2.81}$$

where $\sigma_{1,2}$ is the surface tension at the interface between the particle and the liquid. If only molecular and iono-electrostatic forces are considered, the expression for the force barrier $P$ is

$$P = (1/r)(\beta/\delta - 2\sigma) \tag{2.82}$$

where $\beta = aD(kTze)^2$, $a$ is a numerical coefficient depending on the ratio between the valences of two ions, $D$ is the dielectric permeability, $e$ the charge of the electron, and $z$ the electro-valence of the counter-ion. This equation demonstrates that the tensile strength of such a powdered material is inversely proportional to the particle radii.

In the case of rather loosely bound powders it may be difficult to differentiate between frictional and cohesive forces. Methods for doing this have been suggested by Cremer, Kraus and Conrad[104] and by Patat and Schmid.[105] The former authors suggested the following equation relating angle of repose of a powder, $\alpha$; the coefficient of friction, $k_f$; the force of cohesion, $F_a$; and the mass of a grain of the material $m_0$:

$$m_0 g \sin \alpha = k_f m_0 g \cos \alpha + F_a \qquad (2.83)$$

Patat and Schmid applied this equation to the study of a number of powders and proposed the empirical equation

$$\log F_a = A \log (l/d) + \log C \qquad (2.84)$$

where $A$ and $C$ are constants which depend upon the type of powder.

Table 2-5 shows some of their results which demonstrate the effect of particle size on the force of cohesion.

An interesting aspect of the cohesion of particles is their behavior in a vacuum. This is of practical interest with respect to landings on the moon, since the suggestion has often been made that a thick dust layer exists on the lunar surface into which a space vehicle might sink. Qualitative experiments undertaken in the author's laboratories suggest that even if such a dust layer exists, a vehicle would not necessarily sink into it. Two test tubes were partially filled with a powdered rock and a ball bearing placed in each. The two tubes were then sealed, one containing air at atmospheric pressure and the other at a fraction of a millimeter of mercury pressure. The tubes were held in a vertical position and the bearings raised to the tops of the tubes with magnets. Withdrawing the magnets released the bearings. The one in the tube at atmospheric pressure sank to the bottom, but the one in the evacuated tube only slightly dented the surface of the dust layer.

A quantitative study of the effect of gas pressure on the cohesive behavior of silicate powders was undertaken by Salisbury, Glaser, Stein, and Vonnegut.[105] The rocks tested included chondrite, tektite, obsidian, basalt, andesite, dunite, and pyroxenite. They were cut to obtain fresh surfaces and powdered in a tungsten carbide ball mill in an argon atmosphere. Eighty percent or more of the particles in all the powders were less than 3 microns in diameter, 90 percent were less than 17 microns, and 99 percent were less than 70 microns.

The experiments were undertaken in a stainless steel vacuum chamber which contained an internal sieving mechanism operated with a bellows. Comparisons were made of the angle of repose of samples of the powders sifted at atmospheric pressure, $10^{-9}$ mm Hg, and $10^{-10}$ mm Hg. The angle of repose was very much greater at the lower pressures and in places was as great as 90°. The vacuum-sieved powders clung to the undersides of wires beneath the sieving mechanism and in general the results indicated a strong high-vacuum cohesion.

An effort was made to obtain semi-quantitative information concerning the strength of the cohesive bonds by applying vibration to the holder of the sieved samples. The powder behaved as a solid, breaking up into large fragments. The quantitative measurements were made using an accelerometer mounted at the top of the sample holder column. Assuming that the bonding is electrostatic and direct bonding is not required to produce cohesion, the shear stress was estimated to be 350 dynes/cm$^2$ at very low pressures.

The strength of the bonds was also studied by determining how thick a layer of powder would cling to a metal or glass slide when the slide was inverted. Layers up to 2 mm in depth could be repeatedly inverted or left inverted indefinitely in the air outside the chamber. Again assuming electrostatic bonding, the normal between the particles and the substrate was estimated to be 750 dynes/cm$^2$. These values seem reasonable when compared with those obtained by Patat and Schmid[105] (Table 2-5) at atmospheric pressure.

Several experiments were undertaken to determine whether electrostatic forces were responsible for the increased cohesion in a vacuum. The results all indicated that they were not. During one electrostatic experiment the sample became contaminated with oil vapor from the vacuum pump. Upon being sifted this sample exhibited negligible cohesion, although the distribution and intensity of charge appeared to be unchanged. These results suggest that atomic forces such as van der Waals forces and covalent and ionic bonds are responsible for high-vacuum cohesion.

Powder flow properties in general seem to result from a combination of cohesive properties, frictional resistance, and granular structural resistance. Brown[107] elaborates on this by stating that the flow of powders is determined by a number of factors including the transmission of external and body forces through the system, particle size and shape distribution, ruggedness and resilience of the particles, cohesion, adhesion of particles to surfaces, and adsorbed films, especially of water. The angle of repose indicates the ease of initiating the flow of a powder, and equations such as 2.83 are probably oversimplifications. Thus Brown points out that Train[108] has showed that the size of the pile of powder influences the angle of repose, small piles forming steeper slopes than large ones. In fact, Brown suggests that the angle of repose is largely independent of particle size. However, for particles smaller than 100 microns diameter there is considerable evidence that the angle of repose increases with decreasing particle size. It seems likely however, that the nature of the particle size distribution and its effect on porosity plays a larger role in cohesion and flow properties than any average particle size; the smaller the porosity, the larger would be the expected cohesion for any given type of material. This is supported by the fact that the angle of repose is markedly influenced by the degree of compaction, higher compaction causing greater angle of repose.

Other flow properties, such as the blocking of an aperture and the pattern of flow through an aperture seem to have a similar relationship to cohesion and particle size.

### Compression

The compression of powders is also related to porosity and to particle size. A study of particle size effects in the compression of several nonmetallic powders has been made by Huffine and Bonilla.[109] The compressions were made with a laboratory press in a uniform diameter die. Three crystalline powders were employed: sodium chloride, sucrose, and quartz. They were separated into various fractions according to size using 14 screens of 24 to 200 mesh. The maximum nominal deviation from average size within a fraction was $\pm 9$ percent.

The results were interpreted in terms of the integrated Bal'shin equation:

$$\log P = -LV_0 + b \qquad (2.85)$$

where $P$ is the applied pressure, $L$ and $b$ are constants, and $V_0$ is the ratio of the volume of the powder to the volume of the continuous material.

Plots of relative volume, $V_0$, vs. log pressure were straight lines throughout most of the pressure range for sodium chloride and sucrose, and the entire range for quartz. However, the compaction achieved for quartz was considerably less than for the other powders. The maximum pressure applied was 61,200 psi. This was sufficient to remove all the voids from the sodium chloride ($V_0 = 1$), but it was estimated that 2,000,000 to 6,000,000 psi would be required to remove the voids from quartz.

The effect of particle size was essentially the same for each powder, namely that the result of increase in particle size was to increase the slope or pressing modulus $L$ of equation 2.85. Both the initial volume and the decrease in volume for a given pressure increase decreased with increasing particle size.

The effect of particle size was expressed by the equation

$$\log((P_1/P)/V_0 - 1) = kd^a \qquad (2.86)$$

where $k$ and $a$ are constants for the various materials and $P_1$ is the extrapolated intercept at the $V_0 = 1$ axis. Huffine and Bonilla[109] suggest that $k$ and $a$ should be related to the mechanical properties of the material, but if so, the relationship was not apparent. It is interesting that the initial values of $V_0$, which are measures of porosity, decreased with increasing particle size. This should not be so if the packing arrangement is the same for all sized fractions of a given powder. Thus the difference in slopes may have reflected the effects of differences in the packing arrangements among the different size fractions, which in turn may have resulted from progressive variations in the nature of the size distributions. Carrying this speculation one step further, the variations in $k$ and $a$ may have resulted as much from variations in the size distributions of the original unfractionated powders as from differences in the mechanical properties of the continuous materials.

Huffine and Bonilla explain the effect of particle size by assuming that the decrease in pressure may take place in several ways, that the initial way for powders such as these is slippage of particles over each other to new equilibrium positions, and that the volume change accompanying slippage is greater than for subsequent action. They suggest that the pressure at which each slip is completed is greater for finer particles, and that the slippage phase of compression of the large particles at low pressures has been largely supplanted by the subsequent compression mechanisms, such as deformation. According to this suggestion, slippage remains predominant for the small particles to a much higher pressure, and the pressing modulus is low. This may be correct, but it hardly explains the original high values of $V_0$ for the fine powders.

A series of compressions was made with mixtures of a coarse fraction and a fine fraction of sodium chloride. A plot of pressing modulus vs. weight percent of the coarser fraction was a straight line showing an increasing modulus with increasing weight percent up to about 70 percent of the coarser fraction. Increasing the percentage of the coarser fraction beyond 70 percent had little additional effect. Probably above 70 percent the larger particles were in contact with each other and insufficient fine material was present to fill the voids.

## Thermal conductivity

The thermal conductivity of powders is also very closely related to porosity, but the effect of particle size, except as the size distribution affects porosity, remains in considerable doubt. The difficulty is similar to that experienced in developing equations to describe other phenomena of bulk powders, namely constructing a model that represents reasonably well the complex system that characterizes the usual powder.

Marathe and Tendolkar[110], studied the thermal conductivities of powdered marble, hematite and copper. They concluded that thermal conductivity is a linear function of porosity and is independent of particle size for a given porosity. The results also suggested that the conductivity is determined largely by the conductivity of the continuous phase.

On the other hand, Wakashima[111] found that the thermal conductivity of several glass powders of differing particle size and of several metallic oxides decreased with decreasing particle size.

A number of equations have been developed for rather special situations. Lord Rayleigh derived the following equation for the cubical arrangement of uniform spheres:

$$\frac{K}{K_m} = \frac{(2 + \nu)/(1 - \nu) - 2p}{(2 + \nu)/(1 - \nu) + p} \tag{2.87}$$

where $K$ is the effective conductivity of the two-phase medium, $K_m$ is the conductivity of the continuous phase, $p$ is the fractional volume of the obstacles, $\nu$ is $K_0/K_m$, and $K_0$ is the conductivity of the obstacles.

Russell[112] calculated the conductivity of cubes in a cubical array, assuming that the isotherms are planes perpendicular to the direction of heat flow, and obtained the following equation:

$$\frac{K}{K_m} = \frac{\nu p^{2/3} + (1 - p^{2/3})}{\nu(p^{2/3} - p) + (1 - p^{2/3} + p)} \tag{2.88}$$

Woodside[113] made a similar assumption for a cubical array of spheres, obtaining the equation

$$\left(\frac{K}{K_m}\right)^{-1} = 1 - R\left[1 - \left(\frac{\alpha^2 - 1}{2\alpha}\right)\ln\left(\frac{\alpha + 1}{\alpha - 1}\right)\right] \tag{2.89}$$

where

$$\alpha = \left[1 + \frac{4}{\pi(\nu - 1)R^2}\right]^{1/2}$$

and $R$ is $(6p/\pi)^{1/3}$.

Laubitz[114] determined the effective thermal conductivity of three dense magnesium oxide powders and one dense aluminum oxide powder, all of very uniform particle size; powders consisting of porous bubbles of aluminum oxide and zirconium oxide, again of quite uniform size; and an aluminum oxide powder with a wide size distribution. There was a marked temperature effect which could not be explained by any of the previously derived equations and consisted of a marked increase in conductivity with temperature. Laubitz suggested that this was caused by radiation between the particles and modified Russel's equation (2.88) to account for radiation:

$$K_1 = 2K(R) + 4\sigma T^3 \epsilon \frac{d}{p} (1 - p^{2/3} + p^{4/3}) \qquad (2.90)$$

where $\epsilon$ is the emissivity of the material constituting the powder, $d$ is the linear dimension of the particles, $p$ in this case is the fractional volume of the particles, and $\sigma$ is the Stefan-Boltzmann constant. According to this equation, particle diameter should be important if radiation makes an important contribution to the thermal conductivity.

This equation predicted quite well the thermal conductivities of the uniform powders, but failed for the aluminum oxide having a very wide size distribution and a small median particle size. Nonetheless, it seems likely that radiation must often be considered in interpreting the results of thermal conductivity studies.

## RHEOLOGY OF SLURRIES

The flow properties (rheology) of a fluid are to a large extent characterized by the viscosity of the fluid and the influence of such factors as temperature and the rate of shear on the viscosity. Qualitatively, viscosity is the resistance of a fluid to shear and quantitatively it is the ratio of shearing stress to rate of shear. It can also be defined as the force required to produce unit velocity between two parallel unit areas separated by a layer of the fluid of unit thickness. When the viscosity is independent of the rate of shear the liquid is called Newtonian, and when it varies with the rate of shear it is called non-Newtonian. Many slurries behave in a non-Newtonian manner in which case, if the viscosity is large, they are often called plastic.

Viscosity is often of interest because of its effect on the rate of flow through tubes. The classical relationship between rate of flow $q$ and the viscosity $\eta$ is Poiseuille's equation:

$$q = \frac{\pi D_c^4 P}{128 \eta L} \qquad (2.91)$$

where $D_c$ is the tube diameter, $P$ is the pressure, and $L$ the tube length. Bingham[115] regarded the force on a plastic material as made up of two portions, one which overcomes solid fractional resistance $P$ and the remainder, $p$. He suggested the equation:

$$-\frac{dv}{dx} = \frac{P - p}{\eta'} \qquad (2.92)$$

where $v$ is the velocity at a point $x$ perpendicular to the flow direction, and a modification of the Poiseuille relation for flow of plastic material under the influence of gravity:

$$\eta' = \frac{\pi g D_c^4 t \psi_0 (h - h_0)}{128 QL} \qquad (2.93)$$

where $Q$ is the volume of material of density $\psi_0$ flowing in time $t$, and $h$ and $h_0$ can be considered to be the hydrodynamic heads of plastic material corresponding to $P$ and $p$. In (2.92) and (2.93), $\eta'$ is a constant having a significance similar to that of $\eta$ for Newtonian fluids. However, the variation of viscosity with shear rate for slurries is often much more complicated than is indicated by Bingham's equations.

Einstein in his doctoral thesis developed the following equation for the viscosity of suspensions:

$$\eta'' = \eta(1 + f\theta) \qquad (2.94)$$

where $\eta''$ is the viscosity of the suspension, $\eta$ is the viscosity of the suspending medium, $\theta$ is the ratio of the volume of suspended material to total volume, and $f$ is a constant varying between 2.5 and 2.9. According to Dalla Valle,[99] Einstein's equation gives an approximate value of the viscosity when the concentration of suspended material does not exceed 2 percent and the particles are relatively large (20 to 200 microns).

An important aspect of the Einstein equation is that $\eta''/\eta$ is independent of particle size. However, this will only be true if all the particles are geometrically similar, and may or may not be true for concentration regions where Einstein's equation does not apply. The Einstein equation is discussed in considerable detail by Reiner.[116] He suggests that the non-Newtonian behavior of suspensions in Newtonian liquids results from a change of structure (including orientation) of the dispersed phase with changing rate of shear.

Ree and Eyring[117] developed an equation for non-Newtonian viscosity based on the concept that the relaxation process of viscous flow can be considered to be the sudden shifting of a small patch on one side of a shear surface with respect to the neighboring material on the other side of the shear surface. A shear surface can then be considered to divide a mosaic of such patches lying on either side of the surface. The mosaic is usually heterogeneous and can be described by groups of patches each characterized by a mean relation time $\beta_n$, the fractional area of the shear surface that the group occupies, $x_n$, and by $\alpha_n$, which is a characteristic shear volume divided by $kT$, where $k$, as usual, is the Boltzmann constant. The generalized equation for viscosity is then:

$$\eta = \sum_{n=1}^{n} (x_n \beta_n/\alpha_n)(\sinh^{-1} \beta_n \dot{S}/B_n \dot{S} \qquad (2.95)$$

where $\dot{S}$ is the shear rate.

Maron and Pierce[118] applied the Ree-Eyring flow theory to suspensions of spherical particles, and in particular to the results of an experimental investigation of the flow behavior of X-667 synthetic latex, an aqueous suspension of spherical particles of butadiene-styrene copolymer stabilized with potassium oleate.[119] The flow was found to be Newtonian below a polymer volume fraction of 0.25 and non-Newtonian above this volume fraction. For shear stress in the range 50 to 800 degrees per $cm^2$, $n$ was either 1 or 2, referring to water and to polymer. Thus equation (2.95) became

$$\eta = \frac{x_1 \beta_1}{\alpha_1} + \frac{x_2 \beta_2}{\alpha_2} \left( \frac{\sinh^{-1} \beta_2 \dot{S}}{\beta_2 \dot{S}} \right)$$

$$\equiv a + b \frac{\sinh^{-1} \beta_2 \dot{S}}{\beta_2 \dot{S}} \qquad (2.96)$$

Evaluation of the parameters $a$, $b$, and $\beta_2$ from the experimental results gave an equation which reproduced the dependence of the viscosity on shear rate at all temperatures and concentrations. These parameters are dependent on concentration and temperature. Absolute rate theory predicted correctly their temperature dependence, and empirical equations were developed to express the concentration dependence. These equations were used to calculate the distance between equilibrium positions of the water molecules and also of the latex particles.

Maron and Sisko[120] extended this work to lower shear rates, basing their calculations on experimental studies by Maron and Belner.[121] This region is of particular interest since the Ree-Eyring theory predicts that the flow becomes Newtonian as the shear rate approaches zero. In this case it was necessary to evaluate five parameters letting $\theta_n = (\sinh^{-1}\beta_n \dot{S})/ \beta_n \dot{S}$, (equation 2.95) becomes

$$\eta = \frac{x_1 \beta_1}{\alpha_1} + \frac{x_2 \beta_2}{\alpha_2} \theta_2 + \frac{x_3 \beta_3}{\alpha_3} \theta_3 + \cdots$$

$$\equiv a + b_2\theta_2 + b_3\theta_3 + \cdots \qquad (2.97)$$

where $a$ is the contribution made to the viscosity by the solvent and the $b$'s are the coefficients of the $\theta$'s for the various latex flow units. It was necessary to include the first three terms in (2.97) and the parameters to be evaluated were $a$, $b_2$, $b_3$, $\beta_2$, and $\beta_3$.

Unfortunately, the above theory, useful as it may be for correlating viscosity data, tells us little about the effect of particle size on the viscosity of slurries. Williams[122,123] determined the viscosity of suspensions of glass spheres and concluded that the particle size distribution markedly affects the viscosity at concentrations above 30 percent by volume. He also found that the more nearly uniform the particle sizes, the lower the concentration of particles required to produce a given viscosity. Suspensions of particles may exhibit thixotropy, which is a tendency for the suspension to acquire a gel-like consistency on standing which largely disappears on stirring. Williams observed that for particles less than one micron in diameter the thixotropic tendency increases with decreasing size. He found that the viscosity of the suspensions was Newtonian up to 50 volume percent for particles larger than one micron in diameter. The viscosities of many of his suspensions followed the equation:

$$\frac{V}{X} = \frac{1}{f} - \frac{SV}{f} \tag{2.98}$$

where $X$ is the specific viscosity, which is the ratio of the viscosity of the suspension to that of the liquid medium (the relative viscosity) minus one, $V$ is the volume concentration of the solid, $S$ is the packed volume of solid particles, and $f$ is the Einstein coefficient (equation 2.94).

In connection with equations such as (2.98), Blair[124] has pointed out that the Einstein equation has been modified to allow for non-spherical particles, lyophilic properties, charge, compressibility of the dispersed phase, and other properties, and that Ward[125] has quoted almost fifty modifications of the Einstein equation.

Rigden[126,127] undertook studies to determine the characteristics of dry powders which determine the relative viscosity of powder-in-liquid dispersions over a wide concentration range. They indicated the importance of the porosity (which is related to the size distribution) of the dry powders as a factor controlling the relative viscosity of powder-liquid systems.

Rigden developed a method for experimentally determining the "mean pore radius" of a powder. He prepared suspensions of a large number of powders differing in mineral type and fineness but at a very high concentration. The resulting suspensions were essentially Newtonian in behavior. The liquid phase consisted of a "bitumen" having a viscosity at 15°C of $2.72 \times 10^6$ poises. A plot of the logarithm of the relative viscosity against $C/\sqrt{\bar{r}}$ where $\bar{r}$ was the mean radius of the pores and $C$ the concentration demonstrated the strong relationship between the two over a range of $\bar{r}$

from 0.4 to 4 microns. This result demonstrates a marked dependence of viscosity on mean particle size, since the size of the pores is closely related to particle size, at least for a given type of size distribution.

Orr and Blocker,[128] in a study of the viscosity of suspensions of spheres, dismissed the possibility that particle size could influence the viscosity on the basis of Reiner's[116] analysis of the Einstein equation. However, they emphasized that numerous investigators have observed the influence of particle size distribution on the viscosity.

Examination of experimental data indicated that the relative viscosity of suspensions of spheres increases exponentially with suspension concentration. Therefore, they suggested the empirical equation

$$\frac{\eta'' - \eta}{\eta} = aC^k \tag{2.99}$$

where $a$ and $k$ are constants. They further suggested that $a$ is related to the volume of sediment obtainable from unit volume of suspension ($C_0$) and that $k$ is related to the geometric standard deviation, $s_g$, of the particle size.

Viscosity data from a number of sources were plotted as $(\eta'' - \eta)/\eta$ vs. $C$ on a log-log scale. The plots were essentially straight lines from which $a$ and $k$ were readily obtained. The volume fraction of particles, $C$, varied from about 0.05 to 0.5. The results were presented in tabular form, and although correlation coefficients were not calculated there appeared to be a marked positive correlation between $k$ and $1/s_g$, and between $C_0$ and $1/a$. In fact many values of $k$ were nearly identical with $1/s_g$, and the values of $1/a$ seemed to lie between the values of $C_0$ obtained by sedimentation and those obtained by centrifuging. Unfortunately, the ranges were rather small: 0.315 to 0.456 for $C_0$ obtained by sedimentation and 0.654 to 0.971 for $1/s_g$. Nonetheless, they indicate that a decrease in viscosity accompanies an increase in size distribution over a wide range in concentration.

Sweeny and Geckler[129] determined the rheological properties of concentrated suspensions of sized glass spheres. A suspending medium having a density equal to that of the glass spheres was selected in order to avoid sedimentation. The medium was a solution of zinc bromide in aqueous glycerol in most of the studies, but a non-aqueous medium, an ethylene tetrabromide-diethylene glycol mixture, was used for some experiments. When the aqueous medium was used, the viscosity increased markedly with decreasing particle size, but when the non-aqueous medium was used, the viscosity was independent of particle size.

The authors considered several possible phenomena which might account for the observed effect of particle size on viscosity when the medium was changed. They rejected the possibility that the results were affected by a wall-slippage layer and also the possibility that the decrease in viscosity with increasing size resulted from a change in effective concentration resulting from a double-ionic layer of the suspending medium around the non-conducting charged spheres. They suggested the possibility that each glass sphere was surrounded by an adsorbed layer of fluid which increased its effective size. The resulting increase in volume concentration would be largest for the small particles, producing the observed viscosity-particle size relationship. Possibly a non-aqueous medium would be adsorbed differently from the aqueous zinc chloride-glycerol medium.

They also undertook an investigation of the effect of a change in particle size distribution on the viscosity of the suspensions. The design of the experiments resulted from the following considerations. A close-packed aggregate of spheres contains two types of voids, namely, a reversed spherical cube (a "square hole") and a reversed spherical tetrahedron (a "triangular hole"). In close packing, one square and two triangular holes are associated with each sphere. If a sphere is to fit into a square hole its diameter must be less than 0.414 time that of the spheres producing the hole. If it is to fit into a triangular hole, the diameter of the smaller sphere must be less than 0.225 time that of the larger spheres. When the diameters of the smaller spheres are less than 0.125 time the diameters of the larger ones, the former can pass completely through the aggregate.

Sweeny and Geckler therefore selected pairs of the sized samples such that the small sphere was successively too large to pack into a square hole, small enough to fill a square hole, small enough to fill a triangular hole and barely able to move through the aggregate, and small enough to move easily through the aggregate. Viscosity at rest, viscosity at infinite shearing stress, and thixotropic breakdown of 55 volume percent suspensions in the aqueous medium were determined and plotted against $\bar{d}_{32}$. The viscosity at rest and the thixotropic breakdown at first increased slightly with increasing diameter difference (decreasing ratio) and then decreased markedly. The viscosity at infinite shearing stress increased continuously as the ratio decreased.

Summarizing, relative viscosity seems to increase with decreasing particle size (at least under some conditions) and decreasing width of the size distribution. Departure from Newtonian behavior seems to increase with decreasing size, and suspensions of very fine particles may be thixotropic.

Unfortunately, these conclusions are based on an uncomfortably small amount of published data.

## ELECTRICAL PROPERTIES

### Ion diffusion

As indicated in the section on coagulation, the characteristics of an aerosol may be greatly influenced by its electrical properties. An aerosol may be essentially uncharged (although this is unusual), charged entirely to one or the other polarity, or it may contain particles of both polarities. Furthermore, a given particle may have no charge or one, two, or many units of charge. The charges may be a result of the process by which the aerosols were prepared; they may be acquired by attachment of ions in the natural atmosphere; or they may be deliberately produced, as in an electrostatic precipitator.

Ross Gunn[130,131] has undertaken a theoretical and experimental study of the electrification of atmospheric aerosols by ionic diffusion. Numerous investigators have established that atmospheric dusts are highly charged, and such charges markedly influence the rate of coagulation. Gunn measured the charges on individual cloud droplets and found that they corresponded roughly to earlier measurements on solid aerosols. Since the charges on cloud droplets are largely due to atmospheric diffusion, it seems likely that the same is true of dust particles which have been rather quietly suspended in air for long periods of time. Gunn developed an expression for the average charge on single drops suspended in air which shows the dependence of charge on the ionic characteristics of the environment, the drop size, and the rate of fall. The derivation assumes (1) that the space charge outside the drop is so disperse that it does not appreciably influence ionic motions, (2) that all ions reaching the drop surface will be held by the image forces, and (3) that selective capture due to quasi-crystalline double layers may be ignored. The average charge on a spherical droplet at time $t$ was found to be

$$q = [1 + F(rue/2\pi kTu')^{1/2}]\left[\frac{rkT}{e}\ln\frac{N_+ u_+}{N_- u_-}\right]$$

$$\cdot [1 - \exp -(4\pi e(N_+ u_+ + N_- u_-)t)] \qquad (2.100)$$

where

$$u' = \frac{N_+ u_+ + N_- u_-}{N_+ + N_-} \qquad (2.101)$$

In these equations, $N_+$ and $N_-$ are the ionic densities in the gas, $u_+$ and $u_-$ are their mobilities, $r$ is the droplet radius, $u$ is its velocity of fall, $e$ is the electronic charge, and $F$ is a dimensionless constant close to unity.

The equilibrium charge $q_0$ cannot exceed $4kTr^2/\pi e\lambda$ where $\lambda$ is the mean free path of the gas.

The charging time for a drop is

$$\tau = 1/4\pi e(N_+ u_+ + N_- u_-) \tag{2.102}$$

Gunn estimates that in ordinary air the charging time is in the vicinity of 400 seconds.

Phillips and Gunn[132] tested this theory experimentally. They suspended a metal sphere by means of a fiber in an air stream of known concentrations of both positive and negative ions. The collected charge was measured by induction by lowering the sphere into a Faraday cage. The results agreed very well with equation (2.100).

In any gas where a continuous supply of ion pairs is being produced, as in the air, and a group of droplets is present, a few of the droplets will remain neutral as a result of equal numbers of positive and negative ions striking them. However, according to the laws of probability, some of the droplets will collide with large numbers of ions of one sign and will build up charges of considerable size. The ultimate result is a particle distribution according to charge.

This distribution can be expressed mathematically provided the number of collisions of ions with the droplets is very large, as is the case for drops or dust particles suspended in ionized air. Of course, if ions of one sign collide with the particles more often than those of the opposite sign, the distribution will be distorted. This type of distortion can occur if the concentration of one ion exceeds that of the other, or if the thermal velocity of one exceeds that of the other. Gunn stated that a mathematical analysis demonstrates that the charge distribution approximates a Gaussian (normal) distribution and worked out the constants for the distribution by a direct comparison with the physical requirements. The desired equation is

$$F_x = \frac{Ne}{\sqrt{2\pi rkT}} \exp\left[\frac{-\left(x - \left(\frac{rkT}{e^2}\right)\ln\frac{\lambda_+}{\lambda_-}\right)^2}{2\left(\frac{rkT}{e^2}\right)}\right] \tag{2.103}$$

where $F_x$ is the frequency of occurrence, $N$ is the total number of particles, $x$ is the number of elementary charges on a particle, and $\lambda_+$ and $\lambda_-$ are the conductivities of the positive and negative ions. Equation 2.100 gives the average charge of the aerosol and 2.103 gives the charge distribution.

A number of the characteristics of the charging can be derived from equation 2.103. For example, the fraction of all particles having zero charge is obtained by letting $x$ equal zero and dividing both sides of the equation by $N$ and if, moreover, $\lambda_+ = \lambda_-$, $F_0 = Ne/\sqrt{2\pi rkT}$.

Gunn points out that by substituting appropriate quantities in 2.103 it is readily shown that 99 percent of the atmospheric particles of radius greater than 100 microns will carry at least one elementary charge, but that a particle of 0.01 micron radius will seldom carry a single elementary charge. If the positive and negative charges are equal, the average number of elementary charges on the positive particles, $\bar{x}_+$, is numerically the same as that on the negative particles, $\bar{x}_-$, and

$$\bar{x}_+ = \bar{x}_- = \sqrt{\frac{\pi rkT}{2e^2}} \tag{2.104}$$

while the average charge carried by both the positive and negative fractions of the particles is

$$\bar{q}_+ = \bar{q}_- = \sqrt{\frac{\pi rkT}{2}} \tag{2.105}$$

Equation 2.105 can be written in the form

$$\frac{1}{2}\frac{\bar{q}_+^2}{r} = \frac{\pi}{4}kT \tag{2.106}$$

The terms on the left can be considered to represent the stored electrical energy of the droplet, while $kT$ is its probable thermal kinetic energy. Thus, as Gunn points out, there is an equipartition between the electrical and mechanical energies at equilibrium.

The theoretically predicted distribution curves were compared with those experimentally obtained for silica dust particles by Gillespie and Langstroth.[133] Quite satisfactory agreement was observed.

Woessner and Gunn[134] continued this study by making a number of measurements to compare the initial distribution of charges carried by various aerosols with the final distribution. The dispersed phases of the aerosols were freshly condensed water drops and sulfur particles, freshly dispersed and aged silica dust particles, and sprayed water drops, all having radii of 1–2 microns. The apparatus was an adaptation of that developed by Wells and Gerke.[135] A horizontal electric field was impressed on the aerosols and the radii and electrical charges of the particles were calculated from the observed displacements.

The distribution of charges, if any, in the aerosol cloud was determined immediately after formation and the aerosol was then exposed to large numbers of positive and negative ions produced directly in the aerosol with x-rays. Within one or two minutes the charge distribution was again measured. Regardless of the initial charge, the distribution was rearranged to an equilibrium normal distribution as contrasted to the "aging time" for a typical silica dust cloud of about two hours. The equilibrium distributions, once established, continued for more than an hour regardless of the intensity of the ionization to which they were subsequently subjected. Woessner and Gunn concluded that the charge distributions for aerosols of different initial electrifications achieve the same final equilibrium distribution upon exposure to large numbers of atmospheric ions. The results agree very well with the theoretical development by Gunn described above.

Luchak[136] developed rather elaborate equations describing the changes with time of the charge distribution of coagulating aerosols. The equations agreed well with experimental data from the literature on the charge distribution of initially uncharged ammonium chloride aerosols.

## Blown dusts

The electrification of dust particles by blowing them through tubes was studied by Kunkel.[137] Such electrification is similar to that generally produced when powders are suspended in a gas by blowing. The method was similar to that used by Woessner and Gunn in that the particles were photographed as they fell in a horizontal electric field. When quartz or sulfur particles were blown through tubes lined with the same material, the charge distribution was symmetrical about zero charge and the net charge, accordingly, was zero. The average charge on a particle increased somewhat more slowly than the square of the particle diameter. When the dust material differed from that of the tubes, some asymmetry of the charge distribution was obtained. Kunkel's results suggest that charging occurs when particles which have come into contact are separated, and that asymmetry of charge is caused by particles striking the walls of a containing vessel. Kunkel observed that humidity had little effect, at least for particles that are easily charged. Earlier experimenters had found that particles such as coal dust acquire little charge when moved by an air stream when the humidity is high.

Very little is known about the effect of particle size on the charges carried by particles dispersed by blowing a powder, other than the observation by Kunkel mentioned above. Gillespie and Langstroth[133] developed an instrument for determining the electrical charge distribution in aerosols, which was applied to this as well as other related problems. Aerosol particles were deposited on microscope slides in such a manner that the charge on any particle at the time of deposition could be determined from the size of the particle and its position on the slide. They studied a silica powder with 80 percent of the particles less than 3 microns diameter and a median diameter of less than 1 micron. A plot of average radius against average charge per particle showed that the average charge was proportional to the particle radius, except shortly after generation (about six minutes) when the curve was somewhat concave with respect to the radius axis.

Harper[140] has reviewed the contact charging of powders consisting of conductors, semiconductors, and insulators upon dispersion in gases. He points out that a homogeneous powder should not become charged upon dispersal, but that some apparently homogeneous powders may actually be heterogeneous because of different work functions for different faces of the same particle. Harper suggests that, other things being equal, semiconductors will charge less than metals and that clean electrophobic insulators may hardly charge at all. He states that experiments have indicated that the mutual charging of particles is usually more important than the charging of particles against solid surfaces.

The classic work of Rudge[141] should also be mentioned. His apparatus consisted essentially of a brass tube containing a strip of brass gauze. The latter was connected with an electroscope. The powder to be tested was blown through the tube and imparted its charge to the gauze. Rudge concluded that when the powder has a distinct chemical composition, this composition has a marked effect on the nature of the charge. Thus he observed that non-metallic powders become positively charged, metallic powders become negatively charged, acid-forming oxides become positively charged, base-forming oxides negatively charged, and that the charge of salts depends on the relative strengths of the acids and bases corresponding to the ions. These results were obtained with air, but similar results occurred with other gases.

### Atomization

When aerosols are formed by "atomization," that is, by some sort of spray device, they are highly charged if produced from polar liquids and much less highly charged if from nonpolar liquids. Smoluchowski[142] suggested that the droplet charge is determined by the number of positive and negative ions in the volume of liquid forming the drop immediately prior to the droplet formation. The charge distribution would be expected to be normal and would have the form

$$\frac{dN_c}{ds} = \frac{1}{\sqrt{4\pi N_c V}} \exp(-s^2/4N_c V) \tag{2.107}$$

where $s$ is the number of elementary charges, $N_c$ is the concentration of ions of the same sign, and $V$ is the droplet volume. On the average the mean square charge, $\bar{s}^2$ is given by the expression

$$\bar{s}^2 = 2NV \tag{2.108}$$

According to this theory, the mean square charge is proportional to the cube of the radius, and this has been confirmed by Dodd.[143]

Avy[144] makes the interesting statement that electrification during atomization of a liquid seems to vary with the nature of the orifice; that water vapor passed through an ivory orifice is not charged, but becomes positively charged with other orifices.

## Condensation

As implied earlier, particles prepared by condensation at relatively low temperatures are generally uncharged when first prepared, but rapidly become charged by gaseous ions which diffuse to them. On the other hand, smokes resulting from combustion, such as magnesium oxide smokes, or from electric arcs are often highly charged when first formed. Dalla Valle, Orr, and Hinkle[145] found that about 74 percent of the particles in tobacco smoke and 86 percent of the particles in the smoke produced by burning magnesium ribbon are charged, as contrasted with about 4 percent for stearic acid and ammonium chloride aerosols produced with a La Mer-Sinclair[6] generator. Green and Lane[38] suggest that the large percentage must be due to increased ionization of the air at the high temperature of combustion and in the case of aerosols produced with an arc, to ions produced by the electric discharge. Approximately equal numbers of positive and negative charges are found in aerosols formed by condensation at high temperatures.

## Artificial charging

When small particles are subjected to an electric discharge they become charged and can be collected on a surface having the appropriate polarity. This property of particles is used for sampling and size determination, and also on an industrial scale to remove particles from stack gases to prevent air pollution. The corona discharge is usually used; the ions produced in the corona are attracted to the collecting electrode by the electrical field, and thus strike and become attached to particles suspended in the gas between the electrodes.

Aerosol particles electrified in a corona discharge acquire unipolar charges the number of which depend on the size, other conditions being equal. Drozin and La Mer[146] suggest that the charging law has the form

$$n = kr^\alpha \tag{2.109}$$

where $n$ is the number of charges acquired by the particle, $k$ is a constant, and $\alpha$ is an exponent whose value lies between 1 and 2. The values of $k$ and $\alpha$ are determined experimentally, and the equation is valid for all particles having the same dielectric constant.

Pauthenier and Moreau-Hanot[147] found that the charge $q$ (coulombs) accumulated by a spherical particle is given by the expression

$$q = \left(\frac{3D}{D + 2}\right)\left(\frac{Ed^2}{12 \times 10^8}\right)\left[\frac{t}{t + \dfrac{4K_0}{N\epsilon K}}\right] \tag{2.110}$$

where $D$ is the dielectric constant (electrostatic c.g.s. units), $E$ is the electric field strength (volts/meter), $d$ is the particle diameter in meters, $K$ is the ion mobility (meters$^2$/volt-second), $K_0$ is the dielectric constant of a vacuum ($8.85 \times 10^{-12}$ coulomb$^2$/joule-meter), $N$ is the ion concentration (ions/meter$^3$), $\epsilon$ is the elementary electronic charge, ($1.59 \times 10^{-19}$ coulomb) and $t$ is the time in seconds.

According to this equation, a particle will attain 91 percent of its ultimate charge in $40K_0/N\epsilon K$ seconds. Usually this time is of the order of $10^{-2}$ second, which is a small fraction of the residence time of the aerosol in the field of an electrostatic precipitator.[148] Ion bombardment is the main charging mechanism for particles having a diameter greater than about 2 microns. Both ion bombardment and ion diffusion are important for particles in the size range 2-0.2 microns, while the latter mechanism is controlling for particles smaller than about 0.2 micron.

Note that when $t$ is very large, $q$ is a function of the dielectric constant, the electric field strength, and the particle diameter, since the last term in equation 2.110 approaches unity.

Davies[149] has reviewed the theory of electrostatic charging and precipitation. He states that, given a reasonably long residence time, it should be possible to collect completely particles over 1 micron in diameter, and that very small particles may also be readily removed. However, he suggests that particles about 0.2 micron in diameter may be difficult to collect electrostatically because of the difficulty of charging and the low limiting charge.

Experiments were undertaken in the author's laboratory to determine the collection efficiency of a commercially available electrostatic sampler designed for industrial hygiene applications (MSA Model F). Collection efficiencies of 99 percent or greater were obtained for aerosols of sodium chloride, glycerol, and stearic acid in the diameter range 0.5 to 5 microns.

## Electrical conductivity

The electrical conductivity of powders is determined by the material comprising the particles and the packing arrangement. Obviously, the greater the number of points of contact per unit volume for a given number of particles per unit volume the greater will be the conductivity and the lower the electrical resistance.

The electrical conductivity of powdered galena was studied by Dean and Koster.[150] The conductivity measurements were made for pellets of the powders consisting of various sizes of particles. They observed that Ohm's law was not followed, but rather the equation

$$E = IR + E'$$

where $E$ is the voltage, $R$ the resistance, and $E'$ a constant which is dependent on temperature and grain size. $E'$ was interpreted as a self-induced electromotive force, but the cause was not determined. For a given temperature the resistance increased markedly with decreasing particle size and for a given size it increased with decreasing temperature.

The reason for the increasing resistance with decreasing particle size must be that the number of discontinuities per unit distance in the powder increases with decreasing particle size. However, this argument is valid only for a given type of size distribution. In the case of close-packed spheres, if sufficient powder much finer than the spheres and in sufficient quantity to just fill the voids is mixed with the spheres, the conductivity must be increased.

Harper[140] has theoretically treated the idealized situation of an aggregate of spherical solid particles of uniform size and constitution. If the packing is of the cubic ("most open") type, it may be assumed that contact between particles results in simple elastic deformation. When two spheres are pressed together with a force $F$, Young's modulus is $Y$, and as usual Poisson's ratio is taken to be 0.3, the radius of contact $a$ between the particles can be calculated from the equation

$$a = 1.1(Fr/2Y)^{1/3} \qquad (2.111)$$

If the weight of the powder at a given level in the powder produces a pressure $P$, $F = \pi r^2 P$ and

$$a = 1.1r(\pi P/2Y)^{1/3} \qquad (2.112)$$

The resistance at each contact point is twice that of a circular electrode of radius $a$ feeding into an infinite medium, since $r \gg a$, and is $\rho/4\pi a$ where $\rho$ is the resistance of the continuous phase. Harper next compared the resistance of a column of particles strung like beads on the axis of an enveloping cylinder with that of the solid cylinder. The number of contacts and particles per unit length is $1/2r$ and the resistance per unit length is $\rho/4ar$. Then, since the resistance of the solid cylinder is $\rho/\pi r^2$,

$$\rho_a/\rho = \pi r/4a \qquad (2.113)$$

where $\rho_a$ is the resistance of the powder. Since $r$ may be orders of magnitude larger than $a$, the resistivity of the powder may be orders of magnitude larger than that of the solid material. It is of interest to note that for the special powder considered in this derivation, $\rho_a/\rho$ is dependent only on $Y$ and $P$ and independent of particle size except as it may influence $P$. This can be seen by inserting the value of $a$ in terms of $P$ in equation 2.113, which then becomes

$$\rho_a/\rho = 0.61(Y/P)^{1/3} \qquad (2.114)$$

The electrical conductivity of a powder may be considerably influenced by impurities on the particle surfaces. For example, Harper points out that the resistivity of a powder may be greatly increased if the particles are covered by a film of low conductance which increases the resistance at the points of contact.

## SURFACE PROPERTIES

### Adsorption

The adsorption of gases or vapors on the surfaces of powders is essentially the same as the adsorption on any solid surface. However, the very large amount of surface per unit weight or volume of a powder renders the surface properties of a powder particularly important. In fact, with few exceptions, the influence of particle size on the surface properties of fine particles is restricted to its influence on the specific surface, that is the surface area per unit weight or volume.

Adsorption from the gas phase can be of two kinds: physical adsorption and chemical adsorption ("chemisorption"). Physical adsorption generally results from van der Waals forces, which in turn are the result of polarization at the surfaces. The extent of physical adsorption generally increases with decreasing temperature, and the heats of adsorption are similar in magnitude to the heats of vaporization from liquids. Chemisorption, on the other hand, may increase with increasing temperature, corresponding to a positive chemical activation energy. The heats of adsorption are much higher than those for physical adsorption, corresponding roughly to those for chemical reactions in general.

Decreasing pressure almost always decreases the extent of physical adsorption, but it may or may not decrease the extent of chemical adsorption. In fact serious errors in published results have at times arisen from the assumption that all chemisorption is essentially irreversible. However, in general chemisorbed gases are much harder to remove from surfaces than physically adsorbed gases.

A curve representing the amount, $x$, of gas adsorbed per unit weight of powder at a constant temperature is known as an adsorption isotherm or simply as an isotherm. In the case of a vapor it is often convenient to plot $x$ against $p/p_0$ where $p$ is the partial pressure at saturation.

Most isotherms can be classified using the system developed by Brunauer, Emmett, and Teller.[151] This system divides isotherms into five classes, referred to as types I through V, as shown in Figure 2-16. According to Gregg,[152] only types I, II, and IV are of importance for powders.

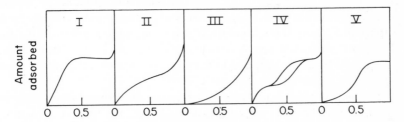

Figure 2-16. Types of van der Waals isotherms.

Type I isotherms are often shaped like an inverted $S$ and have a long almost horizontal portion which may continue to the value $p/p_0 = 1$, but which may also turn upward shortly before reaching $p/p_0 = 1$, as shown in the figure. The flat portion is generally attributed to the presence of pores having a size of the order of that of molecules, while the sharp rise on the right, when it occurs, is attributed to capillary condensation in pores which may be the spaces between the particles. Gregg suggests that the commonest examples of type I isotherms involve charcoal as the adsorbent.

Type II isotherms are more definitely shaped like an inverted $S$ than those of type I. Such isotherms are typical of powders consisting of rather large, non-porous particles. They are the commonest type of isotherms for a powder. It is generally accepted that the curve from the origin to the first inflection represents the formation of a layer only one molecule thick (a monolayer) while beyond this region a multimolecular layer is formed. The very steep portion as the curve approaches $p/p_0 = 1$ represents condensation of the vapor to bulk liquid, which ultimately fills the pores between the particles. Type I and type II isotherms appear rather similar and are differentiated primarily by the fact that the slope of Type I isotherms may be nearly zero over a wide range of $p/p_0$. As Gregg emphasizes, type I isotherms correspond to powders for which the external particle area is small compared with the area of the walls of the pores within the particles, while type II isotherms correspond to powders for which internal area is negligible, or at most comparable in magnitude with the external area.

Type III isotherms, which are convex with respect to the pressure axis, have been obtained for the adsorption of iodine and bromine on silica gel.[153]

Type IV isotherms, having the shape of a double inverted S, are explained on the basis that the particles contain pores up to a few hundred Angstrom units in diameter. These isotherms are characterized by a hysteresis loop, the upper branch of the loop corresponding to desorption. The existence of the upper branch of the loop is attributed to the evaporation of the liquid-like adsorbate from menisci within the pores. The adsorption of benzene by ferric oxide gel yields a Type IV isotherm.

Type V isotherms, shaped like an upright S, are obtained for water vapor adsorbed on charcoal at 100°C.

Brunauer, Emmet, and Teller,[154] assuming the formation of a monolayer of further layers at higher pressures, derived the following equation, oftened referred to as the BET equation:

$$v = \frac{vmcf}{1 - f} \cdot \frac{1}{1 + (c - 1)f} \qquad (2.115)$$

where $v$ is the volume of gas adsorbed, $f$ is $p/p_0$, $v_m$ is the volume of gas adsorbed when the surface is completely covered with a monolayer, and $c$ approximately equals $\exp(E_1 - E_L)/RT$, where $E_1$ is the heat of adsorption of the gas in the first layer and $E_L$ is the heat of liquefaction of the gas.

If $c$ is very much greater than unity, equation 2.115 gives a curve of the form of type II, but if $c$ is less than unity the curve is that of type III. If a single monolayer is formed, a curve of the form of type I without the upturn at very high values of $p/p_0$ is obtained. In this case 2.115 is equivalent to the well-known Langmuir equation,

$$\frac{p}{x} = \frac{1}{k_1 k_2} + \frac{p}{k_2} \qquad (2.116)$$

where $k_1$ and $k_2$ are constants for the given system. At very low gas pressures this equation takes the form

$$x = k_1 k_2 p \qquad (2.117)$$

and the amount of gas adsorbed is directly proportional to the pressure. The condition that 2.116 produce a type IV curve is the same as that for a type II curve, namely $c \gg 1$, while the condition for a type V curve is the same as for type III, namely $c < 1$.

The BET equation is important not only because it aids in the interpretation and correlation of data, but particularly because of its usefulness in connection with determining specific surface. The equation can be written

$$\frac{f}{v(1 - f)} = \frac{1}{v_m c} + \frac{c - 1}{v_m c} f \qquad (2.118)$$

If this equation satisfactorily represents the data, a plot of $f$ against $f/v(1 - f)$ will be a straight line having a slope of $(c - 1)/v_m c$ and an intercept on the ordinate of $1/v_m c$. The values of these two quantities provide a set of two simultaneous equations that can be solved for $v_m$. The surface area can then be calculated as the product of Avogadro's number, the cross sectional area of a molecule (or atom) of the adsorbate, and $v_m$.

Sometimes the value of $v_m$ can be estimated directly from the isotherm. For type I isotherms it is the value corresponding to the horizontal part of the curve. In this case the fine pores are not included. For types II and IV the relatively flat parts of the curves can be extrapolated to zero pressure, $v_m$ being the intercept. Isotherms are used extensively for determining surface area. Nitrogen at $78°K$ is commonly used as the adsorbate. It has a cross-sectional area of about $16.2 A^2/\text{mole}$. Surface areas can readily be converted to a mean particle size if a particle shape or a shape factor is assumed (see Chapter 1).

The BET equation is most applicable to isotherms of type II. Equations have been derived by Brunauer, Emmett, and Teller and by Brunauer, Deming, Deming, and Teller for isotherms of other types.[155]

Several other equations have been developed to aid in estimating $v_m$. An equation developed by Hüttig,[156, 157] like the BET equation, is based on a theory of multilayer adsorption:

$$\frac{p}{v}(1 + f) = \frac{p_0}{c v_m} + \frac{p}{v_m} \qquad (2.118)$$

Generally the BET equation agrees with experimentally determined isotherms for values of $p/p_0$ between 0.05 and 0.30. The Hüttig equation has been found to agree with experimental results for values of $p/p_0$ as large as 0.8.

Harkins and Jura[158] developed the following equation for calculating the specific surface from gas adsorption data:

$$\log f = (B - A)/v \tag{2.119}$$

where $A$ and $B$ are constants. It applies only to isotherms of type I and II. The slope of the straight line obtained by plotting $\log f$ against $1/v$ is $A$. The specific surface $S_w$ is obtained with the equation

$$S_w = kA^{1/2} \tag{2.120}$$

where $k$ is a constant for a given gas at a given temperature. Harkins and Jura determined $k$ for a number of gases, independently determining $S_w$ from the heat of immersion. Values of $A$ were then calculated from experimentally determined isotherms and the values of $k$ were calculated using 2.120. Some of the values obtained were: Water at 25°C, $k = 13.6$; $n$-heptane at 25°C, $k = 16.9$; nitrogen at $-195.8$°C, $k = 4.06$; $n$-butane at 0°C, $k = 13.6$. $S_w$ had the dimension meters square per gram. Values for the specific surface of six nonporous solids calculated using the BET and the Harkins and Jura equations were compared and excellent agreement was obtained.

Powders also adsorb from solution, and some of their important applications result from this fact, the clarification of wines being an example. As in the case of adsorption from the gas phase, adsorption from the liquid phase can be either physical or chemical. Physical adsorption from the liquid phase is often used as a relative method for determining surface areas, since the techniques are much simpler than those for the gas phase. An example is iodine adsorption by carbon blacks.

The attractive forces between the powder and the adsorbate vary, often markedly, from one chemical entity to another. This fact is the basis for a powerful analytical tool, chromatography. At least three variations involving powders are employed, namely gas-liquid partition chromatography, in which the adsorbent is a liquid spread over the surfaces of the powder and the adsorbate is a gas; gas-solid chromatography; and liquid-solid chromatography.

### Permeability

The permeability of a powder may be qualitatively defined as the ease with which a fluid will flow through it. The rate of flow is a function of the pore space, the viscosity of the fluid, various dimensional factors such as the area of the bed of particles, and the specific surface of the powder. Since the specific surface of a powder can be estimated from a knowledge of the rate of flow of a fluid and of the other factors mentioned above, permeability can be used to estimate mean particle size. The relationship between flow rate and specific surface which is usually used to calculate the latter was derived by Kozeny and first applied to determinations of specific surface by Carman.[159,160] The equation is often given in the following form:

$$u = \frac{\epsilon^3}{(1 - \epsilon)^2} \cdot \frac{g\Delta P}{k\eta L S_w^2 \rho^2} \tag{2.121}$$

where

$u$ = linear velocity of the fluid (cm/sec)
$\epsilon$ = fractional void of the bed
$g$ = acceleration of gravity (980 cm/sec$^2$)
$\Delta P$ = pressure difference across the bed (g/cm$^2$)
$\eta$ = viscosity of fluid (poises)
$L$ = thickness of the bed (cm)
$\rho$ = powder density (g/cm$^3$)
$k$ = dimensionless constant

Usually $k$ is assumed to be 5.0 and the fraction of voids is calculated from the volume of the powder in the bed, the weight of the bed, and the density of the material of which the particles are composed.

Fowler and Hertel[161] have investigated the effect of the material constituting the powder and the orientation of the particles on the value of $k$. They found that $k$ can be approximated by the equation

$$k = \frac{3}{\sin^2 \phi} \tag{2.122}$$

where $\sin^2 \phi$ is the square of the sine of the angle between the flow direction and the direction perpendicular to the particle surface elements.

Equation 2.122 is based in part on the assumption that the fluid is stationary at the walls of the channel. However, when a gas is used as the permeating fluid, diffusion or molecular flow is possible which takes the form of a slip at the channel walls.

Equation 2.121 has been corrected for slip, giving rise to the following equation where $Z$ is a constant and $\lambda$ is the mean free path of the gas:

$$u = \frac{g\Delta P}{k\eta L} \left[ \frac{\epsilon^2}{(1 - \epsilon)^2 S_w^2 \rho^2} + \frac{\epsilon^2}{(1 - \epsilon) S_w \rho} Z\lambda \right] \tag{2.123}$$

Values of $Z$ for various substances have been determined by Lea and Nurse,[162] who obtained values ranging from 2.73 to 4.07 and having an arithmetic mean of about 3.3.

Values for specific surface obtained with equation 2.123 obviously should be independent of the porosity, but there seems to be a tendency for $S_w$ to increase with decreasing values of $\epsilon$. A correction has been proposed by the Working Committee on Fineness of the American Society for Testing and Materials which involves substituting $1/(b - \epsilon)$ for $(1 - \epsilon)$ in equations 2.121 and 2.123. The value of $b$ is obtained by plotting $\epsilon^3 g\Delta P/k\eta Lu$ against $\epsilon$; the intercept on the $\epsilon$ axis is $b$. The value of $b$ for cement is 0.85.

The equipment for making permeability measurements is rather simple and this is probably the reason for the popularity of permeability methods for determining mean particle diameters. Several commercial devices for measuring particle size based on permeability are available.

### Chemical reactivity

The chemical reactivity of a heterogeneous system depends in part on the extent of the interface. As a result, many systems which would otherwise be considered rather inert chemically are highly reactive when one phase is in a finely divided form. One of the best-known types of such reactivity is dust explosions. Explosions and fires in bituminous coal dust have been responsible for numerous accidents in mines. Such explosions occur only when the concentrations of dust are very great. Drinker and Hatch[163] suggest that they must be of the order of grams of dust per liter of air and that the propagation of flame through air-borne coal dust usually occurs following a small explosion which disseminates dust at a flammable concentration. The relatively little information available on the effect of particle size on flammability of coal dust suggests that flammability increases with decreasing size.

Flammability of a powder such as coal dust can be defined in several ways. It can be defined as the minimum concentration (grams dust per liter of air) required before an explosion will occur. Another useful definition, since it is related to the destructuveness of the explosion, is the pressure developed by a fixed concentration of dust in a special apparatus and ignited in a specified manner.[164] A third definition is based on the percentages of an inert material which must be added to an explosive dust in order to render the mixture inert.[165] In fact, the dusting of soft coal mines with an inert powdered material such as limestone seems to be an effective method for reducing the hazard from dust explosions.

A number of fundamental studies have been made of the combustion of carbon particles. For example, Golovina and Khaustovich[166] studied the interaction of carbon with carbon dioxide and oxygen at temperatures up to 3000°K. They emphasize that during carbon combustion at temperatures above 1300°K, secondary reactions between carbon and the combustion reaction products, especially carbon dioxide, are very important. Their studies involved the combustion of carbon spheres 15 mm in diameter heated by means of a high-frequency generator. They found (a) that at temperatures below 1600°K so-called kinetic conditions prevail; (b) that in the temperature range 1600°–2300°K, a slowing or "braking" of the carbon-carbon dioxide occurs which is not controlled by diffusion, and (c) that above 2200°K the reaction rate approaches the value determined by diffusion of the carbon dioxide to the surface of the sphere.

Tesner[167] has analyzed experimental results obtained by several investigators relative to the reactions of gases with carbon, and has concluded that the activation energy $E$ in the rate equation

$$v = \frac{P}{\sqrt{2\pi mkT}} \exp(-E/RT) \qquad (2.124)$$

decreases regularly with increasing temperature. In equation 2.124, $v$ is the reaction rate per $cm^2$ of surface, $m$ the mass of the gas molecule, $P$ the pressure, $k$ the Boltzmann constant, and $R$ the gas constant. The gases considered included carbon dioxide, oxygen, and water vapor. The decrease in activation energy with temperature was attributed to an increase in the activity of the surface carbon atom with rising temperature.

Many organic dusts are known to explode, and industrial explosions of wheat flour, starch, cocoa, and powdered soap are well known.[163] As in the case of coal, the little information available suggests that flammability in general increases with decreasing particle size. Hartman et al[168] have found that the ignition temperature of corn starch clouds increases with decreasing particle size.

High concentrations of metal powders in air or oxygen may also be explosive. Magnesium dust is particularly dangerous in this regard, but many other common metals may also produce explosive or flammable dusts, e.g., zinc, aluminum, copper, titanium and a number of others. Essenhigh and Fells[167] suggest that the metal dusts upon ignition melt and then evaporate, finally burning to yield solid combustion products.

The combustion of sprays of liquids is of great economic importance and has been studied extensively. Many of the studies have been made on single drops[170,171,172,173,174] while others have involved the burning characteristics of sprays.[175] The combustion ranges from simple burning to detonation, in which propagation is by means of a shock wave.

The effect of droplet size on the concentration combustion limits and ease of ignition is not simple. If the droplets are less than a few microns in size they may completely evaporate before they burn. For such drops the lower combustion limit is about that of the vapor. When the drops are so large that complete evaporation does not occur before ignition, the vapor concentration in the vicinity of the drop may exceed the combustion limit for the vapor, even if the gross concentration does not, and the low limit of combustion may be decreased.

The kinetics of the combustion of suspensions of liquids and solids in air has been reviewed by Essenhigh and Fells.[169] The simplified kinetic theories for the combustion of both dispersed liquids and dispersed solids are very similar. The simplified theory assumes that the combustion mechanism depends primarily on that of the individual drops or particles and that the combustion is perturbed to only a slight extent by the surrounding particles. The burning rate of the individual particles (liquid or solid) is predicted theoretically to be inversely proportional to the radius, and this is given by the following equation, where $B$ is a constant:

$$dr/dt = -B/r \qquad (2.125)$$

Upon integration this gives the well-known square law for the burning time in an infinite atmosphere:

$$t_b = Kd_0^2 \qquad (2.126)$$

where $t_b$ is the time required for complete burning of the particles, $d_0$ is their initial diameter, and $K$ is the burning constant. Essenhigh and Fells list values for the burning constant taken from 22 scientific papers for both liquids and solids. The tabulation suggests that for liquids and solids the values of the burning constant are of the order of 100 and 1000, respectively. It also indicates that the volatiles from coal particles behave as though they had evaporated from drops.

When the particles are in an enclosed flame, where the oxygen supply is limited, the burning times are increased by a factor $F$, which is a function of the amount of excess air. Introducing $F$ into equation 2.126 we obtain

$$t_b = Fkd_0^2 \qquad (2.127)$$

$F$ can be calculated from the equation

$$F = \left\{ \frac{1 + E_a}{3E_a^{1/3}} \right\} \left\{ 2\sqrt{3} \tan^{-1} \left[ \frac{3}{2E_a^{1/3} - 1} \right] - \ln \left[ \frac{(E_a^{1/3} + 1)^3}{1 + E} \right] \right\} \qquad (2.128)$$

where $E_a$ is the fractional excess air. Values of $F$ were calculated from 2.128 by Essenhigh[176] who found that it rises from 2 to 4 as $E_a$ drops from 0.5 to 0.1 and rises to infinity as $E_a$ drops to zero. Equation 2.128 was derived for solid particles and apparently a similar equation has not been obtained for drops.

The mechanism usually assumed for burning drops is that each drop is surrounded by a flame surface at a finite distance from the liquid surface; the flame is fed by evaporating liquid and the burning rate is controlled by the rate of heat conduction between the flame and liquid surfaces. When the dispersed phase is a solid, the burning rate is controlled by the diffusion of oxygen through the boundary layer surrounding the particle. These assumptions lead to differential equations of the same form which accounts for the applicability of equations 2.125 and 2.126 to both liquids and solids.

In the liquid system, where a steady state is achieved, the total heat arriving at the drop surface in unit time is

$$4\pi r^2 \frac{dq_r}{dt} = 4\pi r^2 \frac{dq}{dt} \qquad (2.129)$$

where $q$ is heat and $x$ refers to any distance from the drop center. Also,

$$\frac{dq}{dt} = -\lambda \frac{dT}{dx} \qquad (2.130)$$

where $T$ is temperature and $\lambda$ is the thermal conductivity of the ambient gas. Then by substitution and integration we obtain

$$\frac{dm}{dt} = -\frac{4\pi\lambda\Delta T/Q}{[1/r - (1/x)]} = -r\frac{4\pi\lambda\Delta T/Q}{(1 - r/x)} \qquad (2.131)$$

where $Q$ is the heat required to evaporate unit mass of the fuel, $\Delta T$ is the temperature difference between evaporation temperature and the flame temperature, $x$ is the radius of the spherical surface from which the heat originates, and $m$ is the mass of a drop. In terms of rate of change of the drop radius,

$$\frac{dr}{dt} = \frac{dm/dt}{4\pi r^2 \rho} = -\frac{1}{r}\frac{\lambda\Delta T/Q\rho}{(1 - r/x)} \qquad (2.132)$$

where $\rho$ as usual is the drop density. This equation has the same form as equation 2.125 if $r/x$ is constant. There are contradictions in the application of this equation to the burning of drops. For example, the use of this equation implies that the flame thickness is essentially zero, while if the burning proceeds with an appreciable activation energy, the flame may be quite thick relative to $r$. However, the validity of 2.132 seems likely in view of the validity of 2.125 and 2.126.

A similar equation can be derived for solids. The controlling factor is diffusion of oxygen, governed by the equation

$$dm_{ox}/dt = -D(dp/dx) \qquad (2.133)$$

where $m_{ox}$ is the mass of oxygen, and $D$ is the diffusion coefficient. The equation for the rate of change of particle radius is

$$\frac{dr}{dt} = -\frac{D(p_o - p_s)}{r(1 - r/x)\rho} \qquad (2.134)$$

where $p_o$ is the ambient oxygen pressure and $p_s$ is the oxygen pressure at the surface of the particle. When $x$ is large relative to $r$, and $p_s$ is zero,

$$\frac{dr}{dt} = -\frac{Dp_0}{r\rho} \qquad (2.135)$$

which has the same form as 2.125. This yields the following equation for the burning constant:

$$K = \rho/3\rho_0' D_0 p_0 (T/T_0)^{0.75} \qquad (2.136)$$

where $\rho'$ is the density of air and the subscript zero refers to standard temperature and pressure. Predicted and experimental values are compared in Table 2-7. Essenhigh and Fells attribute the discrepancies to swelling of the particles. Equation 2.134 may be a considerable over-

TABLE 2-7. VALUES OF BURNING CONSTANT $K$ FOR COKE RESIDUES OF CAR-
BONIZED COAL PARTICLES; COMPARISON OF EXPERIMENTAL AND CALCULATED
VALUES[169]

| Coal | % C (d.m.f.) | Square-Law Index | K (Expt.) | K (Calc.) | Ratio |
|---|---|---|---|---|---|
| 1. Stanllyd | 93.0 | 2.02 | 2125 | 2720 | 1.28 |
| 2. Five ft. | 91.8 | 1.94 | 1290 | 2620 | 2.03 |
| 3. Two ft. Nine | 91.2 | 2.25 | 1470 | 2070 | 1.41 |
| 4. Red Vein | 89.7 | 2.09 | 1475 | 2275 | 1.54 |
| 5. Garw | 88.9 | 2.01 | 1410 | 2030 | 1.44 |
| 6. Silkstone | 86.9 | 2.25 | 1110 | 1655 | 1.49 |
| 7. Winter | 84.0 | 2.18 | 1125 | 1710 | 1.52 |
| 8. Cowpen | 82.7 | 1.94 | 1060 | 1775 | 1.68 |
| 9. High Hazel | 81.9 | 2.14 | 1450 | 1725 | 1.19 |
| 10. Lorraine | 79.3 | 2.20 | 992 | 1890 | 1.91 |
| | | | | mean ratio | 1.55 |

simplification under many circumstances. It does not take into consideration the possibility of burning within pores, reactions with water vapor, or gas-phase reactions such as the burning of carbon monoxide.

Gas-borne particles can, of course, undergo many reactions in addition to burning. Cadle and Robbins[177] have discussed the application of chemical kinetic theory to heterogeneous atmospheric reactions involving aerosols. The considerations are also applicable to many reactions of gas-borne systems.

The reaction rate of a particle at any finite time after introduction of the particle into a gaseous mixture containing a reactive gas may be controlled by diffusion of the reactive gas in the gas phase or in the particle, or by the rate of chemical reaction. When the particle is first introduced into the reactant gas, the initial rate is controlled by the rate of the reaction at the surface of the particle.

Some reactions involving aerosol particles and gases soon achieve a steady state and this steady state may be maintained throughout much of their course. Rashevsky[178] has developed a theory for steady-state diffusion and chemical reactions in living cells which is applicable to aerosols[179, 180] with slight modification. The appropriate differential equations are

$$D_i \left( \frac{d^2 c_i}{dy^2} + \frac{2dc_i}{rdy} \right) + R = 0 \qquad (2.136)$$

and

$$\frac{d^2 c_e}{dy^2} + \frac{2dc_e}{rdy} = 0 \qquad (2.137)$$

with the boundary condition that when $y = r$

$$D_i \frac{dc_i}{dy} = D_e \frac{dc_e}{dy} \qquad (2.138)$$

where $y$ is the distance from the center of the particle, $c$ is the concentration of the reactant gas, $R$ is the rate of reaction of the dissolved gas with the material of the particle, $D$ is the diffusion coefficient, and $i$ and $e$ refer to the interior and exterior of the particle. When the reaction rate is controlled by the rate of diffusion and reaction in the particle, and $R$ is a first-order reaction,

$$R_s = \frac{c_i D_i}{r} [\sqrt{k_r/D_i}\, r \cot h \sqrt{k_r/D_i}\, r - 1] \qquad (2.139)$$

where $R_s$ is the steady-state rate per unit area of particle surface and $k_r$ is the first-order rate constant. When $\sqrt{k_r/D_i}\, r$ is large, equation 2.139

reduces to

$$R_s = c_i \sqrt{D_i k_r} \tag{2.140}$$

When $R$ is a zero order reaction and the penetration of the reactant gas into the particle is small,

$$R_s = \sqrt{2c_i D_i k_r} \tag{2.141}$$

The values of $c_i$ in 2.139–2.141 refer to concentrations just within the particle surface.

If the reaction rate is controlled by gas-phase diffusion, the concentration of the gaseous reactant in the air remains nearly constant with time, and there is essentially no movement of the particle relative to the air, the following equation applies:

$$R_s = \frac{c_e D_e}{r} \tag{2.142}$$

Many reactions involving aerosols never achieve a steady state. Roughton[181] and Crank[182] have developed equations for reactions where the reaction rates vary with time as well as space.

Empirical equations are often used to represent reactions involving aerosols. For example, Cadle and Robbins[177] used the equation

$$\frac{-d[A]}{dt} = k_r \frac{3[B]}{r} (1 - FZ)[A] \tag{2.143}$$

to represent the reaction of ammonia with sulfuric acid drops during which diffusion in the drops controlled the reaction rate. The fraction of the droplet reacted is $Z$, and $F$ is a dimensionless variable multiplier which allows for the rate of diffusion of products and for the surface area represented by each unit of product concentration. $[A]$ is the concentration of the reactive gas, and $[B]$ is the concentration of spherical aerosol particles of radius $r$ expressed in weight or volume units.

### Miscellaneous surface properties of drops

A few other surface properties of droplets should be briefly mentioned, since they are related to droplet size. One of these is that the vapor pressure of a liquid is affected by the curvature of the surface of the liquid. When the liquid surface is convex, the vapor pressure is greater than that of a plane surface, and when the surface is concave the vapor pressure is less. In quantitative terms, the vapor pressures $p$ above a plane surface and $p'$ above a curved surface, whose radius of curvature is $r$, are related to each other and to $r$ by the equation

$$\log \frac{p'}{p} = \frac{2\sigma M}{r\rho RT} \tag{2.144}$$

where $M$ is the molecular weight of the liquid, $\sigma$ is the surface tension of the liquid and $R$ is the gas constant. This equation applies to convex surfaces. The equation is identical for concave surfaces except that the second term is preceded by a negative sign.

When the surfaces are charged,

$$\log \frac{p'}{p} = \frac{M}{R\rho T} \left( \frac{2\sigma}{r} - \frac{q^2}{\epsilon 8\pi r^4} \right) \tag{2.145}$$

where $q$ is the quantity of charge and $\epsilon$ is the dielectric constant.

The effect of curvature on the vapor pressure of most liquids, including water, is not appreciable until the radius of the drop is 0.01 micron or less.

Similarly, the vapor pressure of small solid crystals is greater than that of larger crystals of the same substance. A consequence of this is that a fine powder melts at a lower temperature than the continuous material, provided a continuous liquid is formed.

A related property of droplets is the rate of evaporation. When a small isolated droplet of a pure substance evaporates into still air containing none of the vapor, the rate of change of surface with time is constant and independent of the drop size:

$$-\frac{ds}{dt} = \frac{8\pi Dmc}{\rho} \tag{2.146}$$

where $c$ is the saturation concentration of the vapor in molecules/$cm^3$ and $m$ is the mass of a diffusing molecule. In terms of the rate of loss of particle mass the equation is

$$-\frac{dm}{dt} = 4\pi Dmcr \tag{2.147}$$

The rate of loss per unit area per second is then $Dmc/r$. The droplet life is $r^2\rho/2Dmc$. A difficulty with these equations, due to Langmuir,[183] is that as $r$ approaches zero, the value of the rate of loss of mass per second per unit area approaches infinity. However, the equations hold fairly well down to radii of about one micron.

A more precise theory has been developed by Fuks[184] and refined by Bradley et al.[185] According to this theory, diffusion away from the drop starts from the outer surface of an envelope of vapor surrounding the drop. The radius of the exterior of this envelope is $r + \Delta$ where $\Delta$ has much the same value as the mean free path of the molecules of the evaporating liquid. Actually, few molecules will be in the envelope because $\Delta$ is so small. As would be expected, the introduction of $\Delta$ has little effect except for submicron-sized droplets. The corrected equations corresponding to 2.146 and 2.147 are

$$-\frac{ds}{dt} = \frac{8\pi Dmc}{\rho}\left[1\bigg/\left(\frac{D}{r\gamma\alpha} + \frac{r}{r + \Delta}\right)\right] \qquad (2.148)$$

and

$$-\frac{dm}{dt} = \frac{4\pi rDmc}{D/r\gamma\alpha + r/(r + \Delta)} \qquad (2.149)$$

where $\alpha$ is the fraction of molecules reaching the surface which condenses.

Numerous investigators have studied the evaporation of falling droplets. An equation due to Frössling seems to agree reasonably well with experimental results:

$$\frac{dm}{dt} = 4\pi rD(C_o - C)[1 + a(\mathrm{Re})^{1/2}] \qquad (2.150)$$

Here $a$ is a constant which is characteristic of the material concentrations in the air away from the drop and at the drop surface.

The evaporation of droplets, droplet clouds, and the resulting cooling have been reviewed in detail by Green and Lane.[38]

## DYNAMICS OF PARTICLES IN THERMAL AND CONCENTRATION GRADIENTS

### Thermal forces

When a particle is suspended in a gas through which there is a thermal gradient, a force acts upon it in the direction of decreasing temperature. This force is the basis for a very useful tool for collecting particles from aerosols, namely, the thermal precipitator. The theories explaining this force are very different for the case in which the mean free path of the gas molecules is less than the particle diameter than for the case in which it is greater.

The force on a particle which is large relative to the mean free path is best explained in terms of radiometer theory, which in turn is based on the concept the thermal creep developed by Maxwell. An increment of surface in a thermal gradient is bombarded by more molecules from the direction of the colder gas than from the opposite direction. The molecules will all leave the surface with essentially the same energy (assuming an accommodation coefficient of unity) and the result will be a flow of gas along the surface in the direction of increasing temperature. The combination of this flow and the curvature or discontinuities of particle surfaces (the edges, in the case of radiometer fins) produces the observed force.

Epstein[186] derived an equation for this case, in which a spherical particle is suspended in a gas in which a uniform thermal gradient exists at an appreciable distance from the particle. He calculated the temperature distribution on the surface of the particle on the basis of the thermal conductivities of the particle and of the gas, assuming the applicability of the Fourier equation for heat conduction without convection. Then, using the concept of thermal creep, he obtained an expression for gas flow along the surface of the particle. This was used as a boundary condition for solving the Navier-Stokes equation to obtain an expression for thermal force on the particle. The Epstein equation is

$$F = -9\pi r \left(\frac{k_a}{2k_a + k_i}\right) \frac{\eta^2}{\rho T} G \qquad (2.151)$$

where $F$ is the thermal force, $k_a$ and $k_i$ are the thermal conductivities of the gas and particle material respectively, $\eta$ is the viscosity of the gas, and $G$ is the thermal gradient.

Waldmann[187] has treated the case for the mean free path of a gas larger than the particle diameter. In this case the thermal conductivity of the particles is not important and the thermal force results from the net impulse in the direction of the gradient imparted to the particle by the impinging gas molecules. His equation is

$$F = -\frac{8}{15} r^2 \sqrt{\frac{2\pi m}{kT}} L_{tr} G \qquad (2.152)$$

where $L_{tr}$ is the translational thermal conductivity of the gas, $m$ is the mass of a gas molecule, and $k$ is Boltzmann's constant. Using the equations of classical gas kinetics, this can be put in the form

$$F = -\frac{4.0 P\lambda}{T} r^2 G \qquad (2.153)$$

where $P$ is the gas pressure and $\lambda$ is the mean free path of the gas. A similar equation has been derived by Bakanov and Derjaguin.[188]

An equation was derived by Cawood[189] for the situation where the mean free path of the gas molecules is approximately equal to the particle diameter:

$$F = -\frac{\pi}{2} \frac{P\lambda}{T} r^2 G \qquad (2.154)$$

Its similarity to the Waldmann equation is obvious, but its validity has been questioned on theoretical grounds by Saxton and Ranz.[190]

Numerous experimental studies have been made of thermal forces on gas-borne particles, particularly those which are large relative to the mean free path of the gas molecules. Good agreement was obtained between experimental results and the predictions of the Epstein equation when the thermal conductivities were relatively low, as when the particles were stearic acid.[190,191] This research was undertaken using modified Millikan oil drop apparatus in which thermal gradients as well as electrical fields were provided. The thermal forces were calculated from the rates of fall of individual particles in the presence and absence of thermal gradients, and the electric fields were used for convenience in controlling the location of the particles in the apparatus. The calculations were based on the application of Stokes' equation, and it is interesting to note that the derivation of this equation was based on the assumption that there is no motion of the gas relative to the particle at the surface of the particle, while the derivation of the Epstein equation is based on the concept of thermal creep at the surface. Thus the agreement is surprising.

Schadt and Cadle[192] observed that the Epstein equation predicts that particles of high thermal conductivity should be very difficult to collect with a thermal precipitator, but that no such difficulties had ever been reported. Accordingly, they made a study of thermal forces on aerosol particles in a thermal precipitator under greatly differing conditions of particle size, thermal conductivity of the particles, and thermal gradient. Thermal gradients were produced with a commercially available (Casella) thermal precipitator in which the wire-heating element was replaced with a ribbon filament. Aerosols having a narrow size range were used and thermal forces were calculated from the width of the deposit of particles on the cold slide beneath the hot ribbon, using the Stokes-Cunningham equation.

The thermal forces on stearic acid particles were almost precisely those predicted by the Epstein equation. The effects of particle size and of the thermal gradient on the thermal force were essentially those expected. However, when the particles consisted of materials of much higher thermal conductivity (sodium chloride or carbonyl iron) the measured thermal forces were twenty to forty times those predicted by the Epstein equation.

The thermal precipitator is designed to collect particles, not to measure thermal forces, and these results were difficult to interpret. Therefore thermal forces on aerosol particles of greatly differing thermal conductivity were measured in a modified Millikan oil drop apparatus.[193] The results obtained for particles of tricresyl phosphate, sodium chloride, and mercury confirmed the results obtained with the thermal precipitator.

The results were obtained in two ways. One involved measuring the difference in fall rate in the presence and absence of a thermal gradient. The other involved balancing the thermal and gravitational forces with the electric field so that the particle remained stationary. Within the limits of experimental error the same results were obtained by the two methods.

The results were compared with the Epstein equation by plotting the experimental values of $F/r$ against thermal gradient for a given average temperature. The values for tricresyl phosphate, which has a low thermal conductivity ($4.8 \times 10^{-4}$ cal/cm sec °C), agreed with those predicted by the equation. The measured thermal forces on particles of sodium chloride, which has a much higher thermal conductivity ($1.55 \times 10^{-2}$ cal/cm sec °C), agreed with the predicted dependence on thermal gradient, particle radius, and mean free path. However, the thermal force was about thirty times that predicted by the Epstein theory, as shown by Figure 2-17. This could be accounted for if the thermal conductivity of the particles could be shown to be comparable to that of tricresyl phosphate, about 0.03 time the bulk value for sodium chloride. A difference of this magnitude is difficult to explain. The possibility that the particles might have a microcrystalline structure was negated by electron micrographs of the particles, which indicated that they were single crystals, mostly cubic in form. The possibility that the particles were actually drops of supersaturated salt solution was eliminated by maintaining an atmosphere of very low humidity in the chamber of the Millikan apparatus.

The droplets of mercury, like the sodium chloride particles, agreed with the Epstein theory with regard to the effects of particle size, thermal gradient, and mean free path. However, the thermal force was about fifty times the theoretical value. The mercury aerosol was produced with a condensation-type aerosol generator[6] using dry nitrogen and a very small amount of nitrogen dioxide to produce condensation nuclei. Examination of many of the mercury droplets in an electron microscope showed that they were spherical and must have been coated with a very thin layer of some material, perhaps an oxide of mercury, which prevented evaporation. The layer must have been very thin relative to the drop size because the drops evaporated leaving no trace of material when the electron beam intensity was raised above a very low level. This is fairly convincing evidence that the high thermal forces for the mercury droplets did not result from a very low thermal conductivity for the droplets as compared with that for bulk mercury ($2.8 \times 10^{-2}$ cal/cm sec °C).

Another possible explanation for the high thermal forces is that the

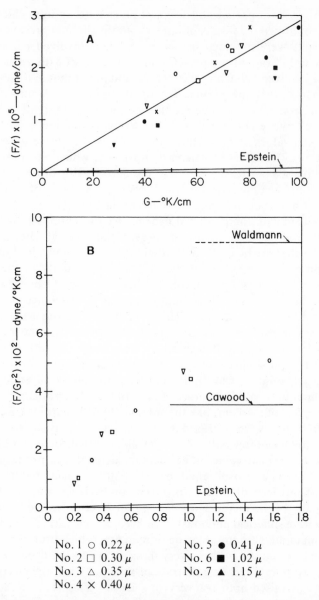

A. Dependence of thermal force on thermal gradient and particle radius at atmospheric pressure. B. The effect of the ratio of mean free path to particle radius. Average temperature was 307°K.

Figure 2-17. Sodium chloride particles, radius of each particle in $\mu$:[193]

particle sizes were so small relative to the mean free path that the Epstein equation does not apply. However, very high thermal forces were obtained for values of $\lambda/r$ as small as 0.057, so this explanation also seems unlikely.

As shown in Figure 2-17, the Cawood equation was fairly satisfactory for particles about the same size as the mean free path of the gas, and this was found to be true regardless of the thermal conductivity of the particles. The Waldmann equation might have applied if sufficiently large values of $\lambda/r$ could have been used.

Brock[194, 195] has developed an equation for the case $\lambda/r < 1$ to explain the results of Schadt and Cadle. He states that two principal objections can be made to the Epstein theory: (1) that appropriate boundary conditions were not used, and (2) that the continuous energy equation was solved neglecting the convective terms. He met these objections by resolving the steady-state Navier-Stokes equations for the case of a spherical particle suspended in a gas in the presence of a uniform temperature gradient and in the absence of external forces. The effect of convective flow was taken into account with a perturbation method. Brock's equation is:

$$F = -12\pi r^2 \eta \, \frac{C_{tm}(\lambda/r)}{(1 + 3C_m(\lambda/r)} \, x \, \frac{k_a/k_i + C_t(\lambda/r)}{1 + 2(k_a/k_i) + 2C_t(\lambda/r)} \, xG$$

(2.155)

where $C_m$ is the tangential momentum first-order slip coefficient, $C_t$ is the temperature jump first-order slip coefficient, and $C_{tm}$ is the thermal creep first-order coefficient. The evaluation of these coefficients must be made semi-empirically, using methods suggested by Brock. Equation 2.155 is only strictly applicable for values of $\lambda/r$ less than 0.25. Extrapolation of the data of Schadt and Cadle to values of $\lambda/r < 0.25$ indicates agreement with 2.155 within 10 to 30 percent. The agreement of the thermal force data of Rosenblatt and La Mer[19] for tricresyl phosphate aerosols with 2.155 is also very good. Brock suggests that the agreement (within 20% at $\lambda/r \sim 0.1$, 50% at $\lambda/r \sim 0.2$) of the Epstein equation with experimental data for tricresyl phosphate and substances of similar thermal conductivity is merely circumstantial and has been misleading.

### Photophoresis

A phenomenon closely related to the movement of particles in a uniform thermal gradient is photophoresis—the motion which occurs when a suspension of particles is subjected to an intense beam of light. The movement may be toward or away from the light and may be linear or in the form of spirals, loops, etc. It is generally believed to be a radiometer effect, similar to that for particles in a thermal gradient. However, this is not universally accepted, and Ehrenhaft[196] believes that photophoresis is a first-order electromagnetic effect.

Rosen and Orr[197] point out that if radiometer theory underlies the explanation, the relationship between the pressure of the surrounding gas and the photophoretic force $F_r$ must exhibit a maximum value $p_{max}$ at a pressure such that the mean free path is equal to the effective dimensions of the particle. Furthermore, below this pressure the force must be proportional to the pressure, and above it the force must be inversely proportional to pressure. The following equation was derived by Rubinowitz[198] for the low-pressure region:

$$F_r = \frac{\pi \alpha p r^3 G p}{3T} \tag{2.156}$$

where $\alpha$ is the accommodation coefficient and $G_p$ is the thermal gradient *within* the particle; Hettner[199] derived the following equation for the high-pressure region:

$$F_r = \frac{3\pi \eta^2 r R G_p}{pM} \tag{2.157}$$

where $R$ is the gas constant and $M$ is the molecular weight of the gas. He also suggested an empirical equation for the transition region where $r$ is about equal to the mean free path:

$$F_r = \frac{\pi r^2 \eta G_p \sqrt{\alpha R / M T}}{p/p_{max} + p_{max}/p} \tag{2.158}$$

where

$$p_{max} = \frac{3\eta}{r} \sqrt{\frac{RT}{M}} \tag{2.159}$$

Rosen and Orr point out that the major problem in applying these equations is in evaluating the gradient $G_p$. Rubinowitz suggests that at high pressures for spherical black particles exposed to a beam of light of intensity $I$,

$$G_p = \frac{I}{2(k_i + k_a)} \tag{2.160}$$

For a particle that is absorbing but not truly black, $I$ must be multiplied by the light absorption coefficient.

Avy[144] points out that colorless or white particles usually do not exhibit photophoresis, as would be expected.

Rosen and Orr studied photophoretic forces on carbon black particles using an experimental technique which compared the photophoretic force with the force of gravity. They first visually followed particle movement upward in an upward-directed light beam, allowing the particle to fall under the influence of gravity. The exposure and shielding times were adjusted so that the particle repeatedly traversed the same path. The photophoretic force was calculated from the particle velocity in the presence and absence of the light beam, the particle density, and the gas pressure.

The apparatus consisted of (1) a light source, (2) a chamber in which airborne particles were exposed to the light beam, (3) a solenoid-operated beam interrupter activated and timed by a thyratron unit, (4) a slide-wire variable resistor which recorded the vertical displacement of the particles, and (5) gas-pressure indicators and a vacuum pump.

Rosen and Orr observed many variations of photophoretic movement during the course of the experimentation. They attributed this to the fact that the temperature distribution in a particle exposed to a light beam is greatly affected by its shape and state of agglomeration. Spiral paths and closed elliptical and circular paths were common. These varied from orbits of very small diameter and high angular velocities to much larger orbits and smaller velocities. Decreasing beam intensity was found to increase the orbital diameter and decrease the angular velocity of orbiting particles. However, quantitative data were obtained only for particles which exhibited a linear vertical motion.

Of the various types of particles studied, only the black particles of wood charcoal and gas carbon produced a measurable photophoretic force. These particles were agglomerates which were about five to twenty-five microns in diameter.

Log-log plots of photophoretic force versus particle radius were straight lines as predicted by equations 2.156, 2.157, and 2.158.

According to these equations, the force should vary as the cube of the radius at low pressure, as the square at intermediate pressures, and linearly at high pressures. A small pressure effect was observed, particularly for the larger particles, as shown in Table 2-8. However, it it interesting to note that at the lowest pressure the mean free path was about seven

TABLE 2-8. EXPONENT ON RADIUS TERM FOR CARBON
PARTICLES AS A FUNCTION OF GAS PRESSURE[197]

| Pressure (mm. Hg) | Exponent |
|---|---|
| 8.3 | 2.72 |
| 15.3 | 2.78 |
| 25.6 | 2.30 |
| 35.4 | 1.86 |
| 46 | 1.8 |

microns; thus the particles were never small relative to the mean free path, and equation 2.156 would not be expected to apply, and at high pressures the exponent of $r$ is closer to 2 than to 1, as predicted by 2.157.

Photophorisis in an electric field has been called electrophotophoresis, and in a magnetic field has been called magnetophotophoresis.[144]

### Diffusiophoresis

Motion is impacted to particles suspended in a mixture of gases in which there is a concentration gradient. Several situations are possible. The particles may be large or small relative to the mean free path and the particles themselves may be growing or evaporating. The case of the non-volatile particle smaller than the mean free path was examined theoretically by Bakanov and Derjaguin,[188] who considered the effects of both the temperature and concentration gradients in the vicinity of a surface at which condensation or evaporation was occurring. The equations are quite involved and to demonstrate their application calculations were made for the behavior of a small non-volatile aerosol particle in the vicinity of a drop of carbon tetrachloride in a helium atmosphere. The calculations were made for three temperatures, 277, 300, and 330°K. The results demonstrated that under some circumstances an inversion of the particle velocity occurs, that is, the particle may be attracted to an evaporating drop and repelled from a growing one.

The behavior of very small particles in a concentration gradient was also investigated by Waldmann,[187,200] who proposed the following equation for the velocity $u$ of a sphere in an isothermal binary mixture:

$$u = - \frac{\delta m^{1/2}}{<m^{1/2}>} D \frac{\partial C_1}{\partial x} \qquad (2.161)$$

where

$$\delta m^{1/2} = m_1^{1/2}\left(1 + \frac{\pi}{8}\, a_1\right) - m_2^{1/2}\left(1 + \frac{\pi}{8}\, a_2\right)$$

$$<m^{1/2}> = m_1^{1/2} c_1 \left(1 + \frac{\pi}{8}\, a_1\right) + m_2^{1/2} C_2 \left(1 + \frac{\pi}{8}\, a_2\right)$$

$\dfrac{\partial c_1}{\partial x}$ is the concentration gradient of gas 1

$C_1$ is the concentration of gas 1

$a_1$ is the coefficient of diffuse reflection

$m_1$ is the molecular mass of gas component 1

$D$ is the binary diffusion coefficient.

If $a_1 = a_2$, equation 2.161 can be written

$$u = -\frac{m_1 - m_2}{m + (m_1 m_2)^{1/2}} D \frac{\partial c_1}{\partial x} \qquad (2.162)$$

The droplet migrates in the direction of the diffusion of the heavier component. Note that according to equations 2.161 and 2.162, the velocities due to concentration gradients of particles which are small relative to the mean free path are independent of particle size.

When the particles are large relative to the mean free path of the gas in which they are suspended, the situation is more involved and the problem has not been completely solved. This situation has been discussed by Waldmann[200] and by Derjaguin et al.[201] The latter point out that an exact and complete theory can be set up for the special case where the particles are volatile and of the same material as the diffusing vapors. A force results if there is a net unidirectional flow of the vapors, and a first approximation is given by the equation

$$F = \frac{4\pi\beta}{\rho''} \frac{\partial \rho'}{\partial x} r \frac{\rho'_1 - \rho'_0}{\rho''} \qquad (2.163)$$

and

$$\beta = 2D\eta\left[\left(\frac{4}{3} - \frac{\eta'}{\eta}\right)\left(\frac{m''}{m'} - 1\right) + \frac{D}{\eta} \rho''\right]$$

Here $\rho''$ is the partial density of the gas, $\rho'_1$ is the density of the saturated vapors at the drop surface, $\rho'_0$ is the vapor density at distances which are large in comparison with the drop radius, $\eta$ is the viscosity of the mixture, $\eta'$ is the bulk viscosity and $m''$ and $m'$ are the molecular masses of the gas and vapor. If 2.163 is substituted in the Stokes' equation and the result solved for velocity, $r$ will again cancel out.

Waldmann[200] suggests the following equation for the force on a non-volatile particle in a diffusion gradient which is derived neglecting friction and diffusion heat slip:

$$F = -6\pi\eta r\sigma_{12}D \frac{\partial c}{\partial x} \qquad (2.164)$$

where

$$\sigma_{12} = \frac{m_1 - m_2}{m + (m_1 m_2)^{1/2}} \qquad (2.165)$$

In terms of velocity instead of force, 2.164 leads to the same equation as for very small particles (2.162).

Experiments reported by Waldmann showed that in only one was the velocity the same for small as for large droplets. Accordingly, he postulated an empirical formula for the diffusion slip factor, $\sigma_{12}$, of equation 2.164:

$$\sigma_{12} = A \frac{m_1 - m_2}{m_1 + m_2} + B \frac{d_1 - d_2}{d_1 + d_2} \qquad (2.166)$$

where $d_1$ and $d_2$ are the molecular diameters and $A$ and $B$ are empirical constants.

Goldsmith, Delafield, and Cox[202] undertook an experimental study of the role of diffusiophoresis in the scavenging of radioactive particles from the atmosphere. The size range of the aerosol particles ("Nichrome") was about 0.01 to 0.1 micron radius. They were rendered radioactive by mixing the aerosol with thoron gas. The thoron decayed to thorium B which became irreversibly attached to any particulate material in the air. The aerosol was passed between parallel plates across which water vapor diffused. The gas channel was about 30 cm long, 10 cm wide, and a few mm across. The vapor-pressure gradient was produced by waterproof backed absorbent paper along each wall. The paper on one side was saturated with water while that on the opposite side was saturated with sulfuric acid of known concentration. After the aerosol had flowed through the "diffusion box" for a given period of time, the box was dismantled and a series of discs was cut from the side papers. These discs and also membrane filters through which the aerosols were drawn in the absence of the diffusion box were assayed using a gamma scintillation counter.

The results showed that the velocity (cm sec$^{-1}$) imposed on the particles when the water vapor pressure was small compared with the total pressure was governed by the equation

$$u = -1.9 \times 10^{-4} \, dp/dx \qquad (2.167)$$

where $dp/dx$ is the water vapor pressure gradient expressed in millibars per cm. This result agrees very well with the theoretical equation for particles small relative to the mean free path (equation 2.162).

Diffusiophoresis can occur in liquids as well as in gases. This case is discussed by Dukhin[203] in a paper primarily concerned with diffusional forces in the neighborhood of a liquid interface. Again, the rate of diffusiophoresis is not affected by particle size, and the force is directly proportional to the particle radius.

## REFERENCES

1. Rayleigh, Lord (J. W. Strutt), *Phil. Mag.*, **41**, 107, 274, 447 (1871).
2. Sinclair, David, Optical properties of aerosols, in "Handbook on Aerosols," Atomic Energy Commission, Washington, D.C., 1950.

3. Oster, G., *Chem. Rev.*, **43**, 319 (1948).

4. Ligda, M. G. H., Radar storm observations, in "Compendium of Meterology," T. F. Malone, ed., Am. Meteor. Soc., Boston, 1951.

5. van de Hulst, H. C., "Light Scattering by Small Particles," Wiley, New York, 1957.

6. Sinclair, David, and V. K. La Mer, *Chem. Rev.*, **44**, 245 (1949).

7. Tabibian, R. M., and W. Heller, *J. Coll. Sci.*, **13**, 6 (1958).

8. Tabibian, R. M., W. Heller, and J. N. Epel, *J. Coll. Sci.*, **11**, 195 (1956).

9. Gucker, F. T., and R. L. Rowell, in "The Physical Chemistry of Aerosols," General Discussion No. 30 of the Faraday Society, Aberdeen, 1961.

10. Aden, A. L., and M. Kerker, *J. Appl. Phys.*, **22**, 1242 (1951).

11. Churchill, S. W., G. C. Clark, and C. M. Sliepcevich, in "The Physical Chemistry of Aerosols," General Discussion No. 30 of the Faraday Society, Aberdeen, 1961.

12. Hodkinson, J. R., I. C. E. S., P. 87, Pergamon Press, New York, 1963.

13. Neuberger, H., Panofsky, H., and Sekera, Z., Physics of the atmosphere in "Air Pollution Handbook," Magill, P. L., F. R. Holden, and C. Ackley, ed., McGraw-Hill, New York, 1956.

14. Sinclair, D., *J. Optical Soc. Am.*, **37**, 475 (1947).

15. Gumprecht, R. O., and C. M. Sliepcevich, *J. Phys. Chem.*, **57**, 90, 95 (1953).

16. Kohler, H., *Trans. Faraday Soc.*, **32**, 1153 (1936).

17. Pijper, A., *S. African Med. Record*, 8 (1919).

18. Ponder, E., in Medical Physics, O. Glasser, ed., The Year Book Publishers, Chicago, 1944.

19. Hogben, M., *Nature*, **155**, 576 (1945); **157**, 484 (1946).

20. Humphries, W. J., "Physics of the Air," McGraw-Hill, New York, 1940.

21. Einstein, A., *Ann. Phys.*, **17**, 549 (1905).

22. Cunningham, E., *Proc. Roy. Soc.*, **83A**, 357 (1910).

23. De Broglie, M., *C. R. Acad. Sci. Paris*, **148**, 1316 (1909).

24. Millikan, R. A., "The Electron," Univ. of Chicago Press, Chicago, 1917.

25. Perrin, J., "Atoms," Tr. D. H. Hammick, Constable and Co., London, 1920.

26. Perrin, J., *Compt. Rendue*, **149**, 549 (1909).

27. Fuks, N. A., "The Mechanics of Aerosols," Tr. M. E. Lackowicz, distributed by U. S. Dept. of Commerce, Office of Technical Services, Washington (1955).

28. Cadle, R. D., and W. C. Thuman, *Ind. Eng. Chem.*, **52**, 315 (1960).

29. Thomas, J. W., "The Diffusion Battery Method for Aerosol Particle Size Determination," O R N L 1648, Instrumentation, January 5, 1954.

30. De Marcus, W. C., and J. W. Thomas, "Theory of a Diffusion Battery," O R N L 1413, October 16, 1952.

31. Nolan, J. J., and P. J. Nolan, *Proc. Roy. Irish Acad.*, **45A**, 47 (1938).

32. Nolan, P. J., and E. L. Kennan, *Proc. Roy. Irish Acad.*, **52A**, 171 (1949).

33. Sinclair, D., Stability of aerosols and behavior of aerosol particles, in "Handbook of Aerosols," U. S. Atomic Energy Commission, Washington, 1950.

34. Smoluchowski, M. von, *Phys. Z.*, **17**, 557, 585 (1916).

35. Smoluchowski, M. von, *Z. Phys. Chem.*, **92**, 129 (1917).

36. Whytlaw-Gray, R., and H. S. Patterson, "Smoke," Edward Arnold, London, 1932.

37. Quon, J. E., International Journal of Air Pollution, in Press.
38. Green, H. L., and W. R. Lane, "Particulate Clouds: Dusts, Smokes, and Mists," Spon, London, 1957.
39. Derjaguin, B., and G. Vlasenko, *D A N USSR*, **63,** 155 (1948).
40. Zebel, G., *Kolloid Z.*, **156,** 102 (1958).
41. Yaffee, I. S., and R. D. Cadle, *J. Phys. Chem.*, **62,** 510 (1958).
42. Rich, T. A., *Geofisica*, **31,** 60 (1955).
43. Gillespie, T., and G. O. Langstroth, *Can. J. Chem.* **30,** 1003 (1952).
44. Patterson, H., and W. Cawood, *Proc. Roy. Soc.*, **136A,** 538 (1932).
45. Artemov, I. S., *J. Phys., Chem. U.S.S.R.*, **20,** 553 (1946).
46. Artemov, I. S., *Doklady. Akad. Nauk. S.S.S.R.*, **50,** 289 (1945).
47. Artemov, I. S., *Kolloid. Zhur.*, **9,** 225 (1947).
48. Beischer, D., and A. Winkel, *Z. Phys. Chem.*, **176A,** 1 (1936).
49. Gillespie, T., *Proc. Roy. Soc.*, **216A,** 569 (1951).
50. Zebel, G., *Kolloid Z.*, **157,** 37 (1958).
51. Carlin, B., "Ultrasonics," 2nd ed., McGraw-Hill, New York, 1960.
52. Andrade, E. N. de C., *Trans. Faraday Soc.*, **42,** 1111 (1936).
53. Parker, R. C., *Trans. Faraday Soc.*, **42,** 1115 (1936).
54. Brandt, O., and Hiedemann, *Trans. Faraday Soc.*, **42,** 1101 (1936).
55. Podoshevnikov, B. F., *Zh. Prikl. Khim.*, **34,** 2664 (1961).
56. Cassel, H. M., and H. Schultz, A sonic method of determining particle size in aerosols in Lewis McCabe, ed., "Air Pollution," McGraw-Hill, New York, 1956.
57. Gucker, F. T., Jr., Determination of concentration and size of particulate matter by light scattering and sonic techniques, in "Proceedings of the First National Air Pollution Symposium," Stanford Research Institute, Menlo Park, Calif., 1949.
58. King, L. V., *Proc. Roy. Soc.*, **147A,** 233 (1934).
59. Fuks, N., Aerosol studies in the Soviet Union, in Stanford Research Institute Journal, 3rd quarter, 1961, V. 5, "Fine Particles Research . . . Things Small, Effects Big," Menlo Park, California.
60. Varlamov, M. L., E. L. Krichevskaya, G. A. Manakin, A. A. Ennan, L. M. Kozakova, and L. S. Zbrozhek. Primenenie Ul' traakustikik Issled. Veshchestva, Moscow, Sb. 1960, No. 12, 199. (*Chem. Abstracts*, **67,** 14453 (1962).
61. Langstroth, G. O., and T. Gillespie, *Can. J. Res.*, **25B,** 455 (1947).
62. Gillespie, T., and G. O. Langstroth, *Can. J. Chem.*, **29,** 201 (1951).
63. Millikan, R. A., *Phys. Rev.*, **15,** 545 (1920).
64. Millikan, R. A., *Phys. Rev.*, **21,** 217 (1923).
65. Knudsen, M., and S. Weber, *Ann. Phys. Lpz.*, **36,** 982 (1911).
66. Mattauch, J., *Z. Phys.*, **32,** 439 (1925).
67. Arnold, H., *Phil. Mag.*, **22,** 777 (1911).
68. Davies, C. N., in "Symposium on Particle Size Analysis," Institution of Chemical Engineers, London, February 4, 1947.
69. Martin, S. W., in "Symposium on New Methods for Particle Size Determination in the Subsieve Range, Technical Publication No. 51," Am. Soc., for Testing Materials, Philadelphia, 1941.
70. Irani, R. R., and C. F. Callis, "Particle Size: Measurement, Interpretation, and Application," Wiley, New York, 1963.
71. Svedberg, T., *Ind. Eng. Chem., Anal. Ed.*, **10,** 113 (1938).

72. Svedberg, T., and K. O. Pedersen, "The Ultracentrifuge," Oxford University Press, London, 1940.
73. Ranz, W. E., and J. B. Wong, *Ind. Eng. Chem.*, **44**, 1371 (1952); *A.M.A. Archives of Ind. Hyg. and Occupational Med.*, **5**, 464 (1952).
74. Ranz, W. E., "Principles of Inertial Impaction," Bulletin No. 66, Dept. of Engineering Research, The Pennsylvania State Univ., University Park, Pennsylvania, 1956.
75. Hughes, R. R., and E. R. Gilliland, *Chem. Eng. Prog.*, **48**, 497 (1952).
76. Schadt, C., and R. D. Cadle, *Anal. Chem.*, **29**, 864 (1957); Gillespie, T., *J. Colloid Sci.*, **10**, 266 (1955); Gillespie, T., and E. Rideal, *J. Colloid Sci.*, **10**, 281 (1955).
77. Rabin, E., A. R. Schallenmuller, and R. L. Lowhead, "Displacement and Shattering of Propellent Droplets," Rocketdyne Report R-2431. Air Force Report AFOSRTR 60-75, 1960.
78. Ingebo, R., "Vaporization Rates and Drag Coefficients for Isooctane Sprays in Turbulent Air Streams," Nat. Adv. Comm. for Aeronautics, Technical Note 3265, Lewis Flight Prop. Lab., Cleveland, 1954.
79. Richardson, E. G., "Aerodynamic Capture of Particles," Pergamon, New York, 1960.
80. Chen, C. Y., *Chem. Rev.*, **55**, 595 (1955).
81. Dorman, R. G., in "Aerodynamic Capture of Particles," Pergamon, New York, 1960.
82. Langmuir, I., O.S.R.D. Report No. 865, Office of Technical Services, Washington, D. C., 1942.
83. Davies, C. N., *Proc. Instn. Mech. Engr. B*, **1B**, 185 (1952).
84. Green, H. L., and D. J. Thomas, *Proc. Instn. Mech. Engrs. B*, **1B**, 203 (1952).
85. Ramskill, E. A., and W. L. Anderson, *J. Colloid. Sci.*, **6**, 416 (1951).
86. Kraemer, H. F., and H. F. Johnstone, *Ind. Eng. Chem.*, **47**, 2436 (1955).
87. Gillespie, T., *J. Colloid Sci.*, **10**, 299 (1955).
88. Gillespie, T., in "Aerodynamic Capture of Particles," Pergamon, New York, 1960.
89. Langmuir, I., *J. Met.*, **5**, 175 (1948).
90. Hocking, L. M., *Q. J. Roy. Met. Soc.*, **85**, 44 (1959).
91. Picknett, R. G., in "Aerodynamic Capture of Particles," Pergamon, New York, 1960.
92. Greenfield, S. M., *J. Met.*, **14**, 115 (1957).
93. McCully, C. R., M. Fisher, G. Langer, J. Rosinski, H. Glaess, and D. Werle, *Ind. Eng. Chem.*, **48**, 1512 (1956).
94. Oakes, B., in "Aerodynamic Capture of Particles," Pergamon, New York, 1960.
95. Pemberton, C. S., in "Aerodynamic Capture of Particles," Pergamon, New York, 1960.
96. Watson, H. H., *Am. Ind. Hyg. Assoc. Q.*, **15**, 21 (1954).
97. Graton, C. L., and H. J. Fraser, *J. Geol.*, **43**, 785 (1935).
98. Westmen, A. E. R., and H. R. Hughill, *J. Am. Cer. Soc.*, **13**, 767 (1930).
99. Dalla Valle, J. M., "Micromeritics," 2nd ed., Pitman, New York, 1948.
100. Furnas, C. C., *Ind. Eng. Chem.*, **23**, 1052 (1931).
101. Herdan, G., "Small Particle Statistics," Academic Press, New York, 1960.
102. Heywood, H., *Powder Metallurgy*, **7**, 1 (1961).

103. Derjaguin, B. V., in "Powders in Industry," Society of Chemical Industry Monograph No. 14, London, 1961; S. V. Nerpin and B. V. Derjaguin, ibid; B. V. Darjaguin and I. I. Abrikassova, *Quart. Rev.*, **10**, 295 (1956); *Disc. Faraday Soc.*, **18**, 24 (1954); B. V. Derjaguin, *Scientific American*, July, 1960.

104. Cremer, E., Th. Kraus, and F. Conrad, *Angew. Chem.*, **64**, 10 (1952).

105. Patat, F., and W. Schneid, *Chemie-Ing. Techn.*, **32**, 8 (1960).

106. Salisbury, J. W., P. E. Glaser, B. A. Stein, and B. Vonnegut, *J. Geophys. Res.*, **69**, 235 (1964).

107. Brown, R. L., in "Powders in Industry," Society of Chemical Industry Monograph No. 14, London, 1961.

108. Train, D., *J. Pharm., London*, **10**, 129, 143 (1958).

109. Huffine, C. L., and C. F. Bonilla, *A.I.Ch.E. Journal*, **8**, 490 (1962).

110. Marathe, M. N., and G. S. Tendolkar, *Trans. Indian Inst. Chem. Engrs.*, **6**, 90 (1953).

111. Wakashima, H., *Kanazawa Daigaku Kogakubu Kiyo*, **2**, 389 (1961).

112. Russel, H. W., *J. Am. Ceram. Soc.*, **18**, 1 (1935).

113. Woodside, W., *Can. J. Phys.*, **36**, 815 (1958).

114. Laubitz, M. J., *Can. J. Phys.*, **37**, 798 (1959).

115. Bingham, E. C., "Fluidity and Plasticity," 1st ed., McGraw-Hill, New York, 1922.

116. Reiner, M., "Deformation and Flow," Lewis, London, 1949.

117. Ree, T., and H. Eyring, *J. Appl. Phys.*, **26**, 793 (1955).

118. Maron, S. H., and P. E. Pierce, *J. Colloid Sci.*, **11**, 80 (1956).

119. Maron, S. H., and S. M. Fok, *J. Colloid Sci.*, **10**, 482 (1955).

120. Maron, S. H., and A. W. Sisko, *J. Colloid Sci.*, **12**, 99 (1957).

121. Maron, S. H., and R. J. Belner, *J. Colloid Sci.*, **10**, 523 (1955).

122. Williams, P. S., *J. Appl. Chem. (London)*, **3**, 120 (1953).

123. Williams, P. S., *Disc. Faraday Soc.*, **11**, 47 (1951).

124. Scott Plair, G. W., in "Encyclopaedic Dictionary of Physics," Macmillan, New York, 1962.

125. Ward, A. G., "Colloids: Their Properties and Applications," Blackie, London, 1945.

126. Rigden, P. J., *J. Soc. Chem. Ind.*, **65**, 299 (1947).

127. Rigden, P. J., *Nature*, **167**, 197 (1951).

128. Orr, Jr., C., and H. G. Blocker, *J. Colloid Sci.*, **10**, 24 (1955).

129. Sweeny, K. H., and R. D. Geckler, *J. Appl. Phys.*, **25**, 1135 (1954).

130. Gunn, R., *J. Colloid Sci.*, **10**, 107 (1955).

131. Gunn, R., *J. Meteor.*, **11**, 339 (1954).

132. Phillips, B. B., and R. Gunn, *J. Meteor.*, **11**, 348 (1954).

133. Gillespie, T., and G. O. Langstroth, *Canad. J. Chem.*, **30**, 1056 (1952).

134. Woessner, R. H., and R. Gunn, *J. Colloid Sci.*, **11**, 69 (1956).

135. Wells, P., and R. Gerke, *J. Am. Chem. Soc.*, **41**, 312 (1919).

136. Luchak, G., *J. Colloid Sci.*, **12**, 144 (1957).

137. Kunkel, W. B., *J. Appl. Phys.*, **19**, 1056 (1948); ibid, **21**, 820 (1950); ibid, **21**, 833 (1950).

138. Nuckolls, A. H., "Generation of Static Electricity in Blower Systems," Underwriters' Laboratories Inc., Bull. of Research No. 8, 1939.

139. von Walther, R., and Franke, W., *Braunkohle*, **28**, 789 (1929).

140. Harper, W. R., in "Powders in Industry," Society of Chemical Industry Monograph No. 14, Gordon and Breach, New York, 1961.

141. Rudge, W. A. D., *Phil. Mag.*, **25**, 481 (1913).
142. Smoluchowski, M. Von, *Phys. Z.*, **13**, 1069 (1912).
143. Dodd, E. E., *J. Appl. Phys.*, **24**, 73 (1953).
144. Avy, A. P., "Les Aerosols," Dunod, Paris, 1956.
145. Dalla Valle, J. M., C. Orr, and B. L. Hinkle, *Brit. J. Appl. Phys.*, **5**, Suppl. 3, 1954.
146. Drozin, V. G., and V. K. La Mer, *J. Colloid Sci.*, **14**, 74 (1959).
147. Pauthenier, M., and Mme. Moreau-Hanot, *Electrician*, **113**, 187 (1934).
148. Gottschlich, C. F., in "Air Pollution," A. C. Stern, ed., Academic Press, New York, 1962.
149. Davies, C. N., *Proc. Instn. Mech. Engrs. (London)*, **1B**, No. 5, 185 (1952).
150. Dean, R. S., and J. Koster, "Mineral Physics Studies. 10. Electrical Properties of Mineral Aggregates II. Natural and Artificial Aggregates of Crystallized Lead Sulfide," U. S. Bureau of Mines Dept. Investigations 3268, 1935.
151. Brunauer, S., P. H. Emmett, and E. Teller, *J. Am. Chem. Soc.*, **60**, 309 (1938).
152. Gregg, S. J., in "Powders in Industry: Society of Chemical Industry Monograph No. 14, Gordon and Breach, New York, 1961.
153. Brunauer, S., "The Adsorption of Gases and Vapors," Princeton Univ. Press, 1943.
154. Brunauer, S., P. H. Emmett, and E. Teller, *J. Am. Chem. Soc.*, **60**, 309 (1938).
155. Brunauer, S., L. S. Deming, W. E. Deming, and E. Teller, *J. Am. Chem. Soc.*, **62**, 1723 (1940).
156. Hüttig, G. G., *Monatsch.*, **78**, 177 (1948).
157. Hüttig, G. F., and G. Pietzka, *Monatsh.*, **78**, 185 (1948).
158. Harkins, W. D., and G. Jura, *J. Am. Chem. Soc.*, **66**, 1366 (1944).
159. Carman, P. C., *J. Soc. Chem. Ind.*, **57**, 225 (1938).
160. Carman, P. C., in "Symposium on New Methods for Particle Size Determination in the Subsieve Range," Am. Soc. for Test. Mat., Philadelphia, 1951.
161. Fowler, J. L., and K. L. Hertel, *J. Appl. Phys.*, **11**, 496 (1940).
162. Lea, F. M., and R. W. Nurse, *J. Soc. Chem. Ind.*, **58**, 277 (1939).
163. Drinker, P., and T. Hatch, "Industrial Dust," 2nd ed., McGraw-Hill, New York, 1954.
164. Price, D. J., and H. H. Brown, "Dust Explosions," Nat. Fire Protection Assoc., Boston, 1922.
165. Wheeler, R. V., *Trans. Faraday Soc.*, **32**, 1344 (1936).
166. Golovina, E. S., and G. P. Khaustovich, in "Eighth Symposium (International) on Combustion," published for The Combustion Institute, Williams and Wilkins, Baltimore, 1962.
167. Tesner, P. A., in "Eight Symposium (Internal) on Combustion," published for The Combustion Institute, Williams & Wilkins, Baltimore, 1962.
168. Hartmann, I., A. Cooper, and M. Jacobson, "Recent Studies on the Explosibility of Cornstarch," U.S. Bur. Mines, Dept. Invest. 4725, 1950.
169. Essenhigh, R. H., and I. Falls, in "The Physical Chemistry of Aerosols," Discussion No. 30 of The Faraday Society, London, 1961.
170. Godsave, G. A. E., in "Fourth Symposium (International) on Combustion," published for The Combustion Institute, Williams & Wilkins, Baltimore, 1953.
171. Goldsmith, M., and S. S. Penner, *Jet Propulsion*, **24**, 245 (1954).

172. Kobayashi, K., in "Fifth Symposium (International) on Combustion," published for The Combustion Institute, Reinhold, New York, 1955.
173. Miesse, C. C., in "Sixth Symposium (International) on Combustion" published for The Combustion Institute, Reinhold, New York, 1957.
174. Isoda, H., and S. Kumagai, in "Seventh Symposium (International) on Combustion," published for The Combustion Institute, Butterworths, London, 1959.
175. Probert, R. P., *Phil. Mag.*, **37**, 94 (1946).
176. Essenhigh, R. H., 2nd Cong. Pulverized Fuel, Institute of Fuel, London, 1958.
177. Cadle, R. D., and R. C. Robbins, in "The Physical Chemistry of Aerosols," Discussion No. 30 of The Faraday Society, London, 1961.
178. Rashevsky, N., "Mathematical Biophysics," 3rd ed., The University of Chicago Press, Chicago, 1960.
179. Coughanowr, D. R., "Oxidation of Sulfur Dioxide in Fog Droplets," Engineering Experiment Station, Univ. of Illinois, 1956.
180. Johnstone, H. F., and D. R. Coughanowr, *Ind. Eng. Chem.*, **50**, 1169 (1958).
181. Roughton, F. J. W., *Proc. Roy. Soc. B.,* **140**, 203 (1952).
182. Crank, J., *Phil. Mag.*, **48**, 811 (1952).
183. Langmuir, I., *Phys. Rev.*, **12**, 368 (1918).
184. Fuks, N., *Phys. Z. Sowjet*, **6**, 224 (1934).
185. Bradley, R. S., and G. C. S. Waghorn, *Proc. Roy. Soc. A*, **206**, 65 (1951).
186. Epstein, P. S., *Z. Physik.*, **54**, 537 (1929).
187. Waldmann, L., *Z. Naturforsch.*, **14a**, 589 (1959).
188. Bakanov, S. P., and B. V. Derjaguin, in "The Physical Chemistry of Aerosols," Discussion No. 30 of The Faraday Society, London, 1961.
189. Cawood, W., "Disperse Systems in Gases; Dust, Smoke and Fog," Faraday Society General Discussion, Gurney and Jackson, London, 1936.
190. Saxton, R. L., and W. E. Ranz, *J. Appl. Phys.*, **23**, 917 (1952).
191. Rosenblatt, P., and V. K. La Mer, *Phys. Rev.*, **70**, 385 (1946).
192. Schadt, C. F., and R. D. Cadle, *J. Colloid Sci.*, **12**, 356 (1957).
193. Schadt, C. F., and R. D. Cadle, *J. Phys. Chem.*, **65**, 1689 (1961).
194. Brock, J. R., *J. Colloid Sci.*, **17**, 768 (1962).
195. Brock, J. R., *J. Phys. Chem.*, **66**, 1763 (1962).
196. Ehrenhaft, F., *J. Franklin Institute*, **233**, 235 (1942).
197. Rosen, M. H., and C. Orr, Jr., *J. Colloid Sci.*, **19**, 50 (1964).
198. Rubinowitz, A., *Ann. Physik.*, **62**, 691 (1920).
199. Hettner, G., *Z. Physik*, **37**, 179 (1926).
200. Waldmann, L., in "Rarified Gas Dynamics," L. Talbot, ed., Academic Press, New York, 1961.
201. Derjaguin (Deryagin), B. V., S. P. Bakonov, S. S. Dukhin, and G. A. Batova, in "Research in Surface Forces," Deryagin, ed., translated by Consultants Bureau, New York, 1963.
202. Goldsmith, P., H. J. Delafield, and L. C. Cox, *Quart. J. Royal Meteor. Soc.*, **89**, 43 (1963).
203. Dukhin, S. S., in "Research in Surface Forces," Deryagin, ed., translated by Consultants Bureau, New York, 1963.

# Chapter 3    Physiological Action

## INTRODUCTION

Ever since man evolved from more primitive animals he must have been aware of many physiological effects of fine particles. If he lived on the desert he was subjected to sand storms. The caves in which he made his home must have been very dusty habitations. And even the earliest man must have rubbed various types of soils and other powders into his wounds. Pneumoconiosis has been observed in prehistoric man; carbonization of the pulmonary tissues has been seen in Basket Maker bodies; silicosis associated with plural adhesions has been observed in the lungs of another Basket Maker body; and anthracosis and pleural adhesions have been found in Egyptian mummies.[1] Presumably these were all "occupational diseases" caused by the inhalation of particles. As man has become more knowledgeable he has also become increasingly aware of the importance to his well being of the biological action of fine particles. Not only do they affect his own body in a multitude of ways but they can have vastly important effects on the plants and domestic animals that constitute his foods and the insects that interfere with his comfort.

For the most part, man's concern with the physiological action of fine particles has been a negative one. For example, much of medicine is concerned with bacteria and viruses. Another example is the major aspect of industrial hygiene and toxicology which is concerned with toxic dusts. And one of the most frightening aspects of our times is the ever-present danger that a large part of the world's human population will be injured or eliminated by radioactive fallout resulting from nuclear warfare. The chief exceptions to this generalization have been powders that are foods or fertilizers, but in these cases the fact that the materials are powdered is more or less incidental. However, during the last few decades physiologically active sprays and powders which depend for their action to a large extent on their particle size have been developed. These include a multitude of insecticides, therapeutic agents, and, more grimly, chemical warfare agents. And even the insecticides, important as they have proved for man's well-being, may not be an unalloyed benefit.[2]

**159**

Fortunately, a tremendous scientific and technological effort has been made to understand and control the behavior of biologically active fine particles. The purpose of this chapter is to discuss the biologically significant aspects of the behavior of such particles and particularly the importance of particle size to this behavior.

## INHALED PARTICLES

### Collection in the human body

The effect of size on the action of particles on the human body is especially important for particles that are inhaled. Particle size, together with specific gravity, largely determines where the particles are deposited in the respiratory system, the fate of the particles after deposition, and to a considerable extent their physiological action, if any. To understand the deposition process it is necessary to have a rudimentary knowledge of the structure of the human respiratory system. Air entering the nose or mouth passes immediately into the pharynx and then into the larynx, or voice box. From here the air enters the trachea (windpipe) which, upon entering the chest cavity, divides into the right and left bronchi. The bronchi in turn divide into progressively smaller branches called bronchial tubes, which are within the lungs. The smallest of the tubes are known as bronchioles. These end in alveolar air sacs whose walls contain indentations (the alveoli) about 0.015 cm in diameter. The walls of the alveoli contain the pulmonary capillaries, within which the oxygen and carbon dioxide interchanges occur.

The trachea is lined with a mucous membrane, the outermost cells of which are covered with cilia—fine hair-like processes which constantly lash back and forth in the mucous which moistens the tracheal walls.

The ordinary inspiration and expiration by the average man is about 500 cm$^3$ of air called the tidal air. Force inspiration will add about 1600 cm$^3$ of complemental air to the tidal air. Even after the most violent expiration about 1000 cm$^3$ of air (the residual air) remains in the lungs, and after an ordinary expiration there will be an additional 1600 cm$^3$ of supplemental air. Of the 500 cm$^3$ normally inhaled or exhaled, about 150 cm$^3$ is needed to fill the tracheobronchial "tree," or anatomical dead space. The combined supplemental, tidal, and complemental air is known as the *vital capacity*.

Davies[3] points out that the lungs are particularly vulnerable to airborne substances because of the delicacy and complicated structure of the surfaces. The total surface area is probably about 300 square feet, and the structures separating the alveoli from the blood stream are extremely thin. Fortunately, the cilia and the winding passages through which the air must pass remove most airborne particles before they can reach the delicate tissues of the alveoli.  Nonetheless, these defenses are occasionally penetrated, in which case the particles may be deposited in the alveoli and cause trouble.

Particle size has at least two effects on the deposition of particles in the respiratory system. One of these is the over-all percentage of retention of the particles in the system; the other is the location of the region within the respiratory system where most of the particles are deposited.  Numerous experimental studies have demonstrated that there is a particle size corresponding to minimum retention of particles in the lungs.[4,5,6]  For most substances this is about 0.5 micron diameter.  Particles larger than this minimum are deposited mainly by sedimentation, and smaller particles reach the respiratory surfaces mainly by diffusion, as a result of Brownian motion. Larger particles are also removed by interception and impaction.

The tubes leading to the alveoli are very tortuous and decrease in size as the alveoli are approached.  Therefore, most particles larger than about 0.5 micron diameter reach the walls of the bronchial tubes and are removed from the airstream.  Cilia occur from the end of the terminal bronchioles up through the trachea, and particles caught on the mucous membranes are transported to the throat by the beat of the cilia and swallowed.  Since the digestive system is much more sturdy than the respiratory system, the swallowed particles seldom do any harm.

Particles smaller than 0.5 micron (but larger than about 0.03 micron) in diameter are more likely to be deposited in the alveolar air sacs and alveoli than in the bronchial tubes. The walls of the former are closer together than those of the tubes, so that the likelihood that particles will reach a surface by diffusion is greater. The effect of size on deposition in the lungs is indicated by Figure 3-1. The plots are shown as bands instead of lines because of experimental errors and because of variations in the nature of particles, breathing patterns, and human beings.[3]

Deryagin et al[7] have made the interesting suggestion that diffusional forces on particles may play an important role in their deposition in the alveoli. The evolution of carbon dioxide and the absorption of oxygen constitute two countercurrents near the surfaces of the lungs. They point out that although the volume of evolved carbon dioxide is 10 to 15 percent less than the volume of absorbed oxygen, the greater molecular weight of the former assures that the Stefan current will be directed away from the alveoli walls, and will protect the latter from contamination.  When the

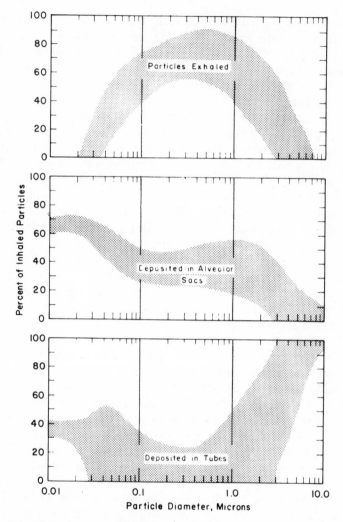

Figure 3-1. The percentage of inhaled particles of various sizes that are exhaled (top), that are deposited in the alveolar sacs (middle) that are deposited in the tubes (bottom).[3] (*Courtesy of Stanford Research Institute*)

particles are very small (less than about 0.03 micron according to Davies) no inhaled particles escape from the lungs and the number reaching the alveolar air sacs is reduced by diffusional deposition on the walls of the trachea, bronchi, and bronchioles.

A number of theoretical studies have been made of particle deposition by diffusion in the lower lung. Landahl[8] based his theoretical calculations on a model structure for the lungs, but the approach has the difficulty that lungs of living persons may vary markedly from one another and from the model. In order to avoid this difficulty, Friedlander[9] used dimensional analysis to derive an expression for the dependence of the particle removal efficiency of the lower lung on the particle diffusion coefficient, the time of breath, and various parameters related to lung structure. He limited the analysis to particles smaller than a few tenths of a micron in diameter, for which diffusion is the controlling removal mechanism. The analysis is particularly useful for correlating and extrapolating experimental data, but it can also be used to estimate the size of the largest particles which are essentially completely removed in the respiratory region. Friedlander defines removal efficiency, $E_r$ by

$$E_r = 1 - \frac{\overline{C}_0}{\overline{C}_i} \tag{3.1}$$

where $\overline{C}_0$ and $\overline{C}_i$ represent the volume average concentrations of particles in the air leaving and entering the lower respiratory region, respectively. They are defined by the equations

$$\overline{C}_0 = \frac{1}{q} \int_0^q C_0 dq' \tag{3.2}$$

and

$$\overline{C}_i = \frac{1}{q} \int_0^q C_i dq' \tag{3.3}$$

where $q$ is the average volume of air entering the respiratory region with each breath, and $C_0$ and $C_i$ represent the instantaneous particle concentrations. The value for the efficiency usually reported is the fraction of particles removed from the tidal air volume. In the absence of deposition in the upper respiratory tract, the efficiency $E_r$ can be calculated from the experimental data using the equation

$$E_r = E_r \text{(reported)} \left(\frac{\text{tidal volume}}{\text{tidal volume} - \text{dead space}}\right) \tag{3.4}$$

Friedlander summarizes the variables on which the efficiency depends as follows:

$$E_r = f_1(D, \tau, l, q/v, g_1, g_2, \text{etc.}) \tag{3.5}$$

where $\tau$ is the average time of breath, $l$ is a characteristic length of the order of the diameter of the alveoli, $v$ represents the functional residual air volume associated with the respiratory region, and $g_1$, $g_2$, etc. are dimensionless shape factors which describe the structure of the lung.

For that size range where diffusion is of controlling importance, but where the diffusion coefficient is small, an equation of the following form should be applicable:

$$E_r = f_2(g_1, g_2, \text{etc.}) [(D\tau)^{1/2}/l] \qquad (3.6)$$

Friedlander compared this equation with experimental data by Altshuler, *et al.*[6] for the deposition of triphenyl phosphate mists in the respiratory tract of three subjects, and came to the following conclusions from the data for two of the subjects:

1. Diffusion controlled the removal when $D\tau$ was greater than $8 \times 10^{-6}$ cm.$^2$

2. Extrapolating the straight line $E_r$ vs $(D\tau)^{1/2}$ to the point where it intersected $E_r = 100$ percent gave a value of $D\tau = 1.5 \times 10^{-4}$ cm.$^2$ This corresponds to the size of the largest particle removed with essentially 100 percent efficiency. The length $2(D\tau/\pi)^{1/2}$ corresponds to the thickness of a region cleared of particles, and when $2(D\tau/\pi)^{1/2}$ is of the order of the characteristic length $l$, the efficiency should approach 100 percent. For these same two subjects the upper cut-off was $2(D\tau/\pi)^{1/2} = 138$ microns, about the alveolar diameter. The line passing through the data for these two subjects is given by the equation

$$E_r = 8000(D\tau)^{1/2} \qquad (3.7)$$

where $D$ has the dimensions cm$^2$/sec and $\tau$ is in seconds.

If we let $E_r$ be 100 percent and $\tau$ be 4 seconds, $D = 3.75 \times 10^{-3}$ cm$^2$/ sec. Diffusion coefficients for spherical particles at body temperature in air at 1 atmosphere pressure, taken from Friedlander's paper, are shown in Figure 3-2. The above value of $D$ corresponds to a particle diameter of 0.04 micron, which is only slightly larger than the figure quoted earlier for the size corresponding to 100 percent collection efficiency.

Thus plotting experimental data for particle removal efficiency vs. $D\tau$ seems to be a useful method for correlating data for the diffusion range.

Charges on particles and particle shape may also influence the deposition of particles, and elongated particles such as fibers may be more easily captured in the tubes than spheres. The possibility that charges on particles might play an important role in lung deposition has been suggested by Landwehr[10] and by Wilson,[11] who investigated the deposition of charged particles in tubes with reference to the retention of charged particles in the respiratory system, and who suggested that unipolar charging might increase lung retention.

The suggestion has often been made that ions in the atmosphere have a marked influence on health, and that the artificial introduction of ions into the atmosphere may decrease the unpleasant effects of airborne

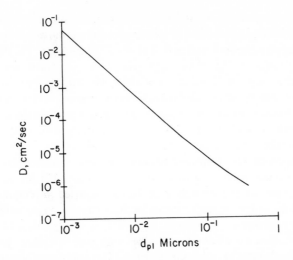

Figure 3-2. Coefficient of particle diffusion in air at 37°C and 1 atm.[9] (*Courtesy of the American Industrial Hygiene Association*)

pollens. Longly[12] suggests that certain effects attributed to ions may actually have been due to much larger charged particles and implies that the effect may have been due to changing the extent of deposition in the lungs. He undertook a series of experiments which showed that placing a high electrical charge on groups of laboratory animals significantly influenced their ability to inhale and that they subsequently showed a pulmonary accumulation of particles of a test aerosol as compared with a control group. He therefore suggested that the electrostatic condition of an animal may have a strong influence on its reaction to an environmental aerosol in either natural or experimental situations.

Soluble particles, even though they are deposited in the tubes, can be absorbed almost immediately into the blood, and the protection of the cilia is by-passed. Thus lead chromate pigments may be inhaled in rather large amounts without ill effects, as the author knows from personal experience. However, acute lead poisoning has occurred during the mining and smelting of lead carbonate ore as a result of inhaling the relatively soluble dust.

The alveoli are not ciliated and cannot get rid of deposited particles by cilial action. Thus they would soon become clogged if they did not have a method of ridding themselves of such particles. The alveoli spaces contain large cells, called phagocytes, that can ingest foreign material and are capable of independent motion. The production of these amoeba-like cells is stimulated by the deposition of particles on the surfaces of the alveoli, and they move about over the alveolar walls picking up foreign particles. Various fates for the phagocytes after particle ingestion have been suggested. Sander[13] states that some of them enter the blood stream and finally lodge in the spleen and liver or move elsewhere within the tissues of the lung, while most make their way to the lymph vessels and eventually lodge in accumulations of lymph tissue. He suggests that in the lymph tissue the particles may be absorbed, may remain inert, or may produce pathological changes such as the formation of silicotic nodules. Davies, on the other hand, states that most of the particle-carrying phagocytes reach the terminal bronchioles and are removed by cilial action. However, according to Davies, some dust particles penetrate into the actual lung tissues where they are found enclosed in phagocyte cells or their remains, and it is these particles that cause occupational dust diseases such as silicosis.

Recent studies by Gross and his co-workers[14, 15, 16] have demonstrated that particles which have remained in the lungs for long periods of time may ultimately become mobile and be removed. For example, black sputum may occur in coal miners who have not been exposed to coal dust for many years, and pulmonary dust mobilization has been shown in animals having pneumonia or simple pulmonary edema. They also found that edema artificially produced by the intratracheal injection of quartz dust combined with dead tubercle bacilli into tuberculin-positive guinea pigs resulted in a lower mean pulmonary silica content than when the same amount of quartz dust was injected alone.

### Classification of effects

It is difficult to classify atmospheric contaminants according to their action on the human body for several reasons. The type of action may vary markedly with length of exposure, concentration of contaminant, susceptibility of the recipient, and whether the effects are acute or chronic. The following classification is a modification of that suggested by Patty[17] for both gases and particles. However, as discussed in detail later, gases and vapors can be adsorbed on or dissolved in particles entering the lungs so the classification of atmospheric contaminants into gases and particles is not as clear-cut as might at first appear.

*Irritants.* Irritants are materials that inflame the membranes. Some of them, such as nitric acid fumes or fine droplets of solutions of sodium hydroxide, partially destroy tissue. In the case of others, while there may be a chemical reaction involved, it is not so obvious. Patty breaks down this category into three parts. The first consists of irritants which chiefly affect the upper respiratory tract; these include alkaline dusts and mists, aldehydes, hydrogen chloride, sulfur dioxide, and sulfuric acid aerosols. The second consists of irritants affecting both the upper respiratory tract and tissues of the lungs. These include the halides, ozone, and compounds of sulfur and phosphorus with the halides. The third category includes those irritants which affect mainly the lower bronchioles and the alveoli, such as nitrogen dioxide and tetroxide, and phosgene. Lung irritants may cause edema and death by asphyxiation. For example, scores of persons died several days after the fire in the Cleveland Clinic in the 1920's as a result of inhaling the nitrogen dioxide fumes produced by burning x-ray film.

**Asphyxiants.** These substances interfere with the normal oxidative processes in the body either by preventing sufficient oxygen from reaching the blood or by interfering with the oxidation of the tissues even if the blood receives sufficient oxygen. The former case may be a simple matter of dilution by relatively inert gases such as carbon dioxide, nitrogen, hydrogen, or methane. Airborne particles cannot, of course, be involved in this type of action. Asphyxiation may also result from irritation producing edema, as by nitrogen dioxide. Severe destruction of lung tissue by substances which at lower concentrations are irritants can cause asphyxia, and so may pollens and other airborne materials if they produce spasms of the upper respiratory system. Numerous well-known poisons are asphyxiants of the second type. These include hydrogen cyanide, carbon monoxide, cyanogen, aromatic amines such as aniline, nitrobenzene, and hydrogen sulfide. This type of poisoning usually results from the inhalation of gases, but this is not always the case. For example, the inhalation of sodium or potassium cyanide dust may cause death.

**Anesthetics and narcotics.** The substances which fall in this category are rather obvious. In general they have a depressant action on the central nervous system. Although such substances may be gases, liquids, or solids, only rarely do liquids or solids in these categories accidentally enter the lungs. On the other hand, they may enter the lungs intentionally, as in opium smoking.

**Systemic poisons.** This category includes various poisons which affect many organs of the body. Particles in this category include numerous toxic metals, various non-metallic compounds such as arsenic oxide and various fluorides, and the relatively non-volatile "nerve gases" and related insecticides. The latter substances might be considered as asphyxiants since death can result from respiratory system paralysis.

**Fibrosis-producing dusts.** These include silica, asbestos, bauxite, and even anthracite.

*Dusts producing allergic reactions.* These include a wide variety of dusts, but pollen and "household dust" seem to be the most common. *Bacteria and other micro-organisms.*

### Pulmonary fibrosis

Pneumoconiosis may be defined as dust particles retained in the lymph depots of the lungs.[13] Thus pneumoconiosis is common to all adults, but it may lead to various diseases.* One of the most common of these is fibrosis, which may take various forms which are usually named in terms of the causative dust. According to Davies,[3] the inhalation of fibrosis-producing particles of such a size that they reach the alveoli stimulates the uncontrolled proliferation of collagen in the connective tissue of the lymph glands.

Fibrosis has been with us for centuries; indeed, silicosis has been observed in the lung of a pre-historic man. The Egyptians, Romans, and Greeks were active in mining. For the most part the miners were slaves and the conditions under which they worked were extremely unhealthful. Highly graphic descriptions, many translated from the original literature, are included[1] in Rosen's "The History Of Miners' Diseases." Numerous crude devices were used by the Roman miners to minimize inhalation of dust, as they apparently recognized that the dust could cause disease. Paracelsus and Agricola both describe miners' diseases during the sixteenth century, and in 1705 Ramazzini described the afflictions of stonecutters who inhaled the dust they produced. However, the specificity of silica as the causative agent for a particular type of fibrosis was not recognized until the early part of the twentieth century, in part because of improved methods for investigating disease, but probably also because of a greatly increased incidence of silicosis as a result of blasting and pneumatic rock drilling. Similarly, other types of fibrosis were hardly recognized until the present century.

The fibrosis problem in the United States has been reviewed by Doyle, Flinn, and Dreessen.[18] They point out that this was such an outstanding occupational disease problem that during the period 1914 to 1940 most of the effort of the Industrial Hygiene Division of the U.S. Public Health Service was devoted to fibrosis research and many cooperative studies were done with the U.S. Bureau of Mines. By 1924 instrumentation and diagnostic procedures were sufficiently developed that environmental conditions could be correlated with pathologic findings. By 1940, three

---

*Many authors limit the use of the term "pneumoconiosis" to the diseased condition.

disabling types of fibrosis had been recognized, namely, silicosis with and without complicating tuberculosis, anthraco-silicosis, and asbestosis. The emphasis on fibrosis research has decreased somewhat since 1940 and the emphasis has been on determining the effectiveness of preventive measures. Nonetheless, research has continued at a high level, as indicated by the fact that the Fifth Decennial Index of *Chemical Abstracts*[19] covering the period 1943 to 1956 contained about 140 entries under silicosis.

**Silicosis.** The most serious form of fibrosis is caused by inhaling powdered quartz, one of the crystalline forms of silicon dioxide ($SiO_2$), and other crystalline forms of $SiO_2$, e.g., crystobalite. The clinical symptoms are shortness of breath, decreased chest expansion, and a decreased capacity for work. Unless complicated by tuberculosis, there usually is no fever. The physiological changes producing these symptoms include the development of a stringy or fibrous character of the tissues and the formation of dust-containing nodules.

Generally, industrially produced silicosis requires many years to develop, although it has been known to occur within a few months. The length of time before symptoms develop varies, as would be expected, with the susceptibility of the individual and the concentration and nature of the dust. Continued exposure to quartz dust after the symptoms become evident increases the seriousness of the disease and renders the patient particularly susceptible to tuberculosis. The patient may contract tuberculosis even if he is removed from exposure to silica dust when the first symptoms are detected. According to Drinker and Hatch[20], death from silicosis is unusual unless tuberculosis develops. The disease can be diagnosed in its early stages by a combination of x-rays and clinical observation; the x-rays reveal a characteristic nodular appearance.

Gross, Westrick, and McNerney[21] distinguish between activity and progression of silicosis. They define activity as the development of the disease as exposure to quartz dust continues, and state that the presence of granulation tissue or immature connective tissue in silicotic lung parenchyma indicates activity. Progression, on the other hand, is the expansion of old lesions or the initiation of new ones, or both, after exposure has ceased. They suggested these distinctions as a result of studies of the progression of experimental silicosis in rats, but progression also seems to be common to human silicosis.

Quartz is one of the most common minerals and is a component of a large percentage of the earth's rocks. Quartz sands derived from such rocks are unusually common, probably in large part because quartz is a particularly inert material. Many mining operations, even if they are not directly concerned with quartz, must work through quartz-bearing rocks.

A large number of industries use or work with finely ground quartz. For example, the abrasives industry uses quartzite, chert, flint, sandstone, quartz sand, tripoli, and diatomaceous earth. Powdered quartz is also used or produced in manufacturing refractories, paint, ceramics, ordinary glass, insulation, various alloys, and a host of other products. Thus it is not surprising that the prevention of silicosis is a very important aspect of modern industrial hygiene.

The effect of particle size on silicosis of the lungs (silica also affects other organs) may be at least two-fold. It affects the percentage of inhaled particles reaching the lungs and also the silicotic activity once the lungs are reached. Tebbins, Schulz, and Drinker[22] investigated the effect of particle size on potency for producing silicosis using four different-sized fractions of silica particles. Ground flint was sized by settling in water, producing "average sizes" of 3.3, 1.7, 1.0, and 0.6 microns. Nine rabbits were used for each size group and each received 400 mg of the powder suspended in saline solution injected into the ear vein in two equal doses at three month intervals.

The sub-micron size particles were found to be the most active in promoting silicotic lesions. At the end of eighteen months the livers of the animals which had received one of the two finer powders were almost entirely replaced by white fibrous tissues. The 1.7 micron powder produced only moderate liver scarring, and rabbits receiving the 3.3 microns dust exhibited only slight enlargement and pitting.

Similar evidence of the size effect was observed in other organs. The finer particles were found in the liver, lungs, spleen, and bone marrow, and lesions were observed in all these organs.

Hatch and Kindsvatter[23] investigated the lung retention of quartz dust less than 0.5 micron diameter. They used commercial pulverized quartz and obtained the desired fraction by settlement in water. Guinea pigs were exposed to this dust daily for periods up to $4\frac{1}{2}$ months, and lung sections of the exposed animals were compared with normal sections. They found that after twenty weeks' exposure the bronchial lymph glands were enlarged to more than three times the diameter of the normal gland. The lung and lymph node sections contained large numbers of the particles. Hatch and Kindsvatter concluded that silica particles smaller than 0.5 micron diameter are of greater importance in the production of silicosis than had previously been thought.

However, the effect of particle size may be more involved than a progressive increase in activity with decreasing size. King et al[24] injected rats intratracheally with sized fractions of flint powder covering the range <0.5 to 8 microns diameter in different amounts having the same total particle surface. On this basis, the powders of 1 to 2 microns size range were more effective than the others. Zaidi et al.[25] obtained a similar result with a higher dosage. They also found an optimum, but wider, size range for liver fibrosis produced by intravenous injection.

The reason that quartz is so effective in producing fibrosis is something of a mystery. At least two theories have been advanced. The older of the two is that silicotic fibrosis results from the abrasive action of the finely divided silica. But silicon carbide particles are hard and sharp and they do not produce fibrosis. The abrasive theory has largely been replaced by the solubility theory, based on the findings of Gye and Purdy,[26] and Gye and Kettle[27] that colloidal silica is highly toxic. According to this theory, at least in its original form, quartz powders produce silicosis because they slowly release a poisonous substance, namely, silicic acid.

However, there are difficulties with this theory. King et al.[28] found that different specimens of quartz, of identical composition but of very different solubilities, may have the same fibrogenic effect on the lungs of animals. They also found that different forms of silica of identical chemical composition and similar solubility may have very different fibrosis-producing capacities.

Hofmann[29] has discussed the relationship of the chemistry of the surface of silicon dioxide to silicosis. He points out that the valences of silicon on the silicon dioxide surface are mainly satisfied by Si-OH bonds and that the free valences can be determined quantitatively by means of reactions such as with $SOCl_2$. The silica dust must remain in the lungs for a long period of time and slowly dissolve to produce silicosis. Hofmann states that if the monomeric silica in solution is responsible for silicosis the physiological action is probably the result either of the silica acting as a phosphatase, or of the formation of a phosphate-containing iron silicate which acts as a protease, oxidase, or a producer of folding isomeric antigens. The silicotic effect may be a catalytic action of the silica surface, in which case the slow dissolving of the particles liberates fresh, active surface.

The inhalation of aluminum powder has often been suggested as a means for preventing and treating silicosis. Its use in the United States and Canada, and the results obtained have been discussed by George.[31] Under experimental conditions, using test animals, small amounts of various kinds of aluminum powder protect against the development of silicosis produced by dusting with large concentrations of silica. It is difficult to establish that similar beneficial effects are obtained for humans exposed to silica dust, but it seems likely that this is the case. Furthermore, there is no evidence that the aluminum as usually administered is in any way harmful.

George suggests that there is enough experimental evidence to justify the use of aluminum powder under the following circumstances: (1) When exposure to silica dust cannot be prevented because of economic considerations. (2) When men show evidence of silicosis in the absence of active tuberculosis. (3) When men are known to have undergone dangerous exposures to silica during the preceding two years. He points out that when the disease is fully developed there is no proof that treatment with aluminum powder in any way modifies the progress of the disease. Any apparent alleviation of the symptoms is probably psychological. Furthermore, aluminum treatment should not be applied to all employees in an industry, but only to those who are likely to receive dangerous doses of silica, and under no circumstances should the use of aluminum be substituted for vigorous control of silica exposures.

A method for administering the aluminum has been described by Oswald,[32] who was concerned with the control of silicosis in a foundry. Aluminum was ground in a small McIntyre mill which produced 3.2 mg of powder per liter of air at the rate of 10 liters per minute. Large particles were removed by settling and impaction in a settling flask, breathing tubes, and breathing valves. Thus although Oswald did not measure the particle size distribution, the largest particles were probably only a few microns in diameter. This large particle removal reduced the amount of powder available for inspiration to about 50 percent of the amount at the mill outlet. Two men could be treated simultaneously by inhalation from mouthpieces. The employees treated received an average of 230 minutes inhalation therapy each year in the form of weekly sessions lasting an average of 5 minutes.

Oswald states that the incidence of new cases of radiologically-diagnosed silicosis dropped to zero after the treatment program was put into effect, the first time it had happened in the history of that foundry.

Dworski[33] reported beneficial effects of both aluminum hydroxide and aluminum for rabbits exposed to silica. Most of the particles were less than one micron in diameter. He found by injecting into animals a suspension containing both quartz particles and aluminum hydroxide that the aluminum compound inhibited the characteristic reaction to quartz. Inhalation of either aluminum or aluminum hydroxide produced the usual silicosis-inhibiting effects.

An interesting aspect of aluminum treatment and prevention of silicosis is its relationship to the solubility theory of silicosis. Denny and Robson[34] noticed that the presence of small amounts of aluminum almost completely prevented silica from passing into solution. Denny, Robson, and Irwin[34] later demonstrated that aluminum powder helps prevent silicosis, and they showed that a relationship exists between the reduced solubility of silica produced by aluminum powder and the effectiveness of preventing silicosis.

**Asbestosis.** Asbestos, the familiar fibrous inorganic mineral, is another common cause of fibrosis. It is a hydrated magnesium silicate and as such may be considered to be a salt of the acid anhydride silica. Actually, the term "asbestos" is applied to a number of fibrous magnesium silicates which differ somewhat in chemical composition and physical properties, including chrysotile, crocidolite, amosite, anthophyllite, actinolite, and tremolite. About 95 percent of the industrially produced asbestos is chrysotile. The largest mines are in Quebec and Africa.

The clinical symptoms of asbestosis are not unlike those of silicosis, but there are some marked differences. Silicosis renders a patient particularly susceptible to tuberculosis, while asbestosis seems to lead to enlargement of the heart and often to death by heart failure. Sander[13] suggests that cyanosis and clubbing of the fingers are likely to appear and that the frequency of lung cancer among asbestosis patients may be considerably greater than among persons in general. A silicosis victim generally gets worse even after exposure to silica has ceased, but according to Wood and Gloyne[30] the condition of patients with asbestosis may remain stationary after exposure to asbestos dust has ceased.

The pathological symptoms also exhibit both similarities and differences. The asbestos fibers tend to accumulate about the necks of the alveoli where they stimulate fibrosis.[30] However, the nodules so characteristic of silicosis do not appear.

King, Clegg and Rae[35] undertook a series of experiments to determine whether short-fiber asbestos is less damaging to the lungs of rabbits than long-fiber asbestos, and also whether aluminum powder will suppress the toxic effect produced by fiber asbestos. They tested four groups of animals and all four exhibited a foreign-body reaction in the lungs. Contrary to the findings mentioned above, the animals exposed to long asbestos fibers developed nodules similar to the experimental silicotic nodule. The animals exposed to short fibers developed a "diffuse interstitial reticulinosis."

Luton and Champeix,[36] after four years of observing workers in a plant using asbestos, concluded that intense functional symptoms appear before any radiological changes can be observed and that the clinical findings do not differ from those of silicosis. However, the radiological findings are more fine and diffuse than those of silicosis, and there is a "stippling" which is finer than that of silicosis.

Perhaps asbestosis in man is not associated with nodules, as it may be in animals, because of differences between man and the other animals or because of differences between experimental and industrial exposure to finely divided asbestos.

**Diatomaceous earth.** Diatomaceous earth consists of the skeletons of myriads of micro-organisms (diatoms) which inhabit both sea water and fresh water, or even moist soil. Unlike the skeletons of most animals, those of diatoms are composed of silica rather than of calcium phosphate or carbonate. However, x-ray diffraction reveals that the silica comprising the skeletons of diatoms is essentially amorphous.

The diatoms are not animals, but plants belonging to the group of algae. Nonetheless, some varieties (of which there are about 15,000) are capable of independent motion, moving over moist surfaces by the ejection of protoplasm or moving about in the water. Most diatomaceous earth (sometimes known as kieselguhr) results from the collection of the shells of the aquatic varieties on the bottom of lakes and seas. Diatoms are primarily cold water plants. The most extensive deposits known to geologists occur in California, although comparable ones are now being formed in the Arctic and Antarctic regions.[35] In Santa Barbara County, California, there is a deposit over a thousand feet thick which is being mined commercially.[37]

Diatomaceous dust which has not been subjected to heat produces a benign fibrosis which is not accompanied by any disability.[38] The lack of progressive, debilitating fibrosis may be related to the fact that the silica is largely non-crystalline. However, when the diatomaceous earth has been calcined, which largely converts it to the crystalline form cristobalite, extensive, progressive fibrosis may follow excessive inhalation. Some cases observed by Smart and Anderson[38] exhibited fibrotic lesions, emphysema, or pleurisy. Unlike most types of silicosis, it was seldom followed by tuberculosis.

Since diatoms are usually considerably greater than ten microns in diameter, a dust consisting of whole diatoms would not be expected to produce fibrosis. However, many diatoms are broken up in diatomaceous earth, and processing may produce further shattering. Sander[13] refers to an unpublished U.S. Public Health Bulletin which describes the results of a survey of the diatomite industry on the West Coast. The particle size (diameter?) of the dust from all types of processing ranged between about 0.5 and 2.2 microns and thus was such that the particles could easily penetrate to the alveoli. The results of this study suggested that the maximum allowable concentrations for dust from crude diatomaceous earth could be placed at 20 million particles per cubic foot of air, and for cristobalite-containing dust at 5 million particles per cubic foot.

**Coal dust.** Fibrosis can occur as a result of coal mining, in which case it is called anthracosilicosis or anthracosis. This apparently is often a type of silicosis, and the extent of its occurrence among miners and the severity of the cases can be related to the exposure to silica dust experienced by the miners. The silica usually occurs as veins between the deposits of coal and must be blasted away to get at the coal. It is more often associated with anthracite than with bituminous coals, which accounts for the names given to this disease. However, the relationship between the fibrosis afflictions of miners and the amount of silica to which they have been exposed is by no means certain. Ray et al.[39] describe results which indicate that coal or graphite containing as little as 2 per cent of silica can produce a fibrosis which is typical of silicosis. Furthermore, soft-coal miners have developed abnormalities that appear on x-ray films and differ considerably from the typical silicosis pattern. The lacy pattern observed on the film is often described as reticulation. Fletcher and Gough,[40] as a result of the study of the effects of different coals, concluded that the relative hazard from the dust was not directly related to the silica content, but possibly was directly related to the percentage of volatile matter. Other studies have shown that persons who worked on coal alone, and were not exposed to the dust from silica veins, as are the underground workers, also have developed fibrosis. Also some workers exposed to coal dust have developed a fibrosis which produced x-ray patterns characteristic of silicosis but differed from it in many clinical symptoms. Undoubtedly the picture is confused by the fact that numerous types of particles enter the lungs of coal miners, and particles of one kind may modify the effects of others.

Doyle, Flinn, and Dreessen[18] have suggested that the following terminology of lung pathology among coal miners is receiving growing acceptance. According to this nomenclature, the term "anthracosis" means merely a blackish discoloration of the lungs produced by carbon deposition and is not necessarily accompanied by pathological changes. Anthracosilicosis refers to a modified form of classical silicosis resulting from long exposure to coal and rock dust containing significant amounts of free silica. The term "coal miners' pneumoconiosis" is a different disease, according to this usage, and is caused by the coal dust itself.

**Bauxite.** Bauxite is impure aluminum oxide, $Al_2O_3 \cdot 2H_2O$, which is the principal ore from which aluminum is manufactured. It is also used to manufacture an abrasive similar to the natural abrasive corundum, also a form of $Al_2O_3$. Bauxite is fused with coke and iron in an electric furnace, accompanied by the liberation of dense fumes. The fume, consisting of particles of submicron size, contains 15 to 55 percent of silica. Prolonged exposure to these fumes has been found to produce a fibrosis which in several cases resulted in death. X-ray patterns of the early disease show the reticulation mentioned earlier, and later patterns may exhibit nodules.

It is of interest that such fine particles can produce fibrosis, since early investigators of silicosis often suggested that only larger particles could produce the disease. It is not known whether the silica or the alumina produces the unpleasant results. As mentioned above, many investigators state that only crystalline silica causes silicosis, and aluminum hydroxide, which can be considered to be a hydrated aluminum oxide, has been used to prevent silicosis. So here we have another uncertainty in the story of fibrosis.

An attempt to at least partially resolve it was made by Christie, Mac-Kay, and Fisher.[41] Male rats and male hamsters were selected for study and were examined at autopsy after intervals of from 4 to 20 months of experiment. The animals were housed in wooden chambers, the dust-tight doors of which could be replaced at night and on week-ends by screens.

The animals were exposed to aluminum in two forms. One was "aluminum powder" composed of 20 percent of aluminum and 80 percent of aluminum oxide, $Al_2O_3$. This powder was dispersed from a dust-containing tube with a blast of compressed air. The ultimate particle size (diameter?) was stated to be 0.05 to 7 microns, although a large percentage of the airborne particles must have been aggregates. The other form was a fume produced by arcing two aluminum electrodes. The ultimate size of these particles was 0.02 to 0.2 micron, and there were between 2 and 100 particles per aggregate.

The aluminum content of the lungs of the rats exposed to the powder was much less than that of the rats exposed to fume, although the weight of particulate matter in the two atmospheres was of the same order. Probably a large fraction of the airborne aggregates produced from the powder was very large and was removed from the lungs by cilial action, or settled out in the chambers prior to inhalation.

Both the powder and fume produced lung changes, including lung enlargement, the development of cysts, and pneumonia. However, there was no evidence of fibrosis, and alumina in these forms at least could not have been responsible for bauxite fibrosis.

## Beryllium poisoning

Beryllium and its compounds are extremely poisonous both to the animal system as a whole and to the lungs. Since the principal hazards from beryllium are from inhaled dusts and the main effects are respiratory, beryllium poisoning is considered here as a topic separate from that of other inhaled poisons.

Lindeken and Meadors[42] point out that two types of respiratory damage, acute pneumonitis and chronic pulmonary granulomatosis, occur in the beryllium industry among workers exposed to beryllium dusts, fumes, and mists. The acute form is an inflammation of the upper respiratory tract and in extreme cases may involve the entire pulmonary system. Usually the patient completely recovers from the acute form, although it may change into the chronic form or result in death.

The chronic form is usually a delayed disease and symptoms may not appear for several years after exposure. The clinical symptoms are rather similar to those of fibrosis, including shortness of breath, general lack of energy, loss of appetite, and a persistent loss of weight. Granulornous lesions occur throughout the lungs. Unlike the acute form, the chronic form is often fatal.

People differ greatly in sensitivity to beryllium. Lindeken and Meadors quote figures from White and Burke[43] to the effect that some persons have worked in atmospheres containing 30 mg/cu meter of beryllium without developing the acute disease, while others working in atmospheres containing only 4 mg/cu meter have suffered fatal acute berylliosis.

Beryllium is used as a minor constituent of various alloys where the major constituent is magnesium, copper, aluminum or iron (steel). Elemental beryllium is used in "space" vehicles and in atomic energy installations. Until 1949 it was used extensively in phosphors for fluorescent lamps. This not only caused an industrial hazard, but also a very real hazard to the users in the event that lamps were broken. The manufacture of lamps coated with beryllium-containing phosphors has now been discontinued in the United States.

According to Donaldson, Hiser, and Schwenzfeier,[44] the particle size of beryllium dust had never been considered in evaluating a worker's environment prior to their study. This is because it is generally considered desirable to keep the concentration in atmospheres to which workers are exposed below 2.0 micrograms/cu meter and this concentration is so low that even collecting enough for analysis is difficult. However, as the result of action by the U.S. Atomic Energy Commission's Division of Licensing and Regulation, this limit may be restricted to those particles that are small enough to penetrate to the alveoli, or are soluble. These authors,[44] on the basis of published results, considered that particles of unit density over 10 microns in diameter are essentially not "respirable"; 5 microns or greater are 25 percent respirable, 3.5 micron particles are 50 percent respirable, and 2 microns and smaller are 100 percent respirable.

Donaldson *et al.* selected two aerosol sampling devices, consisting of cyclones and pumps, which they demonstrated would separate dust according to particle size in essentially the same manner as they attributed to the human respiratory system. They used this system to compare the percentage of respirable beryllium with the total airborne beryllium in various parts of a beryllium production plant. The percentage of respirable beryllium ranged from about 2 to 90 percent depending on the location within the plant. The average value was about 30 percent. In general, the higher total concentrations corresponded to a smaller percentage of respirable dust. Donaldson *et al.* point out that these results reveal that the apparently insurmountable engineering feat of controlling large beryllium production facilities to "target level" or below can be accomplished with good local exhaust ventilation and hooding techniques.

Possibly such considerations of the importance of particle size in determining "respirable" as contrasted with "non-respirable" dust can be used to advantage in defining reasonable standards for other hazardous dusts.

### Mineral oil

Another type of aerosol which produces effects on the respiratory system which do not fit well into the classification of effects described earlier is the oil aerosol, particularly paraffin oil aerosols. The main effect, at least for relatively long exposures, seems to be a chronic lipide pneumonia.[45] Wagner *et al.*[46] conducted acute oil aerosol inhalation studies with mice which showed that single 4-hour exposures and repeated 7-hour daily exposures to about 200 mg/cu meter of mineral oil or motor oil aerosols produced little effect on the lungs. Lushbaugh *et al.*[47] studied the effects of long inhalation of oil fogs on a number of test animals (monkeys, rabbits, rats, mice). The only effect was on the monkeys, which suffered an increased incidence of infectious pneumonia.

Wagner, Wright, and Stokinger[48] investigated the chronic inhalation toxicology of white mineral oil using five species of animals (dogs, rabbits, rats, hamsters, and mice). Exposures were performed at two levels, one at 5 mg/cu meter, "the current threshold level," and the other at 100 mg/cu meter. The mineral oil was composed of naphthene-base saturated hydrocarbons having a molecular weight of 350–410. The oil mists were generated with aspirating-type generators. The mean particle diameter (geometric mean?) was 1.3 microns with a standard geometric deviation of 1.6.

Animal sacrifices were made at 3, 6, and 12 months for the 5 mg/cu meter level; and at 3, 6, 12, 18, and 26 months for the 100 mg/cu meter level.

The results indicated that the lower concentration does not constitute a toxic hazard, even upon prolonged exposure. However, the higher concentrations produced significant deposition in the alveoli and the lymph nodes and various physiological effects including a small amount of fibrosis. The authors concluded that prolonged exposure to mineral oil aerosols at the higher concentration level would in time produce harmful physiological effects.

Oils which are fatty acid esters, such as vegetable oils and animal oils, are for the most part relatively harmless when inhaled in aerosol form since they are rapidly metabolized by lipase action. However, some vegetable and animal oils, such as chaulmoogra, croton, and some fish oils are highly irritating to the tissues of the respiratory system.

## Allergic and related reactions

An allergy can be defined as a hypersensitivity to certain substances by persons who are particularly reactive to usually innocuous substances. The substances producing allergies are known as allergens or antigens. Persons who are allergic to one substance are often allergic to many. Allergens may be airborne, but this is not necessarily the case. Direct contact with the skin, as in the case of poison oak and poison ivy, may cause a reaction, as may eating certain foods. Even such physical agents as light, heat, and cold may act as allergens.

One theory of the action of allergens is that the allergen causes the tissues of a susceptible person to release histamine. Under the influence of the allergens, the blood stream of the body produces antibodies.

Various methods have been developed for treating allergies when it is not practical to prevent an allergen from reaching a susceptible person. Various "antihistamines" have been developed which are drugs for counteracting the histamine. In addition, the injection of extracts of the allergens over long periods of time and in increasing amounts may develop a tolerance toward the allergen.

Airborne substances which often act as allergens include pollen, household dust, bacteria, and various proteins.

Unlike many substances which have highly undesirable effects on the respiratory system, allergens need not reach the alveoli to produce unpleasant effects. In fact, hay fever and asthma are largely diseases of the upper respiratory system. Pollen of various kinds, which for many hay-fever sufferers is the greatest culprit, is so large (10 to 100 microns diameter) that it is almost completely retained by the upper respiratory system.

A respiratory disease affecting workers inhaling dust in cotton mills is byssinosis, which possibly is an allergic manifestation[49] and mainly affects the strippers and grinders. The usual symptoms are those of bronchitis and emphysema.

The disease slowly progresses with the development of fatigue, shortness of breath, decreased working capacity, and asthma-like attacks, especially at night.

Similar diseases result from other vegetable dusts.[50] Bagassosis is a disease occurring among workers who grind bagasse in the dry state. Bagasse is the fibrous residue from sugar cane after the sugar-containing fluids have been expressed. The main symptoms are acute bronchitis, fever, shortness of breath; x-ray pictures show generalized miliary shadows. Grinding the bagasse under water is an effective preventive method.

Similar symptoms among farmers who have been handling mouldy hay during the summer have been called farmer's or thresher's lung. The condition is probably caused by a fungus.[51]

Dock workers who handle grain also at times exhibit an occupational respiratory disease which in many respects, such as x-ray findings, is suggestive of silicosis. As various grains contain small percentages of free silica, the disease may be a form of silicosis.[52]

### Irritants

As mentioned earlier, irritants are materials that inflame the membranes. They may affect only the upper respiratory tract, both the upper and lower tracts, or mainly the lower bronchioles and the alveoli.

Numerous studies of such irritants have been reported in the scientific and technical literature. One that is of particular interest here because of its emphasis on particle size was undertaken by Amdur and Corn.[53] This investigation was stimulated by an earlier paper by Hemeon[54] in which he suggested that zinc ammonium sulfate was partially responsible for the irritating smog which occurred in Donora, Pennsylvania in 1948. He had analyzed a sample of particulate material collected from this smog and found that 22 percent was water-soluble. Of this fraction, 58 percent was zinc ammonium sulfate and 21 percent was zinc sulfate. By combining these values with the measured values for the concentrations of total solids in Donora following the smog, an estimated concentration of 0.3 mg/cu meter was obtained for zinc ammonium sulfate and 0.1 mg/cu meter for zinc sulfate. Concentrations of these compounds were probably higher during the actual smog episode.

The laboratory investigation involved the measurement in guinea pigs of the increase in pulmonary flow resistance produced by exposure to the irritant, zinc ammonium sulfate. A determination was made of the correlation between mass concentration and particle size on the one hand with pulmonary flow resistance, as the criterion of irritant potency, on the other. The pulmonary flow resistance in unanesthetized guinea pigs was measured by making simultaneous tracings of intrapleural pressure, tidal volume, and the rate of flow of gas in and out of the respiratory system. The pulmonary flow resistance, expressed as cm $H_2O$/ml sec, is obtained from these tracings by relating the change in intrapleural pressure to the change in flow rate at places on the tracings corresponding to equal lung volumes.

Respiratory measurements were made on male guinea pigs every five minutes during a half-hour control period. The pigs were then exposed to the aerosol and measurements were again made every five minutes during one half hour. The aerosol was then turned off and flow resistance was measured every fifteen minutes for an hour. The average resistance during the control period was compared with the resistance at the end of the hour of exposure for each animal. The percentage increase of the exposure mean over the control mean for each group of animals was then plotted against particle number concentration and weight concentration.

Aerosols were generated from zinc ammonium chloride solutions using nebulizers, followed by impaction devices to remove the larger droplets and narrow the particle size distribution. Evaporation of the droplets left the desired solid particles. Particle size determinations were made with an electron microscope following collection of the particles with an oscillating thermal precipitator. Four aerosols were used, having mean sizes by weight, $\bar{d}_{30}$, of 0.29, 0.51, 0.74, and 1.4 microns. The corresponding number median diameters were 0.09, 0.18, 0.15, and 0.11.

The results showed that the smaller the particles, the greater the irritation at any given mass concentration. However, for equal number concentrations of particles the larger particles were more irritating. A brief study was made of the response of the animals to mixtures of zinc ammonium sulfate aerosols and sulfur dioxide. The response to the mixture was more than additive, an effect which is discussed in more detail later in this chapter. Brief studies were also made of the irritating action of zinc sulfate and ammonium sulfate aerosols. They had similar actions but were less irritating than the double salt.

Another highly irritating aerosol consists of sulfuric acid droplets suspended in air. The choking effects of this system are well known to most students of elementary chemistry who have inhaled the fumes produced by heating concentrated sulfuric acid.

A considerable and highly unfortunate confusion exists in the literature between sulfur trioxide ($SO_3$) and sulfuric acid ($H_2SO_4$). The former is a colorless, quite volatile, solid formed by the oxidation of sulfur dioxide under anhydrous conditions. It may at times be produced in manufacturing processes, but upon emission to the air it will almost immediately (fractions of a second) be converted to sulfuric acid by reaction with atmospheric water vapor. The confusion has probably arisen from the fact that many analytical chemists report their findings in terms of the oxides of the elements for which they have analyzed. Thus statements in the literature concerning the concentrations and effects of sulfur trioxide in air almost always actually relate to sulfuric acid.

Numerous laboratory studies have been made of the effects of sulfuric acid mists on animals. They have been initiated because sulfuric acid droplets are found in the air of certain industrial plants and of some city smog. Treon et al[55] studied the effect of sulfuric acid aerosols on guinea pigs, mice, rabbits, and rats. The particles were predominantly less than 2 microns in diameter. The guinea pigs died within 2.75 hours exposure to a concentration of 0.087 mg/l, whereas all the mice, rabbits, rats, and a cat survived after being exposed to concentrations of 0.461 mg/l. Some of the symptoms prior to death were coughing, sneezing, labored respiration, and gasping. Pathological changes included edema, acute emphysema, and engorgement of blood vessels.

Stokinger[56] states that numerous studies have shown that sulfuric acid mists are highly lethal to guinea pigs at concentrations as low as 5 ppm and for short exposures (2-3 hr).

Amdur, Schulz, and Drinker[57] state that sulfuric acid has two distinct toxic actions: it produces laryngeal spasm and also produces deep-seated lung damage.

The effect of particle size on the irritant effects of sulfuric acid aerosols has been studied by Thomas et al[58] and by Pattle et al.[59] The former study was undertaken with guinea pigs and mainly with aerosols of three mean diameters ($\bar{d}_{10}$): 0.6, 0.9 and 4 microns. The aerosol containing medium size droplets was the most active. The latter study indicated that 2.7 micron diameter droplets killed guinea pigs at a lower mass concentration than did 0.8 micron droplets for a given exposure time. There is an apparent discrepency between these two investigations with respect to optimum droplet size. However, as Stokinger points out, the latter were mass median diameters and were probably considerably larger than the number mean-diameters ($\bar{d}_{10}$) for the same aerosols.

Goldsmith[50] states that the concentration which is known not to produce an effect on humans is 0.12 mg/cu meter and that detectable responses begin to occur at about 0.25 mg/cu meter for a particle size of about one micron.

An interesting study of the effect of particle size on the irritating effects of a chemical was undertaken by Owens and Punte[61] utilizing *o*-chloro-benzylidene malonitrile aerosols. This is a substance that has a very low toxicity but is highly irritating to both the respiratory system and the eyes. The symptoms include eye irritation, burning of the nose, throat, and lungs, lacrimation, and profuse salivation.

Six volunteers were exposed singly to the aerosol produced in a small wind tunnel at a constant air speed of 5 mph. The eyes only, the respiratory system only, or both could be exposed to either small or large particles.

The mass-median diameter for small particles was 0.9 micron and for large particles was 60 microns. Concentrations for the small and large particles in the aerosols were almost identically 90 mg/cu meter.

Tolerance time was taken to be the time beyond which a subject could no longer remain in the wind tunnel. Recovery time was considered to be the time after exposure when the subjects were able to sort and arrange playing cards from which the corners had been removed.

The results showed that the small particles were more effective than the larger ones in rapidly producing eye irritation. However, the recovery time of those exposed to the small particles was shorter than that for those exposed to the large ones. Respiratory effects were more severe following exposure to the smaller particles and recovery from these symptoms was slower.

The effect of particle size on eye irritation was explained as follows. Impaction efficiency of small particles on the surfaces of the eyes is small, as explained in the last chapter. However, ocular response may have been rapid because of the high rate of solution of small particles in the eye fluids. The larger particles were probably impacted on the eyes with greater efficiency, but the onset of irritation may have been delayed by the slowness of solubility of the large particles. The effect of particle size on the intensity of respiratory effects was explained by the fact that only the small particles could penetrate to the lower respiratory tract.

When both the eyes and the respiratory systems were exposed, the response was mainly respiratory with the small particles and ocular with the large ones.

## Toxic dusts, fumes, mists

Numerous systemic poisons can enter the body by way of the respiratory system. Entrance may be achieved both by absorption through the lining of the respiratory system and by transfer via the cilia to the digestive system. The effect of particle size will thus depend both on the relative retention of particles in the various parts of the respiratory system, and on the rate of assimilation of particles of various sizes in the respiratory and digestive systems. Thus the effect of particle size on the toxicity of substances which are readily assimilated by both systems will be largely the effect of size on over-all retention by the respiratory system.

According to Drinker and Hatch,[20] one is much more liable to be poisoned by inhaling a toxic dust than by swallowing it. This is because dusts reaching the lungs may pass directly into the blood stream and are almost immediately pumped all over the body. However, dust swallowed with food may be largely excreted directly, and that picked up by the portal blood circulation may be removed by the liver. This distinction is particularly important in the case of industrial environments where a worker may be subjected to airborne toxic particles for many years. Thus Drinker and Hatch emphasize that chronic poisoning is a much more difficult problem than acute poisoning. They suggest that the finer the particles the greater the risk, presumably because the smaller particles reach the lower portion of the respiratory system where they cannot be readily removed by cilial action. Also, smaller particles, having a greater surface per unit weight than larger particles, may dissolve before they can be transferred to the digestive systems.

In spite of the large number of poisons that can enter the respiratory systems as dusts, only a few are likely to be encountered.

**Lead.**    Lead poisoning as an occupational hazard has been recognized at least since the early 19th century. Rosen[1] quotes Thackrah[62] writing in 1832 as evidence of high mortality rates among lead miners, "there were in the village of Arkendale (in the heart of the mining district) not less than thirty widows under thirty years of age," and states that the diseases causing the deaths were largely diseases of the lungs and bowels. Since that time a particularly voluminous literature has accumulated concerning lead poisoning, reflecting the fact that it has been and remains an industrial toxicology problem of major proportions.

Lead is used in a wide variety of applications including the manufacture of pigments, the ceramic industry, file making, glass making, painting, copper working, printing, the manufacture of storage batteries, and various agricultural applications. Today the danger from finely divided airborne lead compounds is well-recognized and various codes have been designed to prevent excessive exposures. As a result, acute lead poisoning from dust inhalation seldom occurs, but chronic cases are not infrequent.

Lead poisoning affects the entire body, but particularly the gastrointestinal tract and the nervous system. Victims become very pale, have a poor appetite, and suffer from a painful colic accompaned by constipation. As the effects of the poison advance, considerable weakness develops which is particularly apparent in the fingers, hands, and wrists. Optic atrophy may cause blindness.

The poison is cumulative, but once exposure to lead has ceased the patients are usually curable. Prevention usually involves care to avoid excessive exposure combined with periodic physical examinations including urine analyses for lead.

**Cadmium.** Cadmium is another industrially important metal which has been responsible for numerous toxicity problems. The poisoning is usually caused by the inhalation of cadmium oxide in the form of fume or dust,[63] although the statement is sometimes seen that coarse particles are relatively non-poisonous. However, Drinker and Hatch[20] question the existence of chronic cadmium poisoning, at least in the United States.

The usual symptoms of cadmium poisoning are nausea and diahrrea. Mild cases recover in one or two hours but severe exposures may cause extensive lung damage and be fatal.

Cadmium is used mainly for electroplating iron and steel for protection against corrosion. It is also used for special solder alloys and low-melting fusible alloys, in cadmium batteries, and as the sulfide in pigments.

It is a by-product of the treatment of the ores of other metals which contain it, especially ores of zinc. The separation depends on the relatively high volatility of cadmium oxide and chloride, the pure metal finally being isolated electrolytically, melted, and cast.

### Insecticides

Insecticides by definition are toxic to certain animals, and it is not surprising that many of them are toxic to man. Since they are usually applied as dusts or sprays, poisoning by inhaling them is not unusual. The action of most of them, such as the lead, copper, and arsenic compounds is well-known and will not be discussed in detail here. However, it is probably worth while to mention briefly one of the newest classes of insecticides, the organic phosphorus compounds.

Most of these substances are members of the family of so-called "nerve gases." Dubois and Coon[67] classify them into three groups. The first group consists of the organic pyrophosphates, such as $(CH_3O)_4P_2O_3$ and $(C_2H_4O)_4P_2O_3$. The second group consists of alkyl thiophosphates and includes the well-known parathion (p-nitrophenyl diethyl thionophosphate and malathion (S-(1,2-dicarbethoxyethyl)-0,0-dimethyl dithiophosphate). The third group consists of the phosphoramides and includes ethyl bis (dimethylamido) phosphate. The first and second groups are of the nerve gas variety. They interfere with muscle relaxation by strongly inhibiting the action of cholinesterase. The third group acts mainly on peripheral tissues.

Little is known of the effect of these substances upon man except that many of them are unusually poisonous. For example, a disturbingly large number of persons have been killed accidentally with parathion and others have used it to commit suicide. Golz[68] has reported one of the few laboratory studies using human subjects. Several panels of four human subjects in each were exposed to malathion in air for one hour twice daily for six weeks. The concentrations used were 0, 0.15, 0.60, and 2.4 grams malathion per 1000 cu ft of air. No effects were observed that could be attributed to anticholinesterase action. Air containing the highest concentration did produce slight nasal and conjunctival irritation. Golz concluded that aerosol bombs containing 5 percent malathion solutions are safe for household use.

Studies such as this one are certainly valuable. However, care must be taken not to extrapolate the results very far. Results obtained for a few healthy persons may not be applicable to those with certain diseases or who are particularly sensitive to the chemical in question. Perhaps our greatest ignorance and therefore our greatest danger lies in the chronic effects of insecticides. These may be chronic effects of acute exposures or the cumulative effects of low levels of exposure. Rachel Carson[2] points out that the phosphorus-containing organic insecticides may be particularly dangerous because of their ability not only to poison immediately but also to interfere with various vital processes. Her book very dramatically describes the present and potential dangers from the thoughtless use of insecticides.

### Synergism between particles and gases.

The proposition that the physiological effects of mixtures of gases and gas-borne particles may be greater than for the gases or particles alone has been examined by numerous investigators.

There are several reasons why the effects of mixtures of irritating or toxic gases and particles might be other than additive. One is that the irritating gas may be absorbed on the surface of the particle with the result that when the particle comes in contact with a surface in the respiratory system the concentration of the gaseous material at the place of contact is much greater than it would be in the presence of the gas alone. Another reason is that the gas or the particles or both may modify the tissues of the respiratory system so that the effect of the active air constituents is modified. A similar situation seems to exist for certain organic phosphate insecticides. Some of these, particularly malathion, have relatively low toxicities for human beings because they are destroyed by certain enzymes in the liver. However, other organic phosphates have been found to inactivate such enzymes, with the result that the pairs of organic phosphates are particularly dangerous. This can constitute an inhalation hazard, as for the man who sprays with different insecticides no more than a few days apart.

One of the early investigations of such a synergistic action was undertaken by the author[69] to determine whether it might contribute to "photochemical" smog, such as that occurring in Los Angeles. The aerosol consisted of crankcase oil, sodium chloride, sulfuric acid, and carbon black. The gases included nitric acid vapor, acrolein, formaldehyde, formic acid, and ozone. The concentrations were comparable to those found in smog. Human subjects were used and the results treated statistically. The mixture produced considerable eye and respiratory system irritation, but removal of the particulate constituents had no measurable effect.

The above investigation was undertaken using a panel of subjects who were unaware of the nature of the atmospheres to which they were being subjected. Dautrebande *et al.* used "expert" subjects who did know in advance the nature of the atmospheres to which they were exposed.[70,71] They concluded that aerosols of sodium chloride, oil, and smoke considerably increased the irritation produced by sulfur dioxide, formaldehyde, and other gases found in smog. Gordieyeff,[72] on the other hand, using rats, mice, and hamsters, did not find any effect of various airborne particles on the physiological action of various toxic substances.

In spite of these rather conflicting early results it now seems to be quite well established that under many conditions the presence of airborne particles can considerably influence the effects of physiologically active gases. The influence is generally to increase rather than to decrease the responses of the test subjects.

Perhaps the first experimental results which demonstrated such a positive effect were reported by Dautrebande[73] in 1939. His results showed that the toxicity of mustard gas for rats was greatly increased by the presence of inert aerosol particles and he attributed this to the adsorption of gas on the particles.

Sulfur dioxide has been a favorite subject for such studies. Amdur[74] investigated the influence of sodium chloride and sulfuric acid aerosols on guinea pigs. She used the increase in pulmonary flow resistance as a quantitative measure of the irritation produced since this is a particularly sensitive method for measuring such irritation. The method was described briefly above (p. 180) in connection with the irritation produced by zinc ammonium sulfate. The criterion used throughout her work on sulfur dioxide was the percentage increase in resistance produced by one hour of exposure to the substance or substances under consideration.

When working with a sulfuric acid aerosol containing sulfur dioxide it was necessary to determine whether the response was greater than the sum of those which would be produced by the sulfuric acid and sulfur dioxide independently, since both are irritating. Since a sodium chloride aerosol is not irritating, all that was needed was to determine its effect on the response to sulfur dioxide. The size of the aerosol particles was expected to have a considerable effect on the irritating properties of the mixtures, so the studies were conducted for two different particle sizes in both aerosols.

The experimental procedure for the mixtures of sulfur dioxide and sulfuric acid mist was first to determine the concentrations of each alone which produced the same resistance increase. The response to a mixture containing both sulfur dioxide and sulfuric acid was then measured and compared statistically with the response to twice the concentration of either alone. A response greater for the mixture than for the higher concentrations of the constituents alone was considered to indicate that the irritation produced by the mixture was more than additive.

Figure 3-3 shows the results obtained by the application of this approach to air containing sulfur dioxide and sulfuric acid of 0.8 micron mass-median diameter, which demonstrate that the response to the mix-

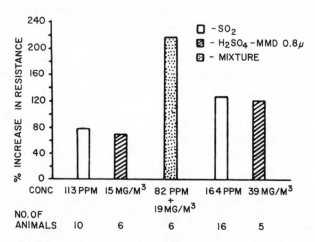

Figure 3-3. Resistance changes produced by exposure to sulfur dioxide and 0.8 $\mu$ sulfuric acid mist.[74] (*Courtesy of The American Industrial Hygiene Association*)

ture was greater than that to the higher levels of either active constituent alone. A similar experiment with sulfuric acid aerosol where the mass-median diameter was 2.5 microns resulted in a response to the mixture which was not greater than the response to either alone.

Amdur explained these results by postulating that sulfur dioxide had been adsorbed by the aerosol droplets and that the smaller droplets penetrated almost entirely to the lower respiratory system, with the result that more sulfur dioxide penetrated to the alveoli. On the other hand, the larger droplets did not penetrate far into the respiratory system. The response to the higher concentration of sulfur dioxide was greater than that to the mixture when the larger sulfuric acid particles were used and Amdur suggested that adsorption of gas on the aerosol has actually decreased the amount of sulfur dioxide reaching the lower respiratory system.

The presence of airborne sodium chloride particles (mass median diameter about 0.2 micron) greatly increased the irritation produced by the sulfur dioxide, but sodium chloride particles of mass-median diameter 2.5 microns had no such effect. Presumably the explanation is the same as for the sulfuric acid aerosols. However, Amdur pointed out that the smaller aerosol particles are more effective than the simple mechanism suggested above indicates and possibly local high concentrations produced by adsorption on the particles were important.

La Belle et al.[75] studied the synergistic effects of aerosol-toxic gas mixtures using white mice exposed in a chamber. Each experiment consisted in exposing two or more successive groups of six white mice until all were dead. A record was made of the time at which each mouse died and the results were treated statistically, the groups being compared on the basis of the geometric mean time of survival (S.T. 50).

Nine materials were used as aerosol particles: triethylene glycol, ethylene glycol, mineral oil, glycerol, sodium chloride, "Dicalite" and "Celite" (diatomaceous earths), attapulgus clay, and "Santocel C F" (a silica gel). The mass-median diameters ranged from 1.8 microns for triethylene glycol to 3.3 microns for "Dicalite." The toxic fumes were formaldehyde, acrolein, and nitric acid.

The results are summarized in Table 3-1. They demonstrate that when aerosols were mixed with atmospheres containing formaldehyde vapors the typical effect was to increase the toxicity. When aerosols were mixed with nitric acid fumes the usual effect was to decrease the toxicity. Addition of aerosols with acrolein produced either no change or some increase in toxicity.

The irritant effect of formaldehyde is largely confined to the upper

TABLE 3-1. SUMMARY OF GEOMETRIC MEAN SURVIVAL TIMES OF MICE EXPOSED TO VARIOUS AEROSOL-TOXIC GAS MIXTURES.[75]

| Aerosol | Formaldehyde | Acrolein | Nitric acid |
|---|---|---|---|
| Triethylene glycol | Shorter | No change | Longer |
| Ethylene glycol | No change | No change | Longer |
| Mineral oil | Shorter | Shorter | Shorter |
| Glycerol | Shorter | No change | No change |
| Sodium chloride | Shorter | Shorter | Longer |
| Dicalite | Shorter | No change | Longer |
| Celite | Shorter | No change | Longer |
| Attapulgers Clay | No change | No change | Longer |
| Santocel C F | No change | Shorter | Longer |

respiratory passages; acrolein produces tensions somewhat deeper; and the effects of nitric acid fumes are confined chiefly to the lungs. La Belle et al.[75] suggest that these differences represent different depths in the respiratory system to which the toxic gases penetrate. They reached the following conclusions. For an aerosol to produce a change there must be a physical "combination" between vapor and aerosol particles (absorption, adsorption, or solution). If such a combination occurs, the effect of the aerosol in changing the toxicity is directly related to the relative penetration of the particles and the toxic vapor. If particle penetration exceeds vapor penetration, toxicity is increased; if vapor penetration exceeds particle penetration, toxicity is decreased. Since particle penetration is closely related to particle size, the size has a large influence on the effect.

Amdur[76,77] also studied the response of guinea pigs to inhalation of formaldehyde and formic acid alone and in the presence of airborne sodium chloride particles. This work differed from that of La Belle et al. in that Amdur used the sensitive intrapleural pressure technique described above. The formaldehyde was introduced into the air by passing the air through 37 percent formaldehyde in a sintered glass bubbler. The formic acid vapor was introduced by passing air over a constant-boiling solution of formic acid in water. The sodium chloride aerosol was prepared from a 1 percent aqueous sodium chloride solution using an aspirating type of generator equipped with baffles to remove large droplets. The geometric mean diameter of the particles was 0.04 micron with a standard geometric deviation of 3.3. Throughout her work, Amdur has measured the particle size of the dried droplets. However, she realized that sodium chloride is hygroscopic above about 75 percent relative humidity and in the lungs must have existed as droplets.

The standard exposure time was one hour. Statistically significant results were obtained with concentrations as low as 0.3 ppm. The formic acid exhibited stronger irritant properties than did formaldehyde.

It is of interest from the standpoint of La Belle's theories that when the protective effect of the upper respiratory system was removed with a tracheal cannula, the response to a given concentration of formaldehyde was increased. This confirms the suggestion that much of the formaldehyde is normally removed by solution during passage through the upper respiratory tract, and that it is an irritant for the lower tract when it can reach it.

The sodium chloride aerosol alone at the concentration used throughout the study (10 mg/cu meter) produced no measurable effect, but as little as 0.07 ppm of formaldehyde produced a statistically significant increase in resistance when the sodium chloride was present. Over the entire concentration range of formaldehyde from 0.07 to 47 ppm the resistance change was greater in the presence of the sodium particles. Amdur states that an explanation of this enhancement would be that of La Belle, namely that the particles provide a means for carrying the formaldehyde deeper into the respiratory system than would otherwise be possible. The degree of enhancement observed, however, could not be explained on this basis alone, since the amount of additional gas reaching the lungs adsorbed on the particles must have been very slight. Amdur therefore had recourse to the other mechanism suggested above, namely that adsorption of the gas on the particles set up very high local concentrations of the irritant. It should probably also be pointed out that along with producing local high concentrations, adsorption can have a catalytic effect which can be negative or positive and thus enhance or decrease the effect of creating a local high concentration.

The response of the animals to breathing the gas-aerosol combination was compared with the response obtained when the scrubbing effect of the upper respiratory system was eliminated with a tracheal connula. The results are shown in Figure 3-4. At all concentrations the effect of using the tracheal cannula was to increase the response, but this effect was not as large as that produced by the sodium chloride particles. Also, note that the curves for the gas alone breathed normally and breathed through the cannula are parallel, but the addition of the sodium chloride particles shifts the slope. These results are consistent with the idea that a portion of the formaldehyde was adsorbed on the aerosol particles (or dissolved in the aqueous NaCl droplets). Amdur also suggests that for each sodium chloride concentration there is a limiting formaldehyde concentration beyond which increasing the latter produces no further increase in the irritating action of the aerosol itself.

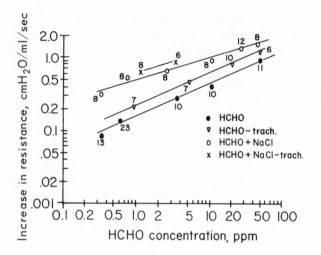

Figure 3-4. Dose-response curves for formaldehyde alone and plus 10 mg/m$^3$ sodium chloride in normal and tracheotomized animals. The increase in resistance at the end of 1-hour exposure is the criterion of response and the concentration is expressed as ppm.[76] (*Courtesy of Pergamon Press*)

The presence of sodium chloride had essentially no effect on the increase in resistance caused by formic acid. However, the sodium chloride did increase the recovery time for both formic acid and formaldehyde.

Rather surprising results were obtained when Frank, Amdur, and Whittenberger[78] applied the pulmonary flow resistance technique to a determination of the effect of sodium chloride particles on the irritating properties of sulfur dioxide to healthy male adults. The geometric mean diameter of the particles was 0.15 micron and the concentration of particles was in the range 10 to 30 mg/cu meter. Sulfur dioxide concentrations varied from 1 to 15 ppm. The sodium chloride particles in these experiments produced no significant difference in response to the sulfur dioxide.

Goetz[79] has developed a theoretical, semiquantitative treatment of the nature of the synergistic action of aerosols to explain the results obtained by Amdur and her co-workers and by La Belle, Long, and Christofano. He made the following assumptions.

(1) The toxic or irritant molecules, which Goetz denotes by $T$, are permanently transferred from the airborne state by adsorption on the particles followed by an irreversible collision with the respiratory system tissues.

(2) The extent of irritation is assumed as a first approximation to be proportional to the number of irritant molecules in contact with unit area of respiratory system tissue.

(3) The airborne particles are physiologically neutral.

(4) In order for a synergistic effect to occur, the irritant molecules must be transferred from the particles to the tissues. Goetz suggests that particles with a high affinity for specific $T$-molecules can attenuate the response but if the tissue has a greater affinity for $T$ than the particle surface, $T$ will be transferred and produce a local increase in the concentration of $T$ on the tissue.

The following model was used to explore the implications of the above assumptions. The unit of tissue surface was represented as a hollow spherical cavity of diameter $D$, inner surface area $A_c(= \pi D^2)$, and volume $V_c(= 0.52D^3)$. The number $N_T$ of $T$-molecules in the cavity is $0.52\bar{N}C_T D^3$ where $C_T$ is the concentration of $T$ in $cm^3/cm^3$ and $\bar{N}$ is the total number of molecules per $cm^3$ of gas. The average surface concentration of $T$ in the cavity assuming every $T$-molecule has collided irreversibly is

$$K_T = N_T A_T / A_c = 0.167\bar{N}C_T D A_T \tag{3.8}$$

where $A_T$ is the area of each $T$-molecule after its transfer to the lung surface.

If the aerosol of concentration $C_p$ is monodispersed, the number of particles in $V_c$ is $C_p D d^{-3}$ and the total particle surface area, $A_p$, is $\pi C_p D^3 d^{-1}$. The fraction of the cavity surface which receives a concentration greatly in excess of $K_T$ is $n' = A_p/A_c$ or $C_p D d^{-1}$.

The number of $T$-molecules associated with $A_p$ for a complete monolayer is $N'_T = A_p/A_T = \pi C_p D^3 (d A_T)^{-1}$, and the ratio of adsorbed to free molecules, $F_T$, is $N'_T/N_T = A_p/A_T N_T = 6C_p(NC_T d A_T)^{-1}$. Thus $F_T$ increases with $C_p/C_T$, decreases with $d$, and is independent of $D$. If we assume a cavity diameter of $10^{-1}$ cm, a particle diameter of 0.3 micron, a $T$-concentration of 1 ppm, $A_T = 1.5 \times 10^{-5}$ $cm^2$, and $C_p = 10^{-9}$ $g/cm^3$, the ratio of bound to free molecules is $5 \times 10^{-3}$.

Goetz then defines the surface concentration if all particles in the cavity are deposited, and all $T$-molecules are transfered from the particles to the surface fraction $n'$, by the equation

$$K'_T = \frac{N'_T A_T}{n' A_c} = \frac{DC_p}{n'd} \tag{3.9}$$

If the particles are covered by a monolayer, $K'_T$ is unity.

For type I or II isotherms the fractional approach to monolayer formation can be written to a first approximation as $kN_T/(1 + kN_T)$ where $k$ is a constant characteristic of the isotherm. Then equation 3.9 becomes

$$K'_T = \frac{DC_p}{n'd} \quad \frac{BC_T}{1 + C_T} \tag{3.10}$$

where $B = 0.52k\bar{N}D^3$.

Since the sorptive properties of the particles are not adequately defined by $A_p/A_T$, and the areas on the cavity surface exposed to transfer of $T$ from the particles are not necessarily equal to $A_p$, Goetz replaces $n'$ by $n(= Cn')$, where $C$ is an empirical constant. The over-all concentration causing irritation is then

$$\overline{K} = K_T + K'_T = D\,\frac{\overline{N}A_TC_T}{6} + \frac{C_pBC_T}{nd(1 + BC_T)} \tag{3.11}$$

This equation of course represents a great oversimplification of the situation, but if the response is a simple function of $\overline{K}$, equation 3.11 furnishes a means of making a qualitative assessment of the influence of several variables on the response. Figure 3-5, obtained by substituting arbitrary values into 3.11, demonstrates the variation of $\overline{K}$ with $C_T$ for four different values of $C_p$. The equation predicts that the effect of the particles will disappear for sufficiently large concentrations of the toxic gas and that the vanishing point will increase with increasing $C_p$.

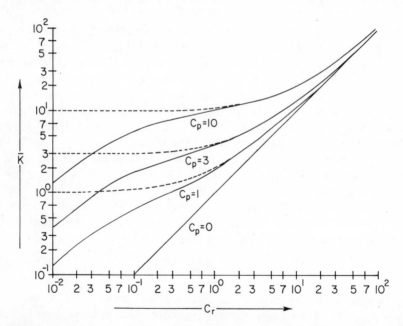

Figure 3-5. Graphic representation equation 3.11 in arbitrary units (AT. $N/6 =$; $(\mathrm{n.d})^{-1} =$; $D = 1$), indicating the variation of $(K)$ with $(C_T)$ in the absence $(C_p = 0)$, and the presence of 3 different concentrations $(C_p = 1,3,10)$ of a synergistic aerosol. The dashed curves represent $BC_T = 1$, the full drawn curves $B = 0.15/C_T$.[79] (*Courtesy of Pergamon Press*)

Goetz applied equation 3.11 to the results of La Belle and of Amdur, obtaining good agreement.

A considerable literature has developed concerning the idea that atmospheric ions have a considerable influence on human well being. It is generally considered that the effects of negative ions are beneficial and those of positive ions are harmful. In addition much published research has suggested that atmospheric ions have effects on micro-organisms, plants, and animals. As might be expected, the subject is quite controversial, particularly since in many of the studies proper controls were not used. Nonetheless, airborne ions have been used for therapeutic purposes in European clinics for many years. The subject has been reviewed by Steigerwald[80] and by Hicks.[81]

Bevilacqua and La Belle[82] have made an interesting study of the synergism of carbon particles and airborne ions. The biological property investigated was the learning rate of rats as determined with a Skinner box apparatus. Each animal received intermittent shocks from the metal floor of the box until it learned to turn off the system by pressing a lever on the wall. The time interval between the start of the intermittent shocks and operating the lever was measured for each trial, successive trials being five minutes apart. Ions were produced with a generator equipped with a high-intensity source of ionizing radiation and electrodes for controlling the polarity of the effluent.

Some of the results are shown in Figures 3-6 to 3-8; the control is shown

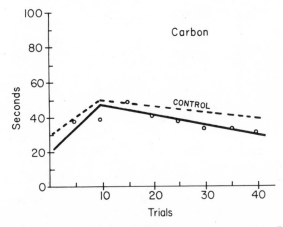

Figure 3-6. Learning curve for rats exposed to carbon particles for periods up to 2 weeks. The dotted line is the regression for control animals.[82] (*Courtesy of the American Industrial Hygiene Association*)

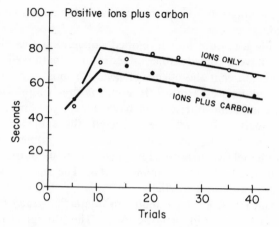

Figure 3-7. Learning curves for rats exposed to positive ions alone, and for rats exposed to positive ions in the presence of carbon particles.[82] (*Courtesy of the American Industrial Hygiene Association*)

in Figure 3-6. The negative ions decreased the learning time and the positive ions increased it. The carbon particles decreased the effect of the positive ions and increased the effect of the negative ions. The carbon particles in air to which no ions had been added decreased the learning time.

These results were explained on the basis that carbon particles preferen-

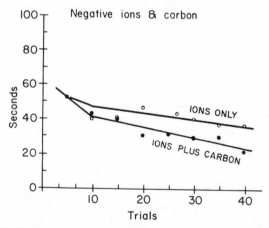

Figure 3-8. Learning curves for rats exposed to negative ions alone, and for rats exposed to negative ions in the presence of carbon particles.[82] (*Courtesy of the American Industrial Hygiene Association*)

tially adsorb positive ions and that each atmosphere tested contained both positive and negative ions even in the absence of added ions. Thus the effect of adding carbon particles was to accentuate the biological effect of the negative ions.

Bevilacqua and La Belle did not speculate concerning the effect of particle size on this effect of carbon. In Chapter 2 it was pointed out (p. 126) that the equilibrium charge per particle varies directly with the diameter raised to a power between 1 and 2. Since the number of particles per unit weight of material varies inversely with the diameter cubed, the synergistic action between carbon particles and ions should increase markedly with decreasing particle size if the explanation given above is correct.

### Radioactive dusts

The ionizing radiations most commonly encountered are alpha, beta, gamma, X-, and cosmic radiation; and X-radiation is merely a soft gamma radiation. The only radiations encountered in radioactive aerosols are the first three.

Radiation dose is usually specified either in terms of the roentgen or the rad. The roentgen is defined as the quantity of X- or gamma radiation and its associated corpuscular emission which produces one electrostatic unit of charge of either sign per cubic centimeter of air at $0°C$ and 760 mm of mercury.

There are a number of difficulties involved in using the roentgen in connection with biological studies. The unit only properly applies to X- and gamma radiation; the energy absorbed by tissue and bone per roentgen varies with the photon energy. For such reasons the rad is a preferable unit for biological work and is defined as the amount of radiation producing an energy absorption of 100 ergs per gram of the material in question.

Equal numbers of rads of alpha, beta, and gamma radiation do not necessarily produce equal biological effects. To take this into account, the Relative Biological Effectiveness (RBE) has been defined as the number of rads of 250-kv X-radiation which produces the same biological action as one rad of the radiation in question. The RBE is about one for X-, gamma, and beta radiation, and as high as ten for alpha radiation. The product of the dose in rads and the RBE is known as the roentgen-equivalent-man or rem.

Another important quantity is the specific activity, which is used to indicate the rate of emission of radiation per unit weight of radioactive material.* It is usually defined in terms of curies (or millicuries) per gram (or milligram). The curie is defined as the quantity of radioactive material which undergoes $3.70 \times 10^{10}$ disintegrations per second.

The biological effects of radiation can be divided into two main types: acute and chronic. Massive doses of radiation destroy cells while those receiving smaller doses may partially or completely recover. Partially recovered cells may become malignant. The radiation may also produce mutations of genes so that offspring may be seriously affected by radiation received by the parents.

Differentiation must also be made between whole-body and local exposure. Exposure of the entire body to gamma radiation exceeding about 2000 r produces death of most animals, including man, in a few hours. The median lethal dose, "LD 50," for most animals is 200 to 1000 r. The acute effects of smaller, sub-lethal, dosages include nausea, diarrhea, thirst, low grade fever, and later loss of hair. There may be ulceration and bleeding in the mouth and pharynx. Local acute external effects include burns and loss of hair.

The effects of internal radiations vary markedly with the distribution of the radiation within the body, the type and intensity of the radiation, and the physical and chemical nature of the source. For example, radium, strontium-90, and calcium-45 become concentrated in the bone, and because of their long half-lives may produce death years after ingestion. The classic example of poisoning from the ingestion of radioactive materials was the jaw necrosis which developed in women applying a luminous paint containing radium to the dials of watches. The girls produced points on their brushes with their mouths and this pointing has been generally blamed for the poisonings. However, Drinker and Hatch[20] pointed out that dust must have played a major role.

The effect of particle size on the radiation hazards from breathing radioactive dust is usually the combined result of several effects of particle size and is apt to vary markedly with the nature both of the particles and the radiation. Of course, one effect of particle size is to control the location of deposition, if any, in the respiratory system. If the dust particles are essentially insoluble, only those reaching the alveoli are likely to have a physiological action, the remainder being eliminated via the gastro-intestinal system. If the particles are somewhat soluble, large ones may be eliminated in this manner; but small ones, being more soluble and dissolving more rapidly, may be largely absorbed by the body. Of course, these same comments can be made for most inhaled poisons,

*Specific activity has been defined in a number of ways.[83] As used in this book it refers to activity per unit weight of particulate material.

but in general, radioactive poisons are $10^6$ to $10^8$ times as hazardous as chemical poisons.[84] When the particles are very soluble, the effect of size will be largely that of determining the extent of deposition anywhere in the respiratory system.

Superimposed on these effects of particle size is the fact that the specific activity of the particle material may vary with particle size. This is particularly likely to be the case when the particles are formed by the condensation of radioactive vapor on inert particles or the agglomeration of radioactive particles with inert particles.

The radioactive isotopes which have the greatest potential for internal hazard are those which have relatively short radioactive half-lives and rather long biological half-lives.[85] These include iodine-131, strontium 89, strontium-90, cesium-137, barium-140, and plutonium-239. Tritium and tritium oxide are also potential hazards and the latter may be inhaled when adsorbed on dust particles. Uranium may also provide a hazard, but as a chemical poison rather than a radiation poison.

Prior to World War II the dial-painting episode was the only well-established case of industrial radiation poisoning by ingestion. Some mining operations were suspected, but it was never definitely established that radiation rather than silicosis was the cause. Today, however, because of the widespread use of radioactive materials, the potential hazard, if not the actual hazard from radioactive particle inhalation, has become quite great. Radioactive particles and vapors may become airborne during operations such as mining and processing radioactive materials, fabricating the materials for various uses, such as atomic energy plants, therapeutic purposes, and weapons, and in the operation of reactors. The dangers from both close-in and world-wide fallout have been well publicized, and inhalation hazards may exist in laboratories using radioactive isotopes.

A number of studies have been made of the deposition of radioactive particles in the lungs. However, relatively little is known about such hazards compared with our knowledge of other types of radiation hazards. A four year investigation of the deposition, retention, translocation, and excretion of radioactive particles at the Hanford Laboratories of General Electric at Richland, Washington, was reported in 1961.[86] The broad objective of the study was to define the hazards of inhaling radioactive particles and to apply experimental results to obtaining maximum permissible concentrations. The isotopes used were $Pu^{239}$, $Ru^{106}$, $I^{121}$, and $Sr^{90}$. Both soluble and insoluble particles containing these isotopes were employed. The animals exposed to the aerosols were dogs, mice, and sheep.

Particles were prepared from plutonium-239 oxide, $Ru^{106}O_2$, $AgI^{131}$, and $Sr^{90}SO_4$. They were suspended in a 0.1 percent (aqueous?) solution of polypropylene glycolethylene oxide and the suspensions were dispersed to form aerosols which were passed into exposure chambers. Samples of the aerosols were collected on membrane filters and used to determine radioactivity concentrations in the air, and particle size distributions using an electron microscope.

The extent of deposition was determined by radiochemical analyses of tissues from both mice and dogs killed immediately after exposures of about 20 minutes for dogs and 1.5 hours for mice. The mice were exposed to $Ru^{106}O_2$ having a number-median diameter (NMD) of 0.38 micron and to $Pu^{239}O_2$ having an NMD of 0.2 micron. The dogs were exposed to $Pu^{239}O_2$ having an NMD of 1 to 5 microns. When the particles were relatively insoluble in the case of mice, 16 to 23 percent of the radioactive material was found in the lungs, 22 to 66 percent in the gastrointestinal tract, and 8 to 14 percent in all other organs. In the case of dogs, 6 percent was found in the lungs and 5 percent in the gastrointestinal tract. The deposition and distribution situation was quite different when the aerosol was composed of soluble particles, since they were rapidly absorbed by the blood and by other tissues. Unlike the mice, the dogs were equipped with plastic dog masks and three-way valves. The low percentage deposition for dogs was explained as being the result of deposition in the masks and valves.

It is interesting to compare these results with Figure 3-1, although this involves comparing mice with men. The band corresponding to particles exhaled by human beings considerably overlaps the percentage of particles not accounted for in the deposition in mice.

The retention of inhaled particles was investigated either by radiochemical analysis of respiratory tract tissue taken from animals which were killed at various times following exposure, or by external monitoring of the live animals. The early clearance of radioactivity from the lungs of mice was rapid, and less than 5 percent was retained for a long time. The biological half-life was 230 days for $Ru^{106}$ and 460 days for $Pu^{239}$. The half-life of $Pu^{239}$ for dogs was evidently very much longer, judging from excretion studies. Gradual movement of the relatively insoluble $Pu^{239}O_2$ and $Ru^{106}O_2$ from the lungs to several other tissues occurred. High concentrations of $Ru^{106}$ accumulated in the ovary and adrenal glands of mice, while the major transfer of $Pu^{239}$ was to tracheo-bronchial lymph nodes. The soluble radioactive materials promptly left the lungs and accumulated in the same tissues that would have occurred following their entry into the body by other routes. The plutonium oxide inhalation was particularly lethal; deposition of 0.3 microcuries ($\mu_c$) caused the death of

80 percent of the mice within nine months, and deposition of 50 to 100$\mu_c$ killed the dogs within three to four months.

The suggestion has often been made that the local high concentrations of radioactivity resulting from contact with radioactive particles might be much more likely to produce malignancies and other undesirable effects than if the same amount of radiation were applied in a less localized manner. Numerous studies have demonstrated that intratracheal injection of radioactive particles into rodents produce benign and malignant tumors and other pathological changes. Studies at Hanford of mice given intratracheal injections of aerosols of $Pu^{239}O_2$ or $Ru^{106}O_2$ confirmed these observations, but when the aerosols were administered by inhalation, malignant tumors were not produced. Bair[86] states that by 1960 there was only one report[87] of carcinoma after inhalation of radioactive particles.

Cember and Watson[88] investigated this effect of high local doses of radiation with beads containing strontium-90 implanted in the lungs of rats. The beads were prepared by mixing strontium carbonate with powdered soft glass using a weight ratio of 1:5 and fusing small amounts of the mixture. The specific activity was 244 $\mu_c$/g of bead material. The median bead diameter was 0.32 mm. They were implanted into the lung with an 18-gauge hypodermic needle.

The death rate was the same for rats treated with radioactive and for rats treated with non-radioactive beads, although the lung puncture had a traumatic effect on both sets of rats. This result is compatible with the hypothesis that energy absorbed from a single radiation source in the lungs is less lethal than the same amount of radiant energy absorbed throughout the lung. However, the radioactive beads were highly carcinogenic. The total malignancy frequency was 30 percent and the carcinoma frequency was 17 percent.

Nelson[89] has reviewed the subject of radiation cancer of the lung and has undertaken studies using radioactive pellets to determine whether lung tissues are more susceptible than others to the carcinogenic action of radiation. He tentatively concludes that they are not.

There is universal agreement on one aspect of the physiological action of airborne radioactive particles and that is that the effects are the result of a complex of many variables, of which particle size and size distribution are but two. For example, Nelson suggests that disease or injury could lead to localized accumulation of radioactive material and produce a high local dosage.

### Aerosol therapy

Almost all the above discussion has dealt with hazards from airborne particles. However, there are a number of therapeutic uses of aerosols, and size plays a major role in such applications since it largely determines the location of deposition within the respiratory system of a major part of the therapeutic agent. One such application of aerosols has been mentioned earlier in this chapter (p. 171), namely, the use of aluminum powder for treating silicosis. A very familiar application is the use of sprays of vaso-constrictors such as phenylephrine hydrochloride, usually sold under the brand name "Neosynephrine," to relieve the symptoms of head colds and hay fever.

The importance of using the appropriate size of aerosol particle has been emphasized by Dautrebande.[90] If the particles are to penetrate deeply into the lung it is important that they be smaller than about one micron in diameter. Furthermore, the size range should be fairly narrow. Otherwise, even if the number-median diameter is less than one micron, the mass-median diameter may be much greater than one micron and a large percentage of the mass of the particles will be collected in the upper parts of the respiratory system. Various techniques are available for preparing nearly monodisperse aerosols, such as the condensation technique of Sinclair and La Mer mentioned in Chapter 2. However, these methods are more appropriate for use as research tools than for producing aerosols for therapeutic purposes.

The above difficulty can be overcome to a large extent by using relatively simple methods to produce aerosols which are polydispersed but which contain large numbers of particles in the size region of interest, which is mostly in the small particle size tail of the size distribution. The larger particles, outside of this size region, are removed by some method which leaves airborne the particles having the rather narrow size range desired. A variation of this approach which has been used successfully in the author's laboratory involves producing the initial aerosol with an aspirating type generator such as one of the commercial nebulizers. The resulting airborne droplets are then passed through a bed of glass beads to remove the larger droplets. The smaller the beads and the higher the flow rate through the bed, the smaller will be the minimum size of particles removed.

The dispersed liquid may be either relatively non-volatile or it may be a solution. In the latter case the solute may be either a solid or a non-volatile liquid and the solvent a volatile liquid which evaporates after the dispersion, leaving airborne particles consisting of the residual non-volatile material. The median size of the residual particles can of course be controlled by the percentage of solute in the solution, but this does not affect the width of the size distribution.

A variation of this method is also useful for dispersing powders. The powder is suspended in a volatile liquid at such a dilution that the largest drops passing through the bed of glass beads are not likely to contain more than one solid particle. The temptation is great to add a wetting agent to aid in dispersing the powder in the liquid, but this should generally be avoided since the concentration of wetting agent needed if it is to be effective is likely to be comparable to that of the powder. The result is an aerosol consisting of both agent-coated particles and, since a large percentage of the droplets will contain no powder particle, particles of pure wetting agent. In fact, often the powder should be extracted repeatedly with the liquid phase before dispersion in the liquid to prevent the production of high number concentrations of very small aerosol particles consisting of soluble impurities in the original powder.

Another variation of this technique was developed by Dautrebande to produce very small airborne particles for therapeutic uses. He employed a technique that he calls "obligatory liquid filtration." The apparatus is a single unit consisting of a nebulizer followed by a series of baffles so arranged that large droplets impinge on them, collecting to form a sheet of liquid on which the aerosol must impinge or through which it must pass. The baffles serve the same purpose as the glass beads, eliminating all but the small particle size tail of the size distribution. Dautrebande has constructed devices based on this principle varying from 2 inches to 2 feet in height and dispersing from 2 to 2000 grams per hour. The particle size obtained will of course vary with the number of baffles, and in the case of a solution with the concentration of the solute. Using six successive "liquid filtering layers" Dautrebande produced aerosols having number-medium diameters of 0.02 to 0.04 micron.

The use of a combination of atomizer and baffles to produce aerosols from which the larger particles have been removed is actually quite old. An atomizer was developed by a Professor Spiers of Frankfort in 1902 which consisted of a nozzle inside a pear-shaped container equipped with a long stem. The container wall served as the baffle. This apparatus was described in detail by Collison[91] after he and Douglas-Hamilton introduced it into England in 1924.

The Dautrebande nebulizer produces unusually small particles. This is no doubt partially due to the elaborate baffle system, but probably just as important is the fact that it operates at a high pressure (about 0.5 to 4 kg/cm$^2$) which in turn produces high velocities of impingement on the baffles and liquid films.

Of course, for many purposes submicron size particles are not particularly desirable. Sprays designed for treatment of the nose and throat should have mass-median diameters no smaller than about 10 microns.

For such purposes conventional commercial nebulizers or "atomizers" used as sold are satisfactory. Examples are the De Vilbiss and the Vaponephrin nebulizers.

Aerosols may stimulate the ortho- or parasympathetic nerve systems of the lungs. Stimulation of the former system dilates the respiratory passages and makes breathing easier, while stimulation of the latter system causes constriction. Constricting substances include the "nerve gases" such as Tabun, Sarin, and Soman; organic phosphorus insecticides such as parathion; acetylcholine; and pilocarpine. Many irritants have a strong constricting effect. The constricting action of the anticholinesterase substances such as the nerve gases and organic phosphorus insecticides can be counteracted by atropine.

Dilating substances include phenylephrine ("Neosynephrine"), clopane isopropylnoradrenalin (Isoproterenol), ephedrine, and adrenaline. A number of substances that are not ortho-sympathicotonics also are dilating. These, as listed by Dautrebande,[90] include histamine, atropine, cocaine, procaine, strychnine, caffeine, calcium and ammonium chlorides, sodium nitrite, barbituates, triethylene glycol, and propylene glycol.

A number of combinations of such substances exhibit a synergistic effect on man. For example, Lilly markets a mixture called "Aerolone" which has the following percentage composition: clopane, 0.5; atropine sulfate, 0.1; isoproterenol, 0.25; procaine hydrochoride, 0.2; propylene glycol, 80; and the remainder water.

Just as certain combinations produce synergism, others result in antagonism, and it is possible to take advantage of this if, for example, a systemic reaction to an aerosol is desired but the aerosol also produces constriction. The best known situation of this kind is the overcoming of an allergic reaction to a dust such as household dust or pollen using a dilator such as neosynephrine. Furthermore, once a dilator has been adminstered, subsequent dosage by a constrictor such as pilocarpine or even dust will probably have little or no effect until the effect of the dilator "wears off." Aluminum powder, when used for preventing or treating silicosis, has a slight constrictor action and it may be able to penetrate deeper into the lungs and be more effective if the patient's lungs are dilated in advance.

The dilating action of many aerosols has an obvious application to patients suffering from shortness of breath and constriction from various causes. Favorable results have been obtained with dilating aerosols in treating both pulmonary and cardiac dyspnea. Patients suffering from asthma and from anthracosilicosis seem to be particularly responsive. Dautrebande has described the results obtained by treating 126 patients having severe asthma with isoproterenol or isoproterenol-phenylephrine aerosols. About 44 percent showed great improvement, 13 percent showed prolonged disappearance of the asthma, and about 20 percent more exhibited definite improvement. Only slightly more than 2 percent experienced aggravation of their symptoms. The study also showed that the younger the subject, the more likely was such treatment to be effective.

The use of dilating materials in aerosol form for treating asthma and other situations where difficult breathing is encountered is of course largely a matter of treating the symptoms and should not be used as a substitute for other treatment, such as desensitization. A few cases have been known where treatment with dilating materials for a few months gave relief for several years, but such cases are rare. Symptomatic treatment of severe asthma by the combined use of adrenocorticoids and dilating aerosols is sometimes highly beneficial.[92] Even though such treatment may be largely symptomatic, it not only permits the patient to live a more nearly normal and pleasant life, it usually increases his appetite, his strength, and his general well-being, and thus almost certainly increases the effectiveness of treatment of the underlying condition.

Antihistamines of various kinds have been found to be very effective for relieving the symptoms of hay fever and asthma. They are generally given orally. Numerous investigations have been made based on the idea[93,94,95,96] of administering them directly to the location of symptoms as aerosols but the results have been conflicting, and there seems to be little if any advantage to the use of antihistamines in aerosol form.

Antibiotics have also been administered as aerosols to treat various infections of the respiratory system, apparently with considerable success. Antibiotics which have been used in this manner include penicillin, streptomycin, "Terramycin," and "Aureomycin." Most of the uses have been for lung infections such as tuberculosis and pneumonia.

The literature is replete with miscellaneous uses of aerosols for treating respiratory ailments, and much of this literature has been reviewed by Dautrebande.[90]

Inhaled aerosol particles which are deposited in the respiratory system may, if soluble, rapidly pass into the blood stream. Therefore, aerosols may constitute effective forms for administering certain systemic drugs. Numerous studies have been made of the concentrations of drugs in the blood and urine following prolonged inhalation of the drugs, and the results indicate that systemic effects following such treatment are common. The main advantage of administering systemic drugs in this manner, if indeed there is an advantage, lies in the fact that prolonged inhalation of the aerosols may have an effect similar to that of slow continuous injection.

A large part of the research concerned with systemic effects of inhaled aerosols has dealt with the fate of inhaled penicillin. Numerous publications have described research which demonstrates that inhaled penicillin is efficiently transported unchanged from the lungs to the general blood system. The fraction of penicillin which reaches the blood seems to be largely independent of the location of the deposition within the respiratory system. Therefore, if penicillin is to be administered for its systemic effects, aerosol generators which produce relatively large droplets (>2 microns in diameter) should probably be used to take advantage of the large mass concentrations of penicillin in such aerosols. If penicillin is to be administered for treatment of lung diseases, generators which produce submicron-sized droplets which reach and are deposited in the lower respiratory system seem more appropriate.

## DEPOSITION ON THE SKIN

### Anatomy of the skin

The skin consists of two distinct layers. The outer is known as the cuticle or epidermis; hair and nails are specially developed parts of the epidermis. The inner layer is called the dermis, cutis vera, or corium.

The epidermis consists of many layers of cells held together by a small amount of binding substance. The deepest cells are elongated or columnar, and arranged with the long ones perpendicular to the corium. Above these are several layers of nearly round cells, and as the surface is approached, the cells become increasingly flattened in a plane parallel to the surface. The outermost layer of the epidermis is composed of a thick layer of nearly flat cells which, unlike the other cells of the epidermis, no longer contain a nucleus. These cells are dead and are constantly being shed from the surface to be replaced by cells from below. This outermost part of the epidermis is known as the horny stratum to distinguish it from the deeper, softer nucous or Malpighian layer. The epidermis is devoid of blood and lymphatic vessels, and is nourished from the corium below.

The corium or dermis consists of a mat of elastic fibrous connective tissue which changes with increasing depth to the subcutaneous areolar tissue. The corium contains a close network of capillaries and numerous lymphatics and nerves. A cut into the corium, unlike one into the epidermis, produces bleeding.

The outer surface of the corium is raised into small elevations called papillae. Some of them contain capillary loops and others, involved in cutaneous senses, contain special organs connected with nerve fibers.

The skin serves many purposes, one of the most important being protection of the rest of the body. According to many authorities, substances that are soluble in both fatty materials and water are more strongly absorbed by the body through the skin than those that are soluble in only one or the other or neither. The gland ducts and the hair follicles are particularly vulnerable portions of the skin, since irritants which otherwise would be innocuous may penetrate the skin through them.

### Effect of particle size

Particle size can influence the physiological action of particles on the body surface in at least three ways. If the particles are airborne before reaching the skin, particle size may play a major role in determining the amounts of the particles deposited on the skin. The size of the particles reaching the skin may influence the physiological action, if any. The retention of particles by the skin following both immediate and prolonged contact is also greatly influenced by particle size.

When particles are introduced into the air at some distance from subjects downwind of the generated cloud, if the particles are sufficiently large and dense, they will settle to the ground before reaching the subjects. On the other hand, if they are large and dense enough to settle rapidly, and the cloud of particles extends to the ground, the closer the subjects are to the source the greater the amount of contamination they will receive by direct sedimentation. This is an important consideration in predicting and evaluating the effects of radioactive fallout, biological warfare, and chemical warfare.

Particles are deposited on the skin by inertial effects as well as by sedimentation. The principles of such deposition were discussed in Ch. 2 (p. 86) for a given wind velocity, or movement of the subject, the impaction efficiency increases with increasing particle diameter. Thus the two main mechanisms for deposition are very ineffective for submicron size particles. Such particles are deposited to some extent by diffusion, by thermal forces, and by electrostatic forces, but these are relatively ineffective.

The effect of size on physiological action once the particles have been deposited is probably determined by the amount of active material in contact with a unit area of the skin. If only a few particles are deposited, large particles may have more effect than small ones. However, if the skin is completely covered with particles, small ones may be more effective. Using the same reasoning, a powder of wide size distribution might be more effective than an essentially monodispersed powder when both have the same number-median diameter. This is largely speculation and there is little or no direct experimental information concerning the effect of size of deposited particles on physiological action.

Other things being equal, small particles adhere to surfaces more strongly than large ones, even when the surfaces are smooth. In the case of skin, with its many irregularities, fine particles adhere tenaciously and are particularly difficult to remove. The same of course can be said of clothing which has become contaminated with hazardous powders and the best "decontamination" may be to discard the clothing.

## Radioactive particles

Extensive studies have been made of the effects of radioactive particles on the skin. They can, of course, produce skin injuries resulting from alpha, beta, or gamma emission. The early fallout produced by a nuclear explosion produces skin damage primarily as a result of the emission of beta particles. If the fission products which are beta emitters come in contact with the skin and remain there for an appreciable time they produce the so-called beta burns.

The most complete information concerning beta burns resulted from a study of the natives of the Rongelab atoll in the Marshall Islands, who were accidentally exposed to radioactive fallout in March, 1964.[85] The fallout started to rain down on the islands about five hours after the nuclear explosion and the natives, who wore little clothing and no shoes, were highly contaminated with it. Since they did not realize its significance, little immediate effort was made to remove the white powder.

The first symptoms of beta burns were an itching and burning sensation. These symptoms disappeared in one or two days and two to three weeks elapsed before further symptoms appeared. The next symptoms were the development of skin lesions and loss of hair. These lesions began as increased pigmentation having the form of dark patches and raised areas. Since the lesions developed on the exposed parts of the body, they must have occurred on the areas coated with fallout. According to Glasstone,[85] they usually occurred in the following order: "scalp (with epilation), neck, shoulders, depressions in the forearm, feet, limbs, and trunk. Epilation and lesions of the scalp, neck, and foot were most frequently observed." The lesions were quite superficial, most of the damage having been done to the epidermis rather than to the corium. The lesions healed rapidly, leaving a depigmented area which gradually disappeared. Glasstone states that the more highly contaminated individuals developed deeper lesions which were ulcerated and later became covered with a dry scab. Even these lesions healed rapidly when given normal burn therapy. However, after the healing of these severe burns abnormal pigmentation persisted for as long as a year.

Regrowth of hair was usually complete in about six months following contamination.

The only other examples of large-scale hazardous exposures to radiation following the detonation of nuclear weapons were those following the two nuclear attacks on Japan. However, in these cases the detonations were air bursts, and most or all of the fallout must have been in the submicron size range so that little of it was deposited locally.

In addition to beta burns there are two other potential hazards from the deposition of fallout on the skin. One is the absorption of radioactive isotopes through the intact skin or through wounds, and the other is receiving an overdose of gamma radiation, particularly to the blood-forming organs.[97]

Numerous studies have been made of methods of removing radioactive contamination from persons and clothing, and of the use of protective clothing to prevent contamination. The U.S. Naval Radiological Defense Laboratory at Hunter's Point, San Francisco, California, has been particularly active in this field. An interesting study was made by Friedman[97] of the decontamination of synthetic radioactive fallout from intact human skin. This was part of a larger investigation in which ton quantities of synthetic radioactive fallout were applied to large areas of land and building surfaces which were subsequently decontaminated. The synthetic radioactive fallout was made from the site top soil using lanthanum-140 as the tracer. Particle diameters ranged from 1.5 to about 47 microns. The investigation was primarily a determination of the efficiency of removal of this synthetic material from the skin by each of nine different removal agents using 45 volunteer human subjects.

The synthetic fallout material was dispersed in air and impacted on the test area of an arm of the subject. Water alone removed more than 90 percent of the measured radioactivity, while scrubbing with a 10 percent solution of a commercial synthetic detergent decreased the activity to less than the detection limit. The pre-application of a protective barrier cream did not significantly increase the decontamination efficiency.

### Irritation

It is rather obvious that substances can irritate the skin and that some persons are much more susceptible than others. Mild irritation may merely produce itching and reddening, while more severe irritation may produce blistering or even destruction of the skin. A technique which has gained wide acceptance both for diagnostic purposes and to determine whether some material may produce skin irritation is the patch test.

The patch test usually involves placing some of the material whose irritating properties are to be examined on the skin of the subject. The material is then covered with an innocuous, impermeable "patch" which is held to the skin with adhesive tape or some similar binder. When the material to be tested is a powder it is placed on a pad of gauze to keep it in place while the patch is being affixed. Since particulate material may consist of liquids dispersed as a mist, patch tests for investigating the irritant properties of such liquids are useful for studying the irritating properties of the corresponding mists. In such cases the gauze is saturated with the liquid and covered with cellophane* which is sealed in place in the usual manner.

The total number of irritants is very large. Schwartz[98] lists more than one hundred merely as examples. Many of them are very reactive chemically, and attack the skin by direct chemical reaction. Many acids, bases, reducing agents, oxidizing agents, reactive elements and substances that precipitate protein are in this category. Other irritants attack the skin physically, such as solvents and emulsifying agents for fats and sterols, and dehydrating agents.

### Allergic reactions

Effects of allergins were discussed above in connection with inhalation. Persons who are susceptible to allergic reactions following inhalation of many substances are also likely to be hypersensitive to many substances upon direct contact with the skin. Many biological materials, both vegetable and animal, cause allergic reactions by susceptible people upon contact. Poison oak and poison ivy are the classic examples, and smoke from the burning of these substances may produce as severe reactions as direct contact with the plants. A characteristic property of allergins is that repeated contact is often necessary before a person becomes sensitized and undergoes an allergic response. For this reason allergic dermatitis is quite common in industries where a worker may be almost continually in contact with some biological material to which he becomes sensitized. Given sufficient time, however, the initial sensitization may give way to a desensitization.

### Absorption

In spite of the fact that the skin is an excellent protective organ, absorption through the skin can and often does occur. Much of what is known about skin absorption has resulted from some of its more dramatic effects. It has long been known that certain substances could poison by

*Schwartz[98] recommends the use of non-waterproof cellophane.

being absorbed through the skin, but such poisoning was apparently quite rare until the development during recent years of very potent insecticides. A number of persons have been poisoned with a chlorinated aromatic insecticide called dieldrin, which produces both acute and chronic effects. There are similar dangers from the related insecticides aldrin and endrin.[2] The organic phosphate insecticides are notorious for poisoning by absorption. A number of accidents have occurred as a result of spray impinging on the arms and legs. It is noteworthy that a device which disperses insecticides in a size range appropriate for spraying or dusting plants may also be very effective for spraying or dusting people, domestic animals, and wildlife.

Other poisonous substances which are said to be rather readily absorbed by the skin include nicotine, strychnine, opium, phenols, salts of various heavy metals, hydrogen cyanide, various nitro-compounds such as nitroglycerine, nitrobenzene, and nitrotoluene, and aromatic amines such as aniline.

It has often been emphasized that absorption through skin lesions is much more rapid than through the intact skin, but this may not be strictly so if large areas of intact skin are sprayed or dusted as compared with small areas of damaged skin.

## REFERENCES

1. Rosen, G., "The History of Miners' Diseases," Schuman's, New York, 1943.
2. Carson, Rachel, "Silent Spring," Houghton Mifflin, Boston, 1962.
3. Davies, C. N., *Stanford Research Institute Journal*, **5**, No. 3, 123 (1961).
4. Wilson, I. B., and V. K. La Mer, *J. Ind. Hyg. Toxicol.*, **30**, 265 (1948).
5. Landahl, H. D., T. M. Tracewell, and W. H. Lassen, *Arch. Ind. Hyg. Occ. Med.*, **3**, 359 (1951); **6**, 508 (1952).
6. Altshuler, B., L. Yarmus, E. D. Palmer, and N. Nelson, *A.M.A. Arch. Ind. Health*, **15**, 293 (1957).
7. Deryagin, B. V., S. P. Bakanov, S. S. Dukhin, and G. A. Batova, in "Research in Surface Forces," B. V. Deryagin, ed., translated by The Consultants Bureau Enterprises, Inc., New York, 1963.
8. Landahl, H. D., *Bull. Math. Biophys.*, **12**, 43 (1956).
9. Friedlander, S. K., *Am. Ind. Hyg. Assoc. J.*, **25**, 37 (1964).
10. Landwehr, M., *Staub*, **18**, 269 (1958).
11. Wilson, I. B., *J. Colloid Sci.*, **2**, 271 (1947).
12. Longley, M. Y., *Am. Ind. Hyg. Assoc. J.*, **21**, 187 (1960).
13. Sander, O. A., The pulmonary dust diseases, in "Industrial Hygiene and Toxicology," vol I, 2nd ed., F. A. Patty, ed., Interscience, New York, 1958.
14. Gross, P., M. L. Westrick, and J. M. McNerney, *Lab. Invest.*, **7**, 348 (1958).
15. Gross, P., M. L. Westrick, and J. M. McNerney, *J. Occ. Med.*, **3**, 258 (1961).
16. Gross, P., J. M. McNerney, and M. A. Babyak, *Am. Ind. Hyg. Assoc. J.*, **23**, 379 (1962).

17. Patty, F. A., Entry and action of toxic materials, in "Industrial Hygiene and Toxicology," vol I, 2nd ed., F. A. Patty, ed., Interscience, New York, 1958.
18. Doyle, H. N., R. H. Flinn, and W. C. Dreessen, *Am. Ind. Hyg. Assoc. J.*, **19**, 317 (1958).
19. "Chemical Abstracts," Fifth Decennial Index, 1947–1956, American Chemical Society, Washington, D.C.
20. Drinker, P., and T. Hatch, "Industrial Dust," 2nd ed., McGraw-Hill, New York, 1954.
21. Gross, P., M. L. Westrick, and J. M. McNerney, *Am. Ind. Hyg. Assoc. J.*, **19**, 201 (1958).
22. Tebbins, D. D., R. Z. Schulz, and P. Drinker, *J. Indus. Hyg. Toxicol.*, **27**, 199 (1945).
23. Hatch, T. F., and V. H. Kindsvatter, *J. Indus. Hyg. Toxicol.*, **29**, 342 (1947).
24. King, E. J., G. P. Mohanty, C. V. Harrison, and G. Nagelschmidt, *Brit. J. Ind. Med.*, **10**, 76 (1953).
25. Zaidi, S. H., E. J. King, C. V. Harrison, and G. Nagelschmidt, *A.M.A. Arch. Ind. Health*, **13**, 122 (1956).
26. Gye, W. E., and W. J. Purdy, *Brit. J. Exper. Path.*, **3**, 86 (1922).
27. Gye, W. E., and E. H. Kettle, *Brit. J. Exper. Path.*, **3**, 241 (1922).
28. King, E. J., S. H. Zaidi, and G. Nagelschmidt, *A.M.A. Arch. Ind. Health*, **13**, 133 (1956).
29. Hofmann, U., *Ber. Deut. Keram. Ges.*, **39**, 272 (1962).
30. Wood, W. B., and S. R. Gloyne, *Lancet*, **2**, 1383 (1934).
31. George, W. E., Supplement to the New South Wales Industrial Gazette, "Use of Aluminum Powder in the Prevention and Treatment of Silicosis" (Sept., 1946). Sidney; Gov't Printer (1946); *J. Ind. Hyg. and Toxic.*, **29**, 90 (abstracts) (1947).
32. Oswald, L. H., *A.M.A. Arch. Ind. Health*, **12**, 221 (1955).
33. Dworski, *A.M.A. Arch. Ind. Health*, **12**, 229 (1955).
34. Denny, J. J., W. D. Robson, and D. A. Irwin, *Canad. M.A. J.*, **37**, 1 (1937); **40**, 213 (1939).
35. King, E. J., J. W. Clegg, and V. M. Rae, *Thorax*, **1**, 188 (1946).
36. Luton, P., and J. Champeix, *Arch. d. Mal. Progr.*, **7**, 365 (1946).
37. Hanna, G. D., in "Geologic Guidebook of the San Francisco Bay Counties," Calif. Div. of Mines, Ferry Bldg., San Francisco, 1951.
38. Smart, R. H., and W. M. Anderson, *Ind. Med. and Surg.*, **21**, 509 (1952).
39. Ray, S. C., E. J. King, and C. V. Harrison, *Brit. J. Indus. Med.*, **8**, 74 (1951).
40. Fletcher, C. M., *Arch. Ind. Hyg. Occ. Med.*, **11**, 17 (1956).
41. Christie, H., R. J. Mac Kay, and A. M. Fisher, *Am. Ind. Hyg. Assoc. J.*, **24**, 47 (1963).
42. Lindeken, C. L., and O. L. Meadors, *Am. Ind. Hyg. Assoc. J.*, **21**, 245 (1960).
43. White, D. H., and J. E. Burke, ed., "The Metal Beryllium," American Society for Metals, Cleveland, 1955.
44. Donaldson, H. M., R. A. Hiser, and C. W. Schwenzfeier, *Am. Ind. Hyg. Assoc. J.*, **25**, 69 (1964).
45. Proudfit, J. P., H. S. Van Ordstrand, and C. W. Miller, *Arch. Ind. Hyg. Occ. Med.*, **1**, 105 (1950).
46. Wagner, W. D., O. J. Dobrogorski, and H. E. Stokinger, *Arch. Environ. Health*, **2**, 523 (1961).

47. Lushbaugh, C. C., J. W. Green, Jr., and C. E. Redemann., *Arch. Ind. Hyg. Occ. Med.*, **1**, 237 (1950).
48. Wagner, W. D., P. G. Wright, and H. E. Stokinger, *Am. Indus. Hyg. Assoc. J.*, **25**, 158 (1964).
49. Gill, C. I. C., *Brit. J. Ind. Med.*, **4**, 48 (1947).
50. McLaughlin, A.I.G., *A.M.A. Arch. Ind. Health*, **12**, 83 (1955).
51. Fawcitt, R., *Brit. J. Radiol*, **9**, 172, 354 (1936); **11**, 378 (1938).
52. Dunner, L., R. Hermon, and D. J. T. Bagnall, *Brit. J. Radiol.*, **19**, 506 (1946).
53. Amdur, M. O., and M. Corn, *Am. Ind. Hyg. Assoc. J.*, **24**, 326 (1963).
54. Hemeon, W. C. L., *A.M.A. Arch. Ind. Health*, **11**, 397 (1955).
55. Treon, J. F., F. R. Dutra, J. Cappel, H. Sigmon, and W. Younker, *A.M.A. Arch. Ind. Hyg. Occ. Med.* **2**, 716 (1950).
56. Stokinger, H. E., Effects of air pollution on animals, in A. C. Stern, Ed., "Air Pollution," Academic Press, New York, 1962.
57. Amdur, M. O., R. Z. Schulz, and P. Drinker, *A.M.A. Arch. Ind. Hyg. Occ. Med.*, **5**, 318 (1952).
58. Thomas, M. D., R. H. Hendricks, F. D. Gunn, and J. Critchlow, *A.M.A. Arch. Ind. Hyg. Occ. Med.*, **17**, 70 (1958).
59. Pattle, R. E., F. Burgess, and H. Cullumbine, *J. Path. Bact.*, **72**, 219 (1956).
60. Goldsmith, J. R., Effects of air pollution on humans, in A. C. Stern, ed., "Air Pollution," Academic Press, New York, 1962.
61. Owens, E. J., and C. L. Punte, *Am. Ind. Hyg. Assoc. J.*, **24**, 262 (1963).
62. Thackrah, C. T., "The Effects of Arts, Trades, and Professions, and of Civic States and Habits of Living, on Health and Longevity, etc.," 2nd ed., London, Longman, 1832.
63. Vance, G. H., *Am. Ind. Hyg. Assoc. J.*, **21**, 107 (1960).
64. Spolyar, L. W., J. F. Keppler, and H. G. Porter, *J. Ind. Hyg. & Tox.*, **26**, 232 (1944).
65. Barrett, H. M., D. A. Irwin, and E. Semmons, *J. Ind. Hyg. & Tox.*, **29**, 279 (1947).
66. Hardy, H., and J. Skinner, *J. Ind. Hyg. & Tox.*, **29**, 321 (1947).
67. Du Bois, K. P., and J. M. Coon, *A.M.A. Arch. Ind. Hyg. Occ. Med.*, **6**, 9 (1952).
68. Golz, H. H., *A.M.A. Arch. Ind. Health*, **19**, 516 (1959).
69. Cadle, R. D., and P. L. Magill, *A.M.A. Arch. Ind. Hyg. Occ. Med.*, **4**, 74 (1951).
70. Dautrebande, L., and R. Capps, *Arch. Internat. Pharmacodynamie*, **82**, 505 (1950).
71. Dautrebande, L., J. Shaver, and R. Capps, *Arch. Internat. Pharmacodynamie*, **85**, 17 (1951).
72. Gordieyeff, V. A., "Toxicity of Vapors in the Presence of Aerosol Carriers," Chem. Warfare Lab. Tech. Repts., CWLR 2053, August 17, 1956.
73. Dautrebande, L., "Bases Experimentales de la Protection Contre les Gaz de Combat," J. Dueulot, Gembloux, Belgium, 1939.
74. Amdur, M. O., *Am. Ind. Hyg. Assoc. J.*, **18**, 149 (1957).
75. La Belle, C. W., J. E. Long, and E. E. Christofano, *A.M.A. Arch. Ind. Health*, **11**, 297 (1955).
76. Amdur, M. O., *Int. J. Air Poll.*, **3**, 201 (1960).
77. Amdur, M. O., in "Inhaled Particles and Vapors," C. N. Davies, ed.,

Pergamon, New York, 1961.
78. Frank, N. R., M. O. Amdur, and J. L. Whittenberger, *Int. J. Air Poll.*, **8,** 125 (1964).
79. Goetz, A., *Int. J. Air and Water Poll.*, **4,** 168 (1961).
80. Hicks, W. W., *J. Franklin Inst.*, **261,** 209 (1956).
81. Steigerwald, B. J., in "Air Pollution," A. C. Stern, ed., Academic Press, New York, 1962.
82. Bevilacqua and C. W. La Belle, *Am. Ind. Hyg. Assoc. J.*, **24,** 448 (1963).
83. Glasstone, S., "Sourcebook on Atomic Energy," Van Nostrand, New York, 1950.
84. Story, E. J., *Am. Ind. Hyg. Assoc. J.*, **20,** 417 (1959).
85. Glasstone, S., "The Effects of Nuclear Weapons," U.S. Atomic Energy Commission, 1962.
86. Bair, W. J., in "Inhaled Particles and Vapors," C. N. Davies, ed., Pergamon, New York, 1961.
87. Lisco, H., *Lab. Invest.*, **8,** No. 1 (1959).
88. Cember, H., and J. A. Watson, *Am. Ind. Hyg. Assoc. J.*, **19,** 36 (1958).
89. Nelson, N., in "Inhaled Particles and Vapors," C. N. Davies, ed., Pergamon, New York, 1961.
90. Dautrebande, L., "Microaerosols," Academic Press, New York, 1962.
91. Collison, W. E., "Inhalation Therapy Technique," Heinemann, London, 1935.
92. Cander, L., and J. H. Comroe, Jr., *J. Allergy*, **26,** 210 (1955).
93. Herxheimer, H., *Brit. Med. J.*, **2,** 901 (1949).
94. Curry, J. J., *J. Clin. Invest.*, **25,** 785 (1946).
95. Schiller, I. W., and F. C. Lowell, *Ann. Allergy*, **5,** 564 (1947).
96. Halpern, B. N., *J. Allergy*, **18,** 263 (1947).
97. Friedman, W. J., *Am. Ind. Hyg. Assoc. J.*, **19,** 15 (1958).
98. Schwarz, L., in "Industrial Hygiene and Toxicology," 2nd ed., F. A. Patty, ed., Interscience, New York, 1958.

# Chapter 4 Air Pollution

For convenience, air pollution can be divided into two general types, although this division must often be rather arbitrary and artificial. One type is commonly called city smog. It is the widespread type of air pollution found in the atmospheres of many large, crowded cities which is a personal nuisance, often causes considerable financial loss, is injurious to health, and has often caused death. The term "smog" is a combination of the words smoke and fog, and is especially appropriate to that type of air pollution which is indigenous to those communities where large amounts of coal, especially bituminous coal, is burned. The smog in such cities is particularly apparent under those meteorological conditions which are conducive to the formation of fog, in which case the particles of soot may serve as condensation nuclei for fog formation. The term "smog" is also commonly applied, although with less justification, to that type of city air pollution which owes many of its properties to photochemical reactions involving hydrocarbons, other organic substances, oxides of nitrogen, and atmospheric oxygen. Fog may also be involved in the formation of this type of smog, but this seems to be rather uncommon.

The other general type of air pollution will be termed industrial air pollution. The word generally refers to single-source or nearly single-source pollution which is emitted to the air from a factory or other industrial operation. An obvious difficulty with this system of classification is that factories may contribute to city smog. However, the pollutants from such factories can be considered to be industrial air contaminants until they have become mixed with the general contamination of the city air.

A third type of air pollution might be added to this classification, namely fission products, which are so often associated with radioactive fallout.

## SMOG

### Photochemical smog

Photochemical smog is the second type of smog mentioned above. It is particularly apparent in cities where little coal is burned and where there are very large numbers of automobiles. Actually, both types can occur in the same city, but the smog of a coal-burning economy may render the presence of photochemical smog difficult to detect.

A large part of the research on photochemical smog has been done in Los Angeles County, California, where such smog is particularly intense. The occurrence of haze in this area had been noted at various times for many years, but it was not until about 1945 that the occurrence of smog had become sufficiently prevalent to cause widespread attention. In particular, it was noticed that the smog not only decreased visibility, but caused eye irritation and even lachrymation.

About this time it was noticed that in several cities in the western United States rubber goods seemed to undergo severe cracking during periods of smog. Bartell and Temple[1] of the United States Rubber Co. noted that the cracking was typical of that produced by ozone in the laboratory and analyzed the air of the cities in question for ozone using a method based on the oxidation of iodide to iodine. The results showed that the atmospheres of these cities did at times have concentrations of ozone many times the 4 to 5 parts per hundred million parts of air (pphm) usually found in uncontaminated atmospheres. Confirmation of the identity of this oxidizing material as ozone, or at least mainly ozone, was obtained by adsorption of gases from Los Angeles smog on silica gel at liquid oxygen temperature ($90°K$), followed by spectroscopic examination of the gases desorbed when the gel was allowed to warm to $195°K$.[2]

Haagen-Smit, Bradley, and Fox[3] discovered that when mixtures of cerain hydrocarbons, nitrogen dioxide, and air, at concentrations comparable to those found in Los Angeles smog, are irradiated with sunlight, ozone is formed in concentrations comparable to those found in smog. It now is quite well established that such photochemical reactions are responsible for the ozone content of what is now called photochemical smog and also for many of its unpleasant properties.

A team at Stanford Research Institute[3] conducted field tests with a number of automobiles driven under various conditions to determine the amounts of hydrocarbons of various kinds that automobile exhaust gases contribute to the atmosphere. The results demonstrated that automobiles emit much larger amounts of hydrocarbons to the Los Angeles atmosphere than all other sources combined. Automobiles are also a major source of the other major photochemical reactants in photochemical smog, i.e., oxides of nitrogen, although these are also emitted in important amounts by other combustion processes occurring in the area.

Atmospheric processes usually are quite effective in diluting and dispersing such contaminants. Therefore, smog of any variety accumulates only under adverse meteorological conditions. These generally consist of the combination of rather still air and the existence of an atmospheric inversion at a relatively low altitude, usually not more than two or three thousand feet above the city streets. Generally, the temperature of the atmosphere decreases with increasing altitude, at least to the tropopause at 12–15 kilometers in middle latitudes. However, at certain times and places this situation is modified. At first the temperature may drop with increasing altitude, but after a few hundred or few thousand feet there is a rather sudden rise in temperature, eventually again followed by the more common decrease in temperature with height. Such an increase in temperature is called an inversion. Little mixing occurs between the warm air and the colder air below, so the inversion provides a sort of lid below which impurities can accumulate. The lower the altitude at which an inversion occurs, and the more marked the increase in temperature with increasing height, the more effective is the lid.

The nature of the terrain beneath the inversion plays a major role in its effectiveness for containing pollutants. For example, the low mountains enclosing Los Angeles on three sides which add so much to its beauty also play a major role in the smog situation. Together with the gentle breeze from the ocean when an inversion exists, they constitute the walls of a bowl covered by the inversion lid. This bowl, the automobiles, and the vaunted sunshine of Southern California provide a remarkably effective factory for the manufacture of photochemical smog.

Similar conditions occur in a number of other cities, although seldom in as insidious a combination. Many cities in the western United States are plagued with such smog, for example, San Francisco, Denver, Phoenix, and San Diego. It has also been detected in various cities in the eastern United States, and almost certainly occurs in several other parts of the world.

As mentioned above, the occurrence of unusually high concentrations of ozone is a characteristic of photochemical smog. Measured variations of ozone concentration and of temperature with altitude in Los Angeles County on two smoggy days are shown in Figures 4-1 and 4-2. Today there is no serious doubt that this ozone is formed by photochemical reactions involving substances emitted into the atmosphere, mainly by

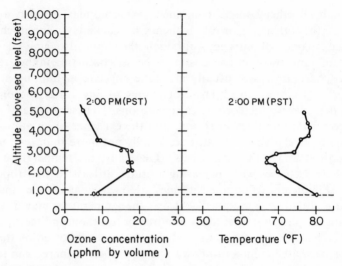

Figure 4-1. Vertical ozone and temperature profiles over Rose Bowl area, July 15, 1952.

automobiles; but even after years of extensive research the mechanisms of the processes producing the ozone and other reaction products remain in considerable doubt.

In order for a photochemical reaction to occur, some constituent of the

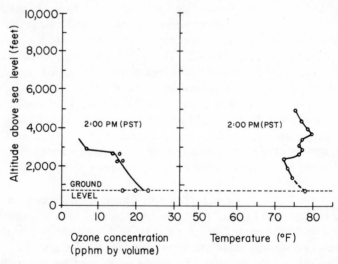

Figure 4-2. Vertical ozone and temperature profiles over Rose Bowl area, July 17, 1952.

reacting mixture must absorb light, and this absorption must decompose this primary photochemical reactant, or at least render it more reactive. Several substances in photochemical smog absorb solar radiation of the wavelengths near the earth's surface, and of these nitrogen dioxide is probably the most important. It absorbs near-ultraviolet radiation, undergoing decomposition in the process:

$$NO_2 + h\nu \rightarrow NO + O \qquad (4.1)$$

The atomic oxygen produced in this manner undergoes numerous reactions, but largely with molecular oxygen of the atmosphere because of its high concentration compared with the concentrations of pollutants:

$$O + O_2 + M \rightarrow O_3 + M \qquad (4.2)$$

M represents any third body which can be $N_2$, $O_2$, O, etc. and which is needed to carry off the excess energy of the reaction, stabilizing the ozone, $O_3$.

Reaction 4.2 produces ozone, but it immediately reacts with the NO produced in 4.1 to regenerate $NO_2$:

$$NO + O_3 \rightarrow NO_2 + O_2 \qquad (4.3)$$

Reactions 4.1 to 4.3 result in a steady state concentration of ozone in photochemical smog which is calculated to be of the order of 3 pphm, much smaller than that usually found in such smog. Nevertheless, all these reactions play a major role in the chemistry of this type of air pollution.

Atomic oxygen can react with various organic compounds to form free radicals, which are very reactive fragments of compounds and usually have a very short life:

$$RH + O \rightarrow R + OH \qquad (4.4)$$

Here the atomic oxygen abstracts hydrogen from the original compound RH to form the radicals R and OH. Radicals such as R react very rapidly with the molecular oxygen of the atmosphere to form peroxy radicals:

$$R + O_2 \rightarrow RO_2 \qquad (4.5)$$

One theory of the mechanism of ozone formation in photochemical smog is that ozone is formed by the reaction of peroxy radicals with molecular oxygen:

$$RO_2 + O_2 \rightarrow RO + O_3 \qquad (4.6)$$

The RO radical produced may perpetuate an ozone-forming chain by the hydrogen abstraction reaction:

$$RO + HR' \rightarrow ROH + R' \tag{4.7}$$

Reaction 4.7 will then be followed by a repetition of 4.5 and 4.6.

Results of research by Calvert at Ohio State University and Haagen-Smit at the California Institute of Technology suggest that ozone is produced by reaction 4.6. For example, when diacetyl is irradiated with visible light it decomposes to form two acetyl radicals. When this photolysis occurs in air, ozone is formed, possibly by the reaction sequence

$$\underset{\substack{\| \\ O}}{H_3C-\overset{O}{\overset{\|}{C}}-\overset{O}{\overset{\|}{C}}-CH_3} + h\nu \rightarrow 2\,H_3C-\overset{O}{\overset{\|}{C}} \tag{4.8}$$

$$2\,H_3C-\overset{O}{\overset{\|}{C}} + 2\,O_2 \rightarrow 2\,H_3C-\overset{O}{\overset{\|}{C}}-OO \tag{4.9}$$

$$H_3C-\overset{O}{\overset{\|}{C}}-OO + O_2 \rightarrow H_3C-\overset{O}{\overset{\|}{C}}-O + O_3 \tag{4.10}$$

Hanst and Calvert[5] found that the photochemical decomposition of diacetyl in oxygen produced acetic acid, but no peroxy acids. This would be expected if ozone is rapidly formed by 4.10.

Leighton[6] has concluded that four types of organic radicals, alkyl, formyl, acyl, and alkoxyl, may each be produced at rates of the order of 1 to 10 pphm hr$^{-1}$ while photochemical smog is forming. He also suggests that hydrogen atoms are produced at about this same rate and hydroxyl radicals at a rate probably below 1 pphm hr.$^{-1}$

Free radicals are formed in smog by reactions other than 4.4. Various aldehydes and ketones are present in smog as a result of combustion processes such as the operation of automobiles. Many of these absorb solar radiation, decomposing to form free radicals.

The concentrations of "oxidant" (mainly ozone) in the Los Angeles atmosphere were measured almost continuously for several years. A typical curve of oxidant concentration vs. time of day is shown in Figure 4-3. Such curves usually follow a characteristic pattern with low concentrations of oxidant at night, increasing to a maximum around noon, and almost disappearing again at sunset. Concentrations at night seldom exceed 5 pphm, while maximum concentrations during conditions of smog often exceed 50 pphm. Presumably the low concentrations of oxidant at night reflect the lack of photochemical reactions involving

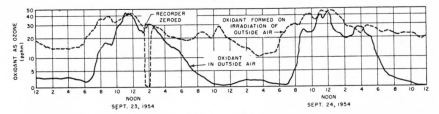

Figure 4-3. Oxidant formed by constant irradiation of outside air—September 23–24, 1954.

sunlight. If night air is irradiated with "artificial sunlight" photochemical smog, typified by the presence of ozone, should be produced. That this is actually the case is shown by the upper curve in Figure 4-3. Extensive investigation of this effect using light of various wavelengths and chemical analyses of both and night and day air lead to the conclusion that ozone is formed at least indirectly by the photochemical decomposition of nitrogen dioxide, aided by a rapid conversion of nitric oxide to nitrogen dioxide.[7]

A compound or type of compound of considerable interest from the standpoint of the mechanism of smog formation was discovered by Stephens and his associates[8] using long-path infrared spectroscopy as an analytical tool. This substance, called at first "compound-X" and later PAN may be peroxyacetyl nitrate,[9] having the structure

$$H_3CCOONO_2 \overset{O}{\overset{\|}{\phantom{CC}}}$$

A secondary photochemical reaction in smog which may play an important role in the plant damage produced by smog is that of ozone with olefins:

$$O_3 + RC\!\!=\!\!CR' \rightarrow \text{products} \tag{4.11}$$

Actually, this is a series of reactions involving various olefins. The reaction rates and the products formed have been studied by numerous investigators.[10,11,12,13] A complex over-all process is involved, but the initial process appears to be kinetically first order with respect to olefin and to ozone. Initial rate constants at about 30°C for several of these reactions, taken from the results of Schadt and Cadle,[10] are shown in Table 4-1. The reactions are sufficiently rapid that they must contribute to an appreciable extent to photochemical smog. For example, for the reaction of ozone with 1-hexene, if the reactant concentrations are 0.2 ppm, the calculated half-life is 380 minutes; if the reactant concentrations are 1 ppm,

TABLE 4-1. RATE CONSTANTS FOR OZONE-OLEFIN REACTIONS[10]

| Olefin | Rate constant $(1 \text{ mole}^{-1} \text{ sec}^{-1}) \times 10^{-3}$ |
|---|---|
| Ethylene | 1.8 |
| Propylene | 3.7 |
| 1-Pentene | 3.2 |
| 1-Hexene | 6.1 |
| Cyclohexene | 35.4 |
| 1-Heptene | 4.9 |
| 1-Octene | 4.9 |
| 1-Decene | 6.6 |

the calculated half-life is 66 minutes. These concentrations are in the range found in Los Angeles smog.

The reaction products vary considerably with the nature of the olefin, as would be expected. When the concentrations are relatively high, of the order of 1 percent, the reaction with many of the olefins produces an aerosol which persists even after dilution to concentrations characteristic of smog. When gasoline vapor was allowed to react with ozone at concentrations comparable to those found in smog, no aerosol was produced.[14] However, when concentrations were increased by only an order of magnitude, aerosols were formed and it remains possible that some olefins react with ozone in smog in this way. Some light is thrown on this question by the fact that the irradiation of nitric oxide-olefin mixtures at concentrations of 1 ppm of the nitric oxide and 3 ppm of the olefin produced no aerosol when the olefin was ethylene, isobutene, or *trans*-2-butene, but produced a relatively high-concentration aerosol when the olefin was cyclohexene.[15,16] Since such irradiation produces ozone, one can conclude that the reaction of ozone with the first three olefins listed does not yield particulate matter, and the reaction of ozone with cyclohexene at low concentrations may do so.

Numerous gaseous products of these reactions have been identified. Eastman and Silverstein,[13] studying the reaction of 1-hexene and ozone, found the gaseous product to be mainly formaldehyde. Other workers studying these reactions found various aldehydes, ketones, organic acids, carbon dioxide, carbon monoxide, and water among the reaction products. Peracids, peroxides, hydroperoxides, and ozonides have also been reported.[17,18]

The reaction mechanism may be the following, which was proposed for liquid-phase reactions of ozone and olefins by Criegee:[19]

$$R_1 \diagdown \atop R_2 \diagup C=C \diagup^{R_3} \diagdown_{R_4} \; + \; O_3 \; \rightarrow \; R_1 \diagdown \atop R_2 \diagup C \underset{\underset{O-O^+}{|}}{-} C \diagup^{R_3} \diagdown_{R_4}$$

$$\underset{O^-}{\overset{|}{\phantom{.}}}$$

$$\rightarrow \; R_1 \diagdown \atop R_2 \diagup C=O \; + \; R_3 \diagdown \atop R_4 \diagup C^+OO^- \qquad (4.12)$$

The zwitterion (the last product in 4.12) may combine with an aldehyde or ketone to form an ozonide, it may dimerize, or it may decompose in various ways.

Leighton has postulated a free-radical chain mechanism to account for much of what is known about the photochemistry of smog.[6] The chain-initiating step is the formation of atomic oxygen which in turn reacts with hydrocarbons to form organic free radicals. Ozone is formed as postulated above by reaction of molecular oxygen with peroxy free radicals. According to this mechanism HOO and HO are among the chain-carrying radicals, and the following reactions are considered to be chain-breaking:

$$2\,HOO \rightarrow H_2O_2 + O_2 \qquad (4.13)$$

$$2\,HO \rightarrow H_2 + O_2 \qquad (4.14)$$

From the standpoint of particle production in photochemical smog, the discovery that the addition of sulfur dioxide to mixtures of air, hydrocarbons, NO and $NO_2$ greatly increases the amount of particulate material produced upon irradiation is of considerable interest. Shuck, Ford, and Stephens[20] reported that adding sulfur dioxide to mixtures of automobile exhaust and air greatly increased the rate of aerosol formation during irradiation. Later the same effect was observed when $NO\text{-}NO_2$-hydrocarbon-air mixtures were irradiated with and without added sulfur dioxide, and it was further noted that the rate of sulfur dioxide disappearance was much greater than could be accounted for by the photochemical oxidation of sulfur dioxide alone.[15, 16]

These results suggest that sulfur dioxide is chemically involved in the $NO\text{-}NO_2$-hydrocarbon-$O_2$ reactions. The particle sizes resulting from the irradiation of such mixtures, as determined by a particle sizer based on light scattering, were almost entirely below one micron diameter and the size distribution was quite large (Figure 4-4).

The chemical composition of this aerosol was studied by Endow, Doyle, and Jones.[21] The apparatus used is shown schematically in Figure 4-5. Most of the experiments involved irradiating a mixture of air of 50 percent

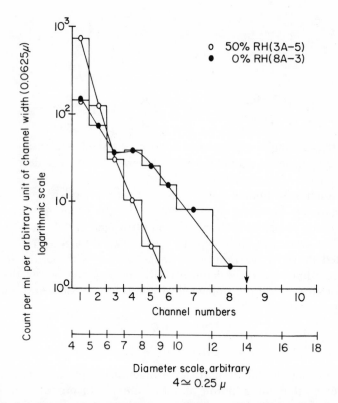

Figure 4-4. Contrasts in counts per milliliter and particle size distribution between aerosols formed by photolysis of 3 ppm 2-methylbutene-2, 1 ppm nitric oxide, and 0.5 ppm sulfur dioxide in dry and in humid air. (*Courtesy of International Journal of Air Pollution.*[15])

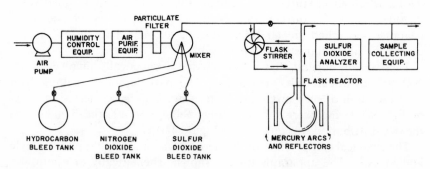

Figure 4-5. Schematic diagram of 52-liter flow reactor system.[21] (*Courtesy of the Air Pollution Control Association*)

relative humidity, 3ppm olefin (propylene, ethylene, isobutylene, or 2-methyl-2-butene), 1 ppm $NO_2$, and 0.5 ppm $SO_2$. An 18-minute residence time was used for all experiments except those involving ethylene, for which the residence time was doubled. Some experiments were also undertaken in a large chamber using 2 ppm of propylene and residence times from 42 to 360 minutes.

Radiation was provided by four medium-pressure mercury arc lamps in borosilicate glass envelopes mounted symmetrically around the reactor flask. According to the authors the light intensity of near ultraviolet radiation was comparable to that of noonday summer sun.

Samples were collected using polystyrene fiber filters, membrane filters, or an electrostatic precipitator. Infrared reflection spectra of the collected aerosols were determined.

The results indicated that aqueous sulfuric acid was the major component. The total carbon content of the aerosol droplets produced from propylene was found by microchemical analysis to be less than 1 percent. In view of these results, and considering the fact that sulfuric acid is not a major constituent of photochemical smog, it seems unlikely that sulfur dioxide contributes to a major extent to the particulate content of such smog.

The particulate composition of photochemical smog (especially of Los Angeles smog) has been the subject of numerous publications. A detailed chemical and spectroscopic analysis[2] was made of particulate matter collected from a Los Angeles smog with a large Westinghouse electrostatic precipitator, which was believed to collect about 90 percent of the particulate material in the air. A typical analysis of such material is shown in Table 4-2. About 60 percent of the collected material consisted of minerals and other inorganic substances. Some of these compounds were undoubtedly of natural origin while others, such as compounds of lead, zinc, and copper, were almost certainly industrial and automobile emissions.

Most of the remaining 40 percent of the material was a complex mixture of organic compounds, carbon, and pollen. Much of the organic material had a tarry consistency and contained among other compounds aldehydes, ketones, and organic acids.

Studies have been made of the organic fraction of photochemical smog by collecting the particles on a filter operating for a relatively long period of time at a high sampling velocity (a "high-volume sampler") followed by extraction of the filter and collected material with an organic solvent such as hexane. The infrared spectrum of the extracted material bore at least a superficial resemblance to the spectrum of the particulate material produced by the reaction of ozone with certain olefins.

Minerals and other inorganic substances about 60 per cent of total

- Water-soluble fraction, about 15 per cent of total
- Water-insoluble fraction, about 45 per cent of total

Elements identified by emission spectrograph:

| | |
|---|---|
| Large amount (10 per cent plus) | Silicon<br>Aluminum<br>Iron |
| Small amount (1 to 9 per cent) | Titanium<br>Calcium |
| 1 per cent | Magnesium<br>Barium<br>Sodium<br>Potassium |
| Very small amount (0.1 to 0.9 per cent) | Lead<br>Zinc |
| 0.1 per cent | Vanadium<br>Manganese<br>Nickel |
| Trace (0.01 to 0.1 per cent) | Tin<br>Copper<br>Zirconium<br>Strontium |
| 0.001 to 0.01 per cent | Boron<br>Chromium |
| 0.001 per cent | Bismuth<br>Cobalt |

Substances identified by Chemical means:

| | PER CENT |
|---|---|
| SiO$_2$ | 14.3 |
| Iron and Aluminum | 7.8 |
| Calcium (As Ca) | 5.2 |
| Fluoride (as F) | 0.05 |
| Sulfate (as H$_2$SO$_4$) | 2.5 |
| Ammonia | 0.70 |
| Nitrate (as HNO$_3$) | 4.8 |
| Chloride (as NaCl) | 0.26 |
| Nitrite | 0.00 |
| Sulfide | 0.00 |
| Sodium (as NaCl) | 4.6 |

Organic compounds soluble in organic solvents, about 10 per cent

- Mainly hydrocarbons
- Also small amounts of organic acids (0.27 per cent), and aldehydes
- Peroxides, 0.04 per cent, (as H$_2$O$_2$)

Fibers, pollen, carbon and highly polymerized organic material, about 15 per cent

Water and volatile organic substances (by difference), about 15 per cent

The nature of the particulate material in Los Angeles smog has been investigated extensively by optical and electron microscopy.[22,23,24] The particles were collected from the atmosphere using methods that permitted examination of the individual particles. For part of the work a plastic impactor was found to be very convenient.[21]

A simple and effective device for qualitatively collecting charged particles was also used. Glass microscope slides were taped to metal plates which were slightly larger than the glass slides. Pairs of such plates were placed on a wooden rack so that the slides faced each other and were about 2 mm apart. Three 300-volt dry cells connected in series were used to produce a field of about 2000 v/cm between the two plates. When an aerosol such as smog was slowly passed through the gap between the plates, charged particles were carried to the surface of one or the other of the slides where they tended to be held on contact. One pair of slides was always left uncharged for comparison. Movement of air between the slides resulted only from the natural breeze, and the apparatus was exposed to the smog for several hours in order to obtain a sample. The slides were then detached and attempts made to identify the particles. This method differs from electrostatic precipitation mainly in that the latter places a charge on the particles.

Sedimentation in a simple, shellacked wooden box (15 by 15 by 122 cm) was used to collect particles from some samples of air, and a thermal precipitator was used where quantitative collection of all particles in the size range 0.1 to 1.0 micron diameter was desired.

Studies of the collected material using optical microscopy involved the technique of chemical micrurgy[25,26,27] combined with the more conventional methods of chemical microscopy.[28]

Micrurgy refers to the use of micro-tools handled by micro-manipulators while observing the working area with a microscope. Such techniques were developed by biologists for studying single cells. The tools include needles, knives, pipettes, and even electrodes. Special manipulators have also been developed for making the tools. Chemical micrurgy thus refers to the application of micrurgic techniques to the study of chemical systems, and particularly to chemical analysis. The following adaptation of this technique has been used by the author. The particles collected on a microscope slide are covered with a thin coating of mineral oil which is spread over the slide with a thin glass rod. The slide is placed oiled-side down on a holder on the microscope stage. Droplets of reagent are deposited through the oil on the individual particles with micropipettes controlled with a micromanipulator. The mineral oil prevents evaporation of the reagent droplets. Pipette tips of two to five microns in diameter are especially convenient. Numerous micromanipulators are commercially available, and those with a large working distance are particularly suitable.

The micrugic techniques were used in a number of ways in addition to depositing reagents on particles and observing precipitates formed or color changes produced. For example, individual particles were washed by depositing and withdrawing the washing liquid using a micropipette.

Much of the material collected from photochemical smog on slides by impaction was a dark brown, gummy, water-insoluble organic material, which occasionally liberated iodine from acidulated aqueous solutions of potassium iodide and formed a blue color with diphenyl benzidine reagent. These results suggest the presence of oxidizing substances such as organic peroxides or ozonides. The organic portion of this material seemed to consist mainly of hydrocarbons.

The material collected by impaction was often very acidic; that collected from relatively clear air was never acidic, that collected from smog was often, but not always, acidic, and on at least one occasion collected fog droplets were acidic. The fact that the material collected from smog was not always acidic conforms with other observations that photochemical smog does not have a constant composition, often varying from hour to hour.

Considerable crystalline material was found on the impactor slides. Some of the crystals had been in the air in the form observed while others had crystallized from droplets of water which were often collected on the slides. Much of the crystalline material was insoluble in water and probably consisted of minerals of natural origin. Most of the material crystallizing from the water droplets was weakly anisotropic and sublimed or decomposed on heating. Tests using the chemical micrurgic technique indicated that the crystals were ammonium sulfate.

Particles of hexagonal form were occasionally observed on impactor slides and on slides from the charged particle collector. These particles had a very low refractive index, slightly greater than 1.43, were very stable when heated, and may have been schairerite ($Na_2SO_4 \cdot Na(F,Cl)$) or pachnolite ($NaF \cdot CoF_2 \cdot AlF_2 \cdot H_2O$). Traces of fluorides were also found in samples of solutions condensed from photochemical smog in liquid-nitrogen traps and in the bulk particulate material mentioned above (Table 4-2).

A very common type of material consisted of droplets which evaporated very slowly. They were collected by impaction from the Los Angeles atmosphere when the relative humidity was as low as 22 percent. Many of these droplets were found to evaporate slowly over a period of several days, and a rather tough film formed over the surface, becoming quite wrinkled as the droplet evaporated. Similar droplets were collected from automobile exhaust gases and from the smoke from burning excelsior. They are probably quite generally produced by the combustion of organic material. Some of these droplets seemed to be largely organic while others were aqueous.

Needle-like crystals identified as gypsum ($CaSO_4 \cdot 2\,H_2O$) were found in smog and in the condensate from gasoline engine exhaust. The finding of similar crystals and of calcium sulfate in smog has frequently been reported in the literature.[29]

The size distributions and concentrations of particles in photochemical smog have been determined by light-scattering particle counters and by collecting the particles with a thermal precipitator followed by microscopic sizing. At least in the size range of 0.2 to 10 microns the size distribution can be represented roughly by the distribution law

$$f(d) = ad^{-b} \qquad\qquad (4.15)$$

where $a$ and $b$ are constants and the value of $b$ is usually about 4.

Numerous determinations have been made of the concentrations of particles having diameters of 0.2 micron or more. Particle concentrations in dense photochemical smog were usually in the range 3000 to 10,000 particles per $cm^3$.

## Smog in coal-burning communities

As suggested earlier in this chapter, smog in coal-burning communities differs in many respects from photochemical smog. The organic gaseous contaminants include the multitude of compounds produced by the partial combustion of coal and thus the atmospheres of such cities contain a multitude of aromatic, aliphatic, and heterocyclic compounds. The main incentive for determining the concentrations of such compounds has been in connection with their possible carcinogenic effects.

Inorganic gaseous constituents are often present at considerably higher concentrations than in photochemical smog. They include sulfur dioxide, hydrogen sulfide, nitric oxide, nitrogen dioxide, hydrogen fluoride, carbon monoxide, and ammonia. Ozone concentrations, on the other hand, may be very low as compared with photochemical smog, or zero. Ozone may be produced to some extent in such smog, at least when the sunlight is not highly attenuated, by much the same photochemical reactions that produce it in photochemical smog. There are at least two reasons why this may not be detected. One is that ozone may be removed as rapidly as it is produced by some of the constituents of a smog, such as hydrogen sulfide. Another reason is that ozone concentrations are very difficult to measure in the presence of comparable concentrations of many reducing substances such as hydrogen sulfide and sulfur dioxide. This is particularly true for those methods of ozone analysis which involve drawing air samples through aqueous reagents.

Evidence that one or both of these effects occurs is furnished by the fact that relatively high concentrations of ozone (about 25 pphm) have been detected in small eastern United States towns such as Edgewood, Md. at times when much lower concentrations were measured in nearby large cities. Thus, as mentioned earlier, smog in coal-burning communities may often in part be photochemical. Also, there is a trend away from coal as a fuel, and as air pollution legislation becomes more widespread and effective, there will be a trend toward more complete combustion of the coal that is used. One result of this may be that as coal-produced smog diminishes, photochemical smog will increase, or at least become more apparent unless simultaneous measures are taken to reduce it.

The particles in smog of the coal-economy type probably vary in nature from city to city and from time to time considerably more than do those in photochemical smog. One reason is that in most of the coal-burning cities various dusts, smokes, and fumes that have little or nothing to do with coal may also be emitted into the atmoshpere from a variety of sources. Many, but by no means all, of these sources are industrial. Backyard incineration and the burning at city dumps are often important contributors to city smog.

Smog in such cities, as the term is generally used today, is only occasionally a combination of smoke and fog, although such a combination is responsible for the most intense smog manifestations. The author observed such a combination a number of years ago in Cleveland, Ohio. About the middle of one afternoon the smog became so intense that day was almost literally turned into night, street lights came on automatically, and many shop owners turned on their neon signs. However, most so-called smog other than the photochemical variety is just dirt in the air, usually accumulating beneath an atmospheric inversion.

Most of the studies of particulate material in the air of highly industrial cities have been concerned with total particle "loadings," that is, mass concentrations. A very extensive study of the concentrations of atmospheric matter in selected urban and nonurban locations has been undertaken as the "National Air Sampling Network" of the United States Public Health Service.[30,31,32] The network was established in 1953 and consists of about 185 urban and 51 nonurban sampling stations in all fifty states, Puerto Rico, and the District of Columbia. The urban stations are in central business or commercial locations, and the nonurban stations are as remote as possible. The latter are on ocean and lake shores, or in desert, forest, mountain, and farmland areas.[32] The locations and sampling times obviously involve a great assortment of smoggy and non-smoggy conditions.

Particulate matter is collected by filtering 70,000 to 80,000 cubic feet of air over a 24-hour period through glass fiber filters. All the samples are analyzed for weight concentrations of particles, benzene-soluble organic matter, and gross beta radioactivity. Some samples are also analyzed for $NO_3^-$, $SO_4^-$, Be, Mn, Pb, Sn, Fe, Cu, Ti, V, Zn, Cr, Ni, Mo, Bi, Cd, and Sb.

A summary of total suspended particulate material in urban areas by geographical region is shown in Table 4-3. It is enlightening to compare

TABLE 4-3. SUSPENDED PARTICULATE MATTER—URBAN STATIONS—REGION AND GRAND TOTALS

| Station | Years | | No. of Stamp. | Micrograms per Cubic Meter | | | | Std. Geo. Dev. |
|---|---|---|---|---|---|---|---|---|
| | | | | Min. | Max. | Arith. Avg. | Geo. Mean | |
| New England Total | 57 | 58 | 595 | 20 | 326 | 100 | 86 | 1.739 |
| Mid Atlantic Total | 57 | 58 | 714 | 23 | 607 | 146 | 125 | 1.772 |
| Mid East Total | 57 | 58 | 516 | 27 | 745 | 123 | 103 | 1.698 |
| South East Total | 57 | 58 | 578 | 15 | 640 | 125 | 104 | 1.689 |
| Mid West Total | 57 | 58 | 967 | 11 | 978 | 158 | 139 | 1.629 |
| Great Plains Total | 57 | 58 | 503 | 22 | 722 | 136 | 120 | 1.622 |
| Gulf South Total | 57 | 58 | 516 | 14 | 630 | 118 | 100 | 1.687 |
| Rocky Mountain Total | 57 | 58 | 247 | 15 | 466 | 99 | 84 | 1.809 |
| Pacific Coast Total | 57 | 58 | 704 | 11 | 639 | 136 | 109 | 2.026 |
| Grand Total | 57 | 58 | 5340 | 11 | 978 | 131 | 111 | 1.772 |

the Pacific Coast data with the Mid West and Mid Atlantic data, since all three regions are noted for smog, and that on the Pacific Coast is primarily photochemical. The particulate concentrations in the Pacific Coast cities are on the average the lowest of the three; this fact conforms with observations that the number concentrations of large particles, which may make an overwhelming contribution to mass concentrations, are relatively much lower in photochemical smog than in that of the coal-burning communities.

Table 4-4 shows data for total particulate matter, benzene-soluble organic matter, sulfate, and nitrate taken from the data of ref. 32 for eight

TABLE 4-4. PARTICULATE CONCENTRATIONS FOR SELECTED CITIES FOR 1958. *Values are arithmetic means.*

| Station location | A<br>Suspended<br>Particulate<br>($\mu$g/m$^3$) | B<br>Benzene Soluble<br>Organic Matter<br>($\mu$g/m$^3$) | % of A | C<br>Sulfate<br>($\mu$g/m$^3$) | % of A | D<br>Nitrate<br>($\mu$g/m$^3$) | % of A |
|---|---|---|---|---|---|---|---|
| Los Angeles | 213 | 30.4 | 21.5 | 14.8 | 7.0 | 8.1 | 3.8 |
| San Francisco | 80 | 10.6 | 13.3 | 6.2 | 7.7 | 2.6 | 3.3 |
| San Diego | 93 | 12.2 | 13.1 | 7.7 | 6.3 | 4.2 | 4.5 |
| Denver | 110 | 11.0 | 10 | 6.1 | 5.5 | 2.3 | 2.1 |
| New York | 164 | 14.3 | 8.7 | 23.0 | 14.0 | 2.2 | 1.3 |
| Pittsburgh | 167 | 13.0 | 7.8 | 15.1 | 9,0 | 2.6 | 1.6 |
| Cincinnati | 143 | 13.7 | 9.6 | 12.2 | 8.5 | 2.6 | 1.8 |
| Louisville | 228 | 18.0 | 7.9 | 20.6 | 9.1 | 4.9 | 2.1 |

cities. The first four cities listed were selected as having chiefly photo-chemical smog. Comparable values for nonurban locations are given in Table 4-5.

The percentage of benzene-soluble organic matter and of nitrate was much higher and the percentage of sulfate lower for the first four cities than for the second four. These results agree very well with our concepts of the origin of photochemical smog. Of course, this comparison is very

TABLE 4-5. PARTICULATE CONCENTRATIONS FOR NINE NONURBAN STATIONS FOR 1958. VALUES ARE ARITHMETIC MEANS.

| Station Location | A<br>Suspended<br>Particulate<br>$\mu$g/m$^3$ | B<br>Benzene Soluble<br>Organic Matter<br>$\mu$g/m$^3$ | % of A | C<br>Sulfate<br>$\mu$g/m$^3$ | % of A | D<br>Nitrate<br>$\mu$g/m$^3$ | % of A |
|---|---|---|---|---|---|---|---|
| Acadia Natnl<br>Park, Me. | 27 | 2.5 | 9.3 | 5.6 | 21 | 0.9 | 3.3 |
| Baldwin Co.,<br>Ala. | 27 | 2.7 | 10 | 3.5 | 12.9 | 0.9 | 3.3 |
| Bryce Canyon<br>Park | 83 | 2.2 | 2.7 | 1.9 | 2.3 | 0.4 | 0.48 |
| Butte Co., Idaho | 23 | 1.4 | 6.1 | 2.2 | 9.6 | 0.6 | 2.6 |
| Cook Co., Minn. | 44 | 2.4 | 5.5 | 4.0 | 9.1 | 0.5 | 1.1 |
| Florida Keys | 36 | 2.0 | 5.6 | 4.7 | 13.1 | 1.2 | 3.3 |
| Huron Co.,<br>Mich. | 44 | 1.6 | 3.6 | 6.5 | 14.8 | 1.5 | 3.4 |
| Shannon Co.,<br>Mo. | 37 | 2.0 | 5.4 | 6.5 | 17.5 | 1.8 | 4.8 |
| Wark Co., N.D. | 28 | 1.9 | 6.8 | 3.2 | 11.4 | 0.9 | 3.2 |

crude but it suggests a type of statistical analysis that might be quite informative.

The main purpose of the network is to determine trends in pollution levels in a given community rather than to determine differences between communities.[32] Preliminary statistical evaluations of some of the early data have been reported by Zimmer *et al.*[31]

Very little information is available concerning the size distributions in smogs other than photochemical smog. Most of the information available was determined for small, isolated portions of the size distribution, limited by the method of particle collection. It is well known that the size distribution is very large. Particles of submicron size have been collected with thermal precipitators and examined with electron microscopes. Large particles have been routinely collected by allowing them to settle onto plates; the collected material was subsequently weighed, studied with a low-power microscope, or chemically analyzed. Thus perhaps the best way of establishing the probable size distribution of such smogs is to consider the size distribution of some of its major components.

When smog is actually a mixture of smoke and fog, dirty fog droplets are probably the major constituent. Small particles may act as condensation nuclei for the fog droplets or agglomerate with them due to Brownian diffusion and coulombic attraction. This does not imply that no small particles (for instance of submicron size) are present, since they are continually being added to the smog by various combustion processes; but the fog droplets largely dominate the smog manifestations.

Measuring the size-distribution of fog droplets is a rather formidable undertaking. This is because the distribution is large and the droplets, of course, are volatile. A number of methods have been developed for making such measurements. A simple and fairly effective method for droplets down to a few microns in diameter is to impact the fog on a slide evenly coated with soot or magnesium oxide. The holes produced by the droplets are measured and a slight correction is applied to yield the desired droplet distribution. Impaction methods, as explained in Chapter II, have the disadvantage that collection efficiency is a function of particle size and discriminate against the smaller droplets. McCullough and Perkins[33] developed a photomicrographic method for determining cloud droplet size from an aircraft. A rotating mirror or prism keeps the images stationary on the film. Light-scattering methods have also been used. For example, the determination of mean fog droplet sizes by Kohler using coronae was mentioned in Chapter 2.

Results obtained by a number of workers indicates that the median diameter of fog droplets in most fogs varies from about 4 to 25 microns and that the distribution is highly skewed, roughly conforming to a log normal distribution. Individual droplets as small as about 1 micron and as large as about 130 microns have been measured. It is entirely possible that at least part of the apparent skewness of the distributions results from overlooking the smaller particles in the fog.

Most measurements in coal-burning communities have been made during the absence of fog and thus of smog in the original sense. The particles in such contaminated air are in general much smaller than those when fog is present.

Nader *et al*,[34] while studying light-scatter instrumentation for the measurement of atmospheric particles, used a "particle size analyzer" on several occasions. This analyzer consisted of a miniaturized light scatter photometer and pulse height analyzer developed for field measurements for the Robert A. Taft Sanitary Engineering center of the U.S. Public Health Service. The sampling station was located in an industrial environment near the downtown area of Cincinnati. The results indicated a predominance in the number of particles below 2 microns diameter, and a peak in the distribution "somewhere below 0.3 micron." These authors conclude that in view of the fact that the atmospheric particle content is a composite of particles from different sources more or less in equilibrium, it is likely that this distribution is representative until a high-output source drastically changes its contribution.

Surprisingly little is known about the size distribution of coal smoke as it comes from a stack or chimney. The "ultimate" particles in the smoke extend over the size range 0.01 to 1 micron. However, coal smoke has a strong tendency to agglomerate, forming long chains and flakes of the ultimate particles. Thus the collection of soot, either from the open atmosphere or from a stack, followed by optical or electron microscope examination, is likely to lead to an erroneous opinion of the size distribution of the smoke particles in the atmosphere. As every dweller in a coal-burning community knows, flakes of soot several millimeters in diameter are all too common.

Even when the coal is burned very efficiently, as in the industrial combustion of pulverized coal, ash is formed and this may escape into the air as "fly ash." Even though coals have the same ash content, the type of fly ash formed may differ among various coals.[35] Fly ash from strip-mine coal may be more difficult to remove before it reaches the atmosphere than that from deep-mine coal. The method of feeding the coal to a furnace will also influence the ash characteristics, and pulverized coal feeders produce smaller ash particles than do stoke-coal feeders. Fly ash is usually in the size range 1 to 300 microns diameter. It is rather easily detected in a sample of particles collected from smog, since it contains numerous spheres which often have a metallic appearance. An interesting discussion of the identification of large particles in contaminated air by their morphology as observed in an optical microscope has been published by McCrone and Salzenstein.[36]

Smog in highly industrial communities often contains metallurgical dusts and fumes which may vary in particle size from 0.001 to 100 microns in diameter.[3]

There is considerable evidence that smog of the coal-burning type is decreasing in importance compared with photochemical smog. Possibly part of this increase is only apparent, resulting from the development of more sensitive methods for recognizing photochemical smog. However, much of it is real and is the result of a number of trends. One of these, of course, is the increased use of automobiles, which are largely responsible for the pollutants causing photochemical smog. Another is the trend in heating equipment away from coal and toward oil-fired and gas-fired furnaces (Table 4-6).[38] A third trend is the increasing control of effluents from various industrial operations.

TABLE 4-6. SALES OF HEATING EQUIPMENT[38] (UNITS)

| | 1950 | 1955 | 1959 |
|---|---|---|---|
| Central heating equipment | | | |
| Gas-fired | | | |
| Warm air furnaces | 599,800 | 874,400 | 1,053,400 |
| Conversion burners[a] | 345,300 | 209,100 | 156,200 |
| Boilers | 79,600 | 90,100 | 147,662 |
| Floor and wall furnaces | 613,000[a] | 554,800 | 546,800 |
| Total | 1,637,700 | 1,728,400 | 1,904,062 |
| Oil-fired | | | |
| Furnaces | 156,700 | 371,200 | 344,000 |
| Conversion burners | 608,000 | 241,000 | 152,900 |
| Boilers | 82,100 | 196,500 | 140,200 |
| Floor and wall furnaces | 73,400 | 59,700 | 40,000 |
| Total | 920,200 | 868,400 | 677,100 |
| Coal | | | |
| Stokers (Domestic and commercial class 1 and 2) | 19,600 | 13,300 | 12,200 |
| Direct heating equipment | | | |
| Gas-fired | 2,023,300 | 1,729,100 | 1,446,300 |
| Oil-fired | 1,320,600 | 634,500 | 473,900 |
| Coal-fired | 888,500 | 654,200 | 727,900 |

[a] Estimated.

An indication of the changes in the proportion of coal-burning to photochemical type smog is the increasing reporting of incidence of photochemical smog in coal-burning communities. Haagen-Smit and Middleton[39] have stated that typical manifestations of photochemical smog have been reported in cities in twenty states and the District of Columbia.

An interesting example of a photochemical smog incident in a city where ozone concentrations have usually been reported to be quite low occurred in Cincinnati in May, 1962.[40] Attention was focused on this incident by complaints of eye irritation, which is usually produced by moderately severe photochemical smog. An atmospheric pollutant monitoring station is operated jointly by the City of Cincinnati and the Robert A. Taft Sanitary Engineering Center. Turbidity measurements were being made during this time at the latter, and particulate material was being collected at the Gest Street Experimental Facility. The oxidant (ozone) recorder indicated peak five-minute average values of 0.17 ppm, 0.20 ppm, and 0.12 ppm on the 16th, 17th, and 18th of May. These values would not be particularly high for Los Angeles, which has had concentrations close to 1 ppm, but they are high for Cincinnati and for most parts of the eastern United States. The continuous records for the three days are shown in Figure 4-6 and as usual exhibit peaks during the daylight hours. Nitrogen dioxide concentrations were also very high on May 16 and 17, on each day reaching a peak at about eight o'clock in the morning.

The atmospheric turbidity level for May 17 was the third highest in two years. Similarly, the concentrations of particulate material determined for that day was the third highest recorded. Niemeyer[40] states that the pollution levels indicated by the gas-monitoring, turbidity, and particulate measurements for those days were extreme for that time of year; and that since domestic and industrial space heating is used less often as spring progresses, records of air pollutant concentrations usually indicate a seasonal decrease from winter to summer.

Apparently the excessive pollution levels were produced by the following conditions. (a) Winds were light, permitting contaminants to remain near the point of emission, especially at night when horizontal air movement near the surface was at a minimum and air stability was at a maximum. (b) During the early morning, additional pollution was emitted to the already contaminated air as the activity of the city's inhabitants increased to the usual daytime level. (c) After sunrise, solar radiation not only produced the usual photochemical reactions which result in photochemical smog, but also brought about a dilution of the contaminants. Niemeyer suggests that as the surface of the earth was heated, the air

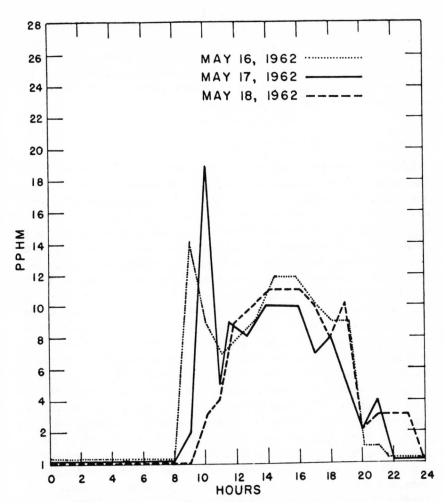

Figure 4-6. Hourly concentrations of total oxidant, Cincinnati continuous monitoring station.[40] (*Courtesy of the Air Pollution Control Association*)

immediately above became heated and turbulent, producing mixing. Ultimately this mixing broke the radiation inversions which formed each night, producing a sudden increase in mixing volume and accounting for the dramatic decrease in pollution shown on the oxidant records for the 16th and 17th.

Replacing one kind of smog by another is hardly a major accomplishment. However, the art of controlling smoke-produced smog is much more advanced than that for controlling photochemical smog. Hopefully, measures currently being developed for controlling automobile exhausts and alleviating photochemical smog will be effective. A trend away from coal-burning smog to photochemical smog would probably change the size distribution in the smoggy air, decreasing the mass-median diameter and producing a less sooty, although irritating, atmosphere.

### Undesirable effects of smog particles

*Visibility decrease.* Perhaps the most obvious manifestation of all types of smog is the decrease in visibility which smog produces. The visibility decrease is caused almost exclusively by small particles and, as will be seen, particle size has a major effect on this aspect of smog.

"Everyone" knows what visibility is, but actually it is rather difficult to define in quantitative terms. For the purpose of weather observing in the United States it is conventional to define it as the greatest distance in a given direction in which it is just possible to identify an object. In the daytime the object should be prominant, dark, and observed against the sky near the horizon. At night the object should be an unfocused moderately intense light source. Visibilities can be reported for different directions or resolved into a single value of "prevailing visibility." This term as used by the U.S. Weather Bureau is defined as "the greatest visibility which is attained or surpassed around at least half of the horizon circle, but are not necessarily in continuous sectors."[41,42]

Visibility reduction caused by haze and smog results largely from light scattering by a large number of particles. Therefore, visibility can vary greatly with direction and time of day as a result of variations in the intensity of scattered light with illumination angle.

A more precisely defined number relating to visibility, although not necessarily a more useful one, is the visual range. It can be defined as the distance at which the contrast between a black object and the adjacent sky becomes equal to $\epsilon$, which is the least fractional difference in intensity the eye can detect. This definition is much the same as that for daytime visibility defined above, except that the object observed must be black, not merely dark. Visual range is often determined by means of instruments, employing an assumed or average value for $\epsilon$.

Airborne particles decrease visibility in at least two ways. One is by decreasing the light from an object that reaches an observer of that object. This decrease is caused largely by scattering of the light by the particles and to some extent by absorption of light by the particles. The other cause of visibility decrease is the scattering in the direction of the observer of sunlight or any other light which illuminates the particles. Visibility decrease is often not so much a matter of decreasing the light from an object as of decreasing the contrast between the object and its background as a result of increasing light intensity from the direction of the object and its background.

Consider a length $dx$ of the light path from the object to the observer. The intensity $I$ of the light from the object will change by an amount $dI$ in traversing the length $dx$. We can now write the equation

$$dI/dx = -kI + a \qquad (4.16)$$

where $k$ is the attenuation coefficient at the point $x$ and $a$ is the scattering coefficient at the same point.[43] This equation can be integrated to yield

$$I = C \exp \int -k\,dx + (\exp \int -k\,dx) \int a(\exp \int k\,dx)dx \qquad (4.17)$$

where $C$ is an integration constant involving the optical characteristics of the object.

If the air is uniform between the object and the observer, $k$ is constant, and if the atmospheric illumination is uniform in this region and for some distance beyond the object, $a$ is also constant. Under these conditions equation 4.17 reduces to

$$I = C \exp(-kx) + a/k \qquad (4.18)$$

Equation 4.18 involves three unknown constants, $C$, $k$, and $a$, so any set of three independent values of $I$ and $x$ will permit evaluation of all three constants.

One way of acquiring such a set is to observe the apparent brightness of a black object silhouetted against the sky near the horizon.[43] Then

$$k = \frac{1}{s} \ln \frac{1}{1 - (I_s/I_\infty)} \qquad (4.19)$$

where $s$ is the distance from the object to the observer, $I_s$ is the intensity of light at the observer, from the direction of the object, and $I_\infty$ is the intensity of the light at the observer from an infinitely distant object in the same direction. $I_s$ and $I_\infty$ provide two of the three independent values of $I$. The third one is $I = 0$ at the object itself since the object is black. (Figure 4-7a).

If for some reason the sky near the horizon cannot be used, the arrangement of Figure 4-7b can be substituted. Equation 4.18 then becomes

$$\frac{I_s}{I_t} = \frac{1 - e^{-ks}}{1 - e^{-kt}} \qquad (4.20)$$

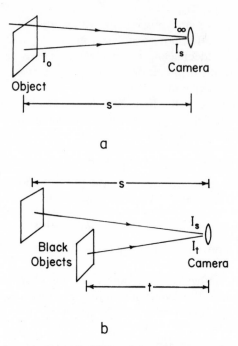

Figure 4-7. Arrangements for determining the attenuation coefficient.[43]

where $I_s$, $I_t$, $s$, and $t$ are defined as indicated by Figure 4-7b. Although this equation cannot be solved explicitly for $k$, a table can be constructed relating $k$ to $I_s/I_t$ for given values of $s$ and $t$.

Steffens and Rubin[43] used this arrangement in a valley in Los Angeles County (the Arroyo Seco Valley) where the sky near the horizon could not be used and where short observation paths were needed.

Attenuation coefficients determined by such methods can be used to calculate visual range. The contrast limen $\epsilon$ is given by the expression

$$\epsilon = \frac{I_\infty - I_v}{I_\infty} \tag{4.21}$$

where $v$ is the visual range and $I_v$ is $I_s$ for the distance $v$. Then

$$v = \frac{1}{k} \ln \frac{1}{\epsilon} \tag{4.22}$$

The contrast limen, sometimes called the psychophysical constant, is often taken as a defined constant, 0.02.* The corresponding value of $v$ is

*The contrast limen is sometimes defined as $(I_v - I_\infty)/I_\infty$, in which case the right side of 4.21 becomes $(1/k) \ln (1/-\epsilon)$ and the limen is negative for a blackbody.

then called the standard visibility, $v_2$, which can be calculated from equation 4.21:

$$v_2 = \frac{1}{k} \ln \frac{1}{0.02} = \frac{3.912}{k} \qquad (4.23)$$

The use of 0.05 instead of 0.02 for the contrast limen often yields calculated visual ranges that are in better agreement with visibilities reported by field workers. The calculated visual range, $v_5$, then equals $2.996/k$.

Note that $a$ of equation 4.18 has disappeared from the subsequent equations because the object observed is assumed to be a blackbody.

Smog is usually far from homogeneous. However, Steffens[44] has calculated that the light obscuring distant objects comes mostly from haze very close to the observer. This is because light from more distant parts of the haze is attenuated by the haze nearer the observer. His calculations show that if the visual range through a uniform fog is 100 yd, half of the obscuration is caused by the 18 yd of fog nearest the observer, and the fog beyond 60 yd would cause only 10 percent of the effect. The importance of airborne particulate material near the observer is probably one reason the above equations yield reasonably satisfactory results.

When the atmospheric aerosol is non-absorbing, as for fogs, clouds, and mists in clean air, $k$ is a scattering coefficient and can be estimated from the Mie equations. When there is no external light source, and secondary scattering of the initially scattered radiation from the direction of the object can be neglected, $a$ becomes zero. This situation occurs when a beam of light is passed through smog at night or through the tube of a transmissometer. In this case, equation 4.17 becomes

$$I = C \exp \int - d\,dx \qquad (4.24)$$

and equation 4.18 becomes

$$I = C \exp(-kx) \qquad (4.25)$$

Steffens has discussed in detail the question of the mass concentration of material $W$ corresponding to a given visual range. This question can be answered only if the identity of the material and the size distribution are precisely known. While the question can be answered quite accurately for a number of pure materials, the problem becomes quite difficult for the mixtures that comprise smog. For material of given radius,

$$W = \frac{4r \ln \epsilon}{3Kv} \qquad (4.26)$$

where $K$ is the ratio of the effective cross sectional area of the particle for scattering to the geometrical cross-sectional area (see Chapter 2, p. 56).

When the dispersed phase is water, the wave length is 5550 Å (close to the maximum sensitivity of the eye), and $v_5$ is 0.5 mile; $W$ is 2.96, 0.57, and 9.0 mg/cu meter for $d$ = 0.0728, 0.728, and 7.28 microns, respectively. Tables of such values for water and for iron are given by Steffens.[44] Note that there is a particle size corresponding to a minimum value of $W$, which thus corresponds to a maximum effectiveness of the dispersed material.

A number of instrumental methods have been developed for measuring the attenuation coefficient $k$. Steffens[45] used a photographic method to measure the intensity ratios for the experimental set-ups indicated by Figure 4-7. The optical density, $D$, of a photographic negative is given by the equation

$$D = g + \gamma \log (\text{exposure}) \qquad (4.27)$$

where $g$ and $\gamma$ are constants over a wide range of densities. The exposure can be considered to be $I \times f(t)$, where $f(t)$ reduces to $t$ if the reciprocity law for photographic materials applies. The desired ratios of intensities can be calculated from the equation

$$\frac{I_2}{I_1} = \log^{-1} \frac{D_2 - D_1}{\gamma} \qquad (4.28)$$

where $D_2$ and $D_1$ are the densities of the images and $\gamma$ is calculated from other measurements of density on the negative. Equation 4.28 combined with 4.20 or 4.19 permits the calculation of $k$ and of the visual range.

Marynowski and Littman[46] developed a continuous-recording visibility meter for air-pollution studies. A single black "target" was used which consisted of a large commercial gasholder which was conveniently painted black. Light from the shady side of this gas holder was focused on the cathode of a photocell. An integrating translucent dome which gathered light from much of the sky served as an artificial horizon. Light from this dome was focused on a second photocell, and the difference in reading between the two photocells was a function of the visibility. Since this instrument depended on natural illumination it could not be used at night. However, it had the great advantage of measuring continuously during the daylight hours. It was used at the Pasadena Field Laboratory of Stanford Research Institute, and the results could be compared with those obtained by continuously operating analytical devices, such as those measuring ozone, nitric oxide, nitrogen dioxide, and sulfur dioxide.

Various transmissometers have been developed for measuring the attenuation coefficient. One used in the author's laboratory at Stanford

Research Institute was based on that of Bradbury and Fryer.[47] A mechanically chopped light beam was reflected back and forth a number of times within a tube containing the air being studied and finally was focused on a photocell. The photocell output was amplified and recorded. Light was focused directly from the source onto the photocell for calibration.

Measured attenuation coefficients can be used to estimate particle size distributions in the atmosphere. The form of the particle size distribution must be assumed and the attenuation measured at two or more wave lengths. Consider the distribution of equation 4.15:

$$f(d) = ad^{-b} \qquad [4.15]$$

where the exponent $b$ is to be determined from the values for the attenuation coefficient. It is readily shown that

$$k = \pi a K \left(\frac{\lambda}{2\pi}\right)^{3-b} \qquad (4.29)$$

where $K$ can be calculated from the Mie equations. For light of two different wavelengths, $\lambda_1$ and $\lambda_2$,

$$b = 3 - \frac{\log(k_2/k_1)}{\log(\lambda_2/\lambda_1)} \qquad (4.30)$$

Steffens and Rubin used this method combined with the photographic technique to determine $b$ in equation 4.15 for Los Angeles smog. They determined attenuation coefficients at different wave lengths over the same path by photographing the black targets on panchromatic film through a series of filters such as Wratten A (No. 25), B (No. 58), and C5 (No. 47), which are red, green, and blue, respectively. The effective wave lengths are about 0.62, 0.54, and 0.45 micron. The arithmetic mean value of $b$ was 4.5, which agreed within the limits of experimental error with values obtained by the direct collection and measurement of the airborne particles.

Steffens and Rubin also calculated the contribution of particles of various sizes to the attenuation coefficient, assuming a size distribution of the form of 4.15, a value of $b$ of 4.5, and a value of the refractive index relative to air of 1.33, that for water. The results are shown in Figure 4-8. The diameter which divides the area under the curve into two equal parts is about 0.8 micron. The diameters which delimit 5 percent of the total area under the curve at each end are also marked. They are about 0.2 micron and 6 microns. While such a curve, which is the result of many approximations, should not be taken too seriously, it demonstrates the

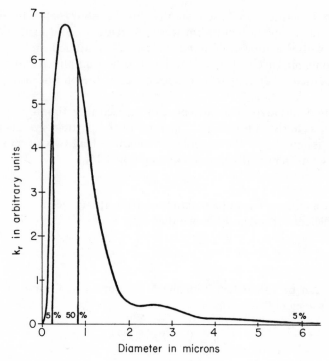

Figure 4-8. Contribution of particles of various sizes to the attenuation coefficient.

importance of particles less than 1 micron in diameter to interference with visibility.

Steffens and Rubin give the following example of a comparison of the results of the photographic technique with those obtained by collecting particles from Los Angeles smog with a thermal precipitator. The number of particles collected with the precipitator was estimated by counting with dark-field microscopy, and was found to correspond to $6 \times 10^8$ particles per cubic foot of air. The average particle size was estimated to be 0.2 to 0.3 micron diameter, and tests with oils of various refractive indices indicated that most of the particles had a refractive index close to 1.5.

The photographic technique yielded a value of 1.7 for the attenuation coefficient with the K2 filter, and 1.95 for the ratio of the coefficients through the C5 and A filters. The mean effective diameter was calculated from these data to be 0.3 micron, in agreement with the estimate for the collected particles.

A further test was made by calculating the attenuation coefficients that would result from different sizes at the particle concentration mentioned

TABLE 4-7. EFFECT OF PARTICLE SIZE ON THE CALCULATED
ATTENUATION COEFFICIENT[43]

| Assumed diameter ($\mu$) | 0.2 | 0.3 | 0.4 |
|---|---|---|---|
| Calculated k (miles$^{-1}$) | 0.4 | 3.4 | 10.0 |

above. The results are shown in Table 4-7. Again, the results agree
with the microscopic estimates. Steffens and Rubin emphasize that because of the great sensitivity of the attenuation coefficient to changes in
the assumed diameter, these comparisons merely demonstrate that the
results with the thermal precipitator are not inconsistent with those of the
photographic technique.

When the smog is actually composed of fog droplets condensed on
smoke particles, the visibility may drop to a few yards. In such cases
the visibility decrease is largely the result of the water droplets which of
course are much larger than the particles responsible for the decrease
caused by photochemical smog.

Much more thorough discussions of visibility through the atmosphere
than are appropriate here are given in references 41, 44, 48, and 49.

**Health.** That intense smog episodes can have drastic acute effects on
human health is very well known. One of the earliest such episodes which
was quite thoroughly studied occurred in the Meuse Valley of Belgium in
December, 1930 and lasted about a week. This valley contained a large
number of industries such as steel mills, coke ovens, and blast furnaces.
During this particular week, unusual meteorological conditions, including
a low atmospheric temperature inversion, largely prevented the escape of
atmospheric pollutants from the valley.

By the third day of the episode many persons were suffering from
respiratory distress, and by the end of the week sixty had died.[50] As is
usually true for the effects of intense smog, older persons, especially those
already suffering from heart or respiratory ailments, had the highest
mortality rate. The symptoms were typical of respiratory system irritation
and included coughing, dyspnea, sneezing, and pain.

A similar episode occurred at Donora, Pennsylvania, in October, 1948.
Judging from interviews with Donora residents the smog consisted of
both fog and industrial fumes, and as in the case of the Meuse Valley
disaster, a low temperature inversion combined with nearly still air to
permit the accumulation of contaminants. Donora is in a highly indus-
trialized valley containing a steel mill and many other industries. Again,
the symptoms of respiratory irritation were the main manifestations of ill
health. There were about nineteen deaths, all among persons with records
of heart or respiratory system disease.

The Donora episode was thoroughly investigated after the smog had cleared. Unfortunately, the Donora smog was not sampled during the episode itself.

Perhaps the most disastrous smog, judging from the number of deaths, was that of London from December 5 through December 9, 1952. This smog was a combination of smoke and fog, the accumulation of which resulted from unusually stable meteorological conditions. The extent of the disaster was not realized until after the event occurred and the statistics relating to death rate were examined. A total excess of about 3500 deaths over those normally occurring at that time of year was recorded. Most of the deaths were among the aged and those with respiratory or heart ailments. Goldsmith[50] states that measurements were made of the amount of suspended smoke and sulfur dioxide and that the highest values reported were 4.46 mg/cu meter and 1.34 ppm, respectively.

Lawther[51] made the following comments concerning this disaster, many of which are pertinent to all such episodes.

"The 1952 smog, like so many disasters, was much better documented than it was observed and anyone reading the reports cannot help but feel that he is contemplating the wreckage without having many clues to the cause. We know that the great majority of the dead were respiratory or cardiac cripples. Evidence from post-mortem material is virtually valueless because of its paucity. No well-defined clinical syndrome was recognized. Many people were found dead in bed. Routine air pollution studies consisted of measurements of smoke and sulfur dioxide and these pollutants reached high levels. The danger we face in interpreting these data is to forget that they might merely be of significance as indicators of atmospheric pollution in general. In ascribing the disaster to either of these substances (which are selected for routine measurement mainly because of the ease with which they are determined, their reliability as an indication of general pollution, and their obvious unpleasant character) we run the risk of following a monstrous red herring."

Goldsmith lists three other such episodes, one in Poza Rica, Mexico, in 1950; a second in Yokohama, Japan, in 1946; and a third in New Orleans, in 1958.

The acute effects listed above are unique only in their intensity. Such effects, particularly on the respiratory system, are very common in coal-burning communities. The effects of London smog have been studied intensively and attempts have been made to correlate the nature of the particles with such smog effects. Lawther[51] in 1955 reported the differences both with respect to physical makeup and physiological effects of two London smogs. One occurred on December 16, 1964 and consisted of large water droplets. Sulfuric acid was present to the extent of 1 mg/cu meter. It had little clinical effect. The other occurred on January 19, 1955, and within two hours of the onset the smoke content increased tenfold and the sulfur dioxide content threefold. This smog had a low relative humidity, and no water droplets were present. Unlike the smog of December 16, it produced definite clinical effects. Of course, such a comparison of just two episodes, while suggestive, really establishes nothing.

In a later paper Lawther[52] again emphasized the fact that large water droplets may not be an important part of such smog, at least so far as acute physiological effects are concerned. He suggested that sulfuric acid droplets may play an important role in causing acute effects, in which case the droplet size would be of limited importance since in the respiratory system inhaled air quickly becomes saturated with water vapor and hygroscopic sulfuric acid droplets grow very rapidly.

Based on the assumption that acidic particulate material is largely responsible for the acute irritating effects of smog in the British Isles, experiments have been undertaken for some time to determine whether the use of low pressure drop filter masks combined with the introduction of low concentrations of ammonia into the air to neutralize the acid would decrease the irritating effects of such smog. Such a cumbersome method of combating smog effects would be inconvenient and in general unnecessary for use by healthy individuals, but might save the lives of persons suffering from respiratory or cardiac disease. However, the results of these experiments do not seem to have been conclusive.

The concept that fog droplets are not important to the acute physiological effects of London smog but that sulfuric acid droplets are important seems to conflict somewhat with the results of Johnstone and Coughanowr[53] mentioned in Chapter 2 (p. 139 ff). Their results demonstrated that the presence of fog droplets greatly accelerates the oxidation of sulfur dioxide to sulfuric acid. Perhaps the answer is to be found in another statement by Lawther[52] to the effect that wet fog is rather rare in central London and usually forms when pollution is rather low.

The acute effects of photochemical smog are superficially, at least, very different from those of smog of the coal-burning variety. Respiratory system irritation is relatively unimportant and deaths from such smog have not been established. Eye irritation, which is unimportant in other types of smog, is a major effect of photochemical smog. It is often severe enough to be accompanied by lachrymation.

Although the acute effects of photochemical smog have been more of a nuisance than a serious health hazard, serious episodes from photochemical smog remain a distinct possibility. Such smog contains a number of hazardous chemicals although the one most frequently considered as a potential acute danger is ozone.

It is ironic that ozone was once thought to have beneficial effects and ozone generators were even installed in some public buildings such as Severence Hall in Cleveland. However, it is now known that ozone is very irritating to the respiratory system and is a highly toxic substance.

The toxicity of ozone to animals has been reviewed by Stokinger.[54] When mice or rats were exposed to ozone for four hours, the concentration which was lethal to 50 percent of the exposed group ($LC_{50}$) was about 6 ppm. Other studies have been made with dogs, cats, rabbits, guinea pigs, and chicks. Although the animals differed markedly in susceptibility, the results all demonstrated that ozone is highly toxic to such animals. Death generally resulted from pulmonary edema and hemorrhage.

Clamann and Bancroft[55] found that when healthy persons are subjected to air containing 2 ppm of ozone for one hour, there may be serious interference with function. It is suggested that such concentrations might produce acute illness in very sensitive persons. Their results suggested that man may be more sensitive to ozone than most other animals.

So-called oxidant concentrations in Los Angeles smog, which are calculated as ozone and as mentioned above consist largely of ozone, have on at least one occassion approached 1 ppm. The potential, if not the actual, hazards to humans from the ozone in photochemical smog has received considerable attention. For example, in Los Angeles a series of "alerts" has been established based on oxidant concentrations designed to limit those human activities, such as automobile use, which ultimately lead to ozone production.

Animals seem to quickly build up a tolerance to ozone when exposed to subinjurious concentrations.[54] This tolerance persisted for from 4 to 6 weeks in rats and as long as 100 days in mice. This finding suggests that humans living in an area subjected to photochemical smog may develop a similar tolerance.

Of course, our interest here is especially in the possible effect of airborne particulates on the toxicity of ozone. Mittler,[56] in looking for agents for reducing the toxic effects of ozone, found no therapeutic effect from aerosols of silicones. However, Stokinger[54,57] found a definite therapeutic effect of aerosols of certain other oils. Rodents were exposed to aerosols of mineral or motor oil and later to ozone or nitrogen dioxide. The results showed that the acute lethal effects of ozone on mice were materially reduced by the pre-treatment, and those of nitrogen dioxide completely eliminated several hours after exposure to the aerosols. No difference could be detected between aerosols of oils of low and high viscosity. However, when the oils were given simultaneously with ozone or nitrogen dioxide a synergistic instead of a protective effect was observed.

The lowest effective concentration of oil in the aerosol against ozone toxicity was about 8.5 ppm for six hours; the lowest effective concentration against nitrogen dioxide toxicity was 0.5 ppm (about 7 mg/cu meter). Stokinger found that the protective effect could still be measured after 9 days but not after 12 days.

The particle size range for greatest protection seemed to be within the limits 0.5 to 1.5 microns diameter. It may be more than a coincidence that this is in a size range of high retention by the lower respiratory system.

Stokinger concludes that certain fractions of petroleum (cycloparaffins) have an extraordinary capacity to reduce or abolish the acute irritant properties of at least two of the gases in photochemical smog. However, it seems that such oils in the smog itself if anything contribute to the irritant properties of these gases.

As mentioned above, eye irritation is the most noticeable acute physiological symptom of photochemical smog. The cause of the eye irritation has been particularly difficult to discover. Cadle and Magill,[58] in 1951, suggested that since no single contaminant identified in Los Angeles smog accounted for the eye irritation, it might be produced by the additive or

TABLE 4-8. FORMULAS FOR ARTIFICIAL SMOG[5]

| Old Formula | Concentrations | New Formula |
|---|---|---|
| Formic acid | 0.04 mg./cu.m. | . . . . . . . . . . . . . . . . |
| Formaldehyde | 0.22 or 0.5 mg./cu.m. | . . . . . . . . . . . . . . . . |
| Acrolein | 0.01 mg./cu.m. | . . . . . . . . . . . . . . . . |
| Nitric acid | 0.5 mg./cu.m., calculated as $HNO_3$ | Nitric acid |
| Sulfur dioxide | 0.5 ppm by vol. | Sulfur dioxide |
| Sulfur trioxide | 0.2 mg./cu.m. | Sulfur trioxide |
| Oil | 0.5 mg./cu.m. | Oil |
| Particulate matter (lamp black) | 1.0 mg./cu.m. | Particulate matter (lamp black) |
| Ozone | 0.35 ppm by vol. | Ozone |
| NaCl | 0.01 mg./cu.m. | NaCl |
| . . . . . . . . . . . . . . . . . . . . | 10 mg./cu.m. | Gasoline |

even the synergistic effect of a number of smog constituents. This theory was tested using a group of about 25 volunteers. Panel members were exposed, two at a time, to test atmospheres passing through a ten cubic meter chamber. Records of the sensations (eye, nose, and throat irritation) of the individual members were treated statistically. For statistical purposes, the atmospheres were compared in pairs and a rank test was used to determine whether differences between pairs of atmospheres were statistically significant.

The test atmospheres used are shown in Table 4-8. The formula for the artificial smog remained essentially unchanged for over a year of testing in order that the results obtained with it could be easily compared. However, eventually the composition was changed to the "new formula" based on increased knowledge of the composition of smog. In compounding the new formula the ozone and gasoline vapors were allowed to react before admission to the "smog chamber."

The following are some of the conclusions drawn from the results of these experiments:

(a) Atmospheres containing all the major constituents of Los Angeles smog (as they were known at that time) at the maximum concentrations at which they had been found produced definite eye irritation, although apparently not so severe as at times experienced in photochemical smog.

(b) Removal of no single constituent of the artificial smog eliminated all the irritating action.

(c) Removal of all the particulate constituents had little or no effect on the eye-irritating action.

(d) Removal of all the gaseous constituents eliminated the eye-irritating action.

It is of interest to note that the new-formula artificial smog, in which the aldehydes were replaced by the products of the reaction of gasoline and ozone, seemed to have more nearly the odor of photochemical smog than did the old-formula smog.

These results strongly indicate that airborne particles do not contribute to an important extent to the eye irritation produced by photochemical smog.

Schuck and Doyle[16] investigated the contribution of formaldehyde and acrolein to the observed eye irritation produced by irradiated dilute automobile exhaust and by irradiated nitric oxide-olefin mixtures. As in the case of the Cadle and Magill experiments, a human panel was subjected to test atmospheres prepared in a "smog chamber." An arbitrary irritation index was again used as a measure of the severity of reaction by panel members. The gases were irradiated in the chamber and the subjects were seated outside in booths. The irritation indices resulting from known concentrations of formaldehyde and acrolein were compared with the indices resulting from the irradiation experiments. The results indicated that formaldehyde and acrolein accounted for about 80% of the irritation. More recent results have indicated that "PAN", mentioned earlier in this chapter, also contributes to the eye irritation resulting from such laboratory experiments.

Buchberg et al.[59] irradiated air containing known amounts of automobile exhaust in a transparent reaction tunnel to simulate the formation of photochemical smog. Eye-irritating properties were determined with a panel of 12 college students. The experiments were designed to establish statistical relationships between various exhaust components, various atmospheric reaction products, amount of irradiation, and the eye irritation produced. Correlation coefficients were determined for the relationship between eye irritation and each of 28 physical variables.

The results suggested that the amount of hydrocarbon reacted accounted for most of the variations in eye-irritation thresholds. Strong correlations were observed between formaldehyde concentration and eye irritation. However, the results suggested that other irritants are also present.

The eye irritation produced by Los Angeles smog seems to be greater than that produced by the laboratory-irradiated mixtures.[9,60] Thus the possibility cannot be entirely eliminated that airborne particles contribute to the eye irritation resulting from photochemical smog. Of course, some undiscovered component of the smog may also be important. For example, Cadle and Johnson[61] suggested that free radicals, and especially peroxy free radicals, may contribute to eye irritation.

The chronic effects of smog are much more difficult to define than the acute effects. Lung cancer and bronchitis are those usually discussed, but there may be a number of others such as heart disease.

Little statistical evidence, other than rather circumstantial, is available relating to the development of chronic ailments among persons living in cities subject to smog as compared with the development of such ailments among persons living in relatively uncontaminated atmospheres. This is almost certainly because of the difficulty in arranging proper controls. Probably all large cities are subject to smog in some degree; small towns and the open country differ from cities as part of the human environment in a number of ways in addition to the incidence of smog. At any rate, most investigations of the chronic effects of smog have been undertaken with test animals.

The few statistical studies that have been made have been reviewed in the Air Pollution Manual.[32] The results have demonstrated a higher incidence of lung cancer in cities than in rural areas, and this higher incidence remains even when the comparison is made on the basis of non-smokers, or of smokers of equal intensity. The U.S. Public Health Service[62] conducted a study of mortality data from 163 metropolitan areas in the United States. Calculations were included of linear correlation coefficients between various causes of death and fuel consumption indices. The diseases considered were (a) malignant neoplasm of the esophagus and stomach; (b) malignant neoplasm of trachea, bronchus, and lung; (c) arteriosclerotic heart disease including coronary disease; and (d) chronic endocarditis not specified as rheumatic, and other myocardial degeneration. The indices of fuel consumption were (a') all fuel; (b') all fuel-coal consumption stressed; (c') gas; (d') home heating units; and (e') service station sales. The highest correlation coefficients were for (a) with a', b', d' (about 0.4); the lowest was (c) with c' (about 0.05) and the rest were between about 0.15 and 0.30. If the positive correlations are largely the result of smog, fuel burning of many types, including coal and gasoline, would seem to be implicated and to cause heart disease as well as cancer of various types.

Comparisons of this type are more convincing for men than for women. However, the few available data indicate an upward trend in lung cancer with population density when women non-somokers or light smokers are compared.[32]

Paul Kotin and his associates have undertaken a long series of experiments designed to establish both the chronic and the acute effects of smog. The experiments have been undertaken both with synthetic smog and with various smog components. Their work up to 1955 was reported by Kotin and Falk.[63] Chambers were used for the exposure of the animals to various atmospheres. A few tests were also made of acute effects on humans using large exposure chambers.

Two artificial smogs were used. One was prepared by irradiating with sunlight a mixture of air, hydrocarbons, and oxides of nitrogen. The other, which replaced the first in later experiments, was prepared by allowing ozone to react with gasoline vapors. The similarity of these synthetic smogs to actual photochemical smog was checked by chemical tests for oxidants and aldehydes, evaluation of damage to plants, and the eye irritation produced.

The results indicated that smog in concentrations of 15 ppm, which is much higher than the concentrations of a smoggy day, produced certain mild physiological changes which rapidly disappeared after removal of the animals from the exposure chambers. Repeated exposures indicated that no cumulative effects of the pollutants occurred "in terms of either increasing reactivity or sensitivity to smog or in terms of ultimate lethal effects." The artificial smog in realistic concentrations produced no demonstrable physiological or morphological changes in presumably healthy animals. These atmospheres presumably contained both gases and particles.

Kotin and Falk emphasized that the above results do not apply to carcinogenic properties of the smog. They stated, "In sharp contrast to the exoneration of the atmosphere [photochemical smog] as a source of biologic morbidity on the acute level, our data suggest that it is capable of being incriminated from a chronic or potentially carcinogenic viewpoint." They reported finding aromatic polycyclic hydrocarbons, including the well-known carcinogen, 3,4-benzpyrene, in Los Angeles smog. Skin cancers were produced by applying extracts of the aromatic materials in smog to the skins of C57 black mice. Similar skin cancers were produced in C57 black mice by applying extracts of gasoline-engine exhaust and diesel engine exhaust. The percentage of tumor production was greater than could be explained by the aromatic polycyclic content of either the atmosphere or vehicular exhausts. Experiments with aliphatic materials collected from the atmosphere demonstrated that they also could produce skin cancers.

The carcinogen 3,4-benzpyrene has the following structure:

It is found in the atmospheres of many cities and may be a semiquantitative index of the presence in air of other polynuclear aromatic hydrocarbons which are also carcinogenic. It melts at 180°C and boils at about 500°C at atmospheric pressure. Thus it exists as particles in contaminated atmospheres, almost always associated with particles of other materials. It is formed by the combustion of numerous organic substances and thus is found in most or all city smogs.

Sawicki et al.[64] reported the results of two series of studies of the 3,4-benzpyrene content of air. One consisted of monthly mean values of samples taken continuously for a year in nine United States cities. The other consisted of a single mean value for each of 94 urban and 28 non-urban sites. The latter were regular samples of the National Air Sampling Network mentioned above. For the most part the concentrations in the urban areas were in the range of tens and hundreds of $\mu$g/1000 cu meter. The concentrations in Los Angeles and San Francisco, both noted for photochemical smog, were very much less than those in most other cities. The lowest urban values occurred in the west and the highest in the eastern and mid-western sections of the United States. The nonurban sites generally had much lower concentrations than the urban sites.

The benzpyrene concentrations in particulate matter were much lower for western cities than for eastern. Thus in Montgomery, Alabama, the concentration was 340 $\mu$g per gram of particles and 2000 $\mu$g per gram of the benzene-soluble fraction of the particles; in San Jose, California the corresponding concentrations were 7.2 and 91.

Essentially no information is available concerning the effect of particle size on the carcinogenic properties of the particulate portion of smogs. However, it is probably worth while speculating as to what this might be. Prindle[62] found that mortality due to almost all forms of cancer is more frequent in the central portion of metropolitan areas of the United States than in nonurban areas. If this difference results from air pollution, not only must the smog carcinogens act upon contact of particles with tissue surfaces but must also be assimilated by the body. If this assimilation can occur through the tissues of both the respiratory and digestive systems, the main influence of particle size on carcinogenic action will be its effect on the total amount of material deposited anywhere in the respiratory system. Of course, this is a tremendous oversimplification. There may be a variation of the concentrations of carcinogens in the particulate material with particle size, but whether such a variation exists is not known. Also, the carcinogenic effects may be greater if deposition occurs in certain parts of the respiratory system than in others, and the location of deposition is of course very sensitive to particle size. Obviously, many questions remain to be answered.

Long exposure to smog probably produces chronic irritation of the respiratory system, with symptoms such as those of chronic bronchitis. Little is known about such chronic effects of smog, but both gaseous and particulate constituents might be expected to contribute. Stokinger *et al.*[65] found that chronic injury to the lungs of small animals resulted when they were exposed to daily doses of ozone at a concentration of 1 ppm. This injury was in the form of chronic bronchitis and bronchiolitis. Dogs did not exhibit such deep lung changes but only a mild irritation of the upper respiratory tract.

The irritating effects of certain types of particles found in smog, such as sulfuric acid droplets, and the effect of particle size on such irritating action, was discussed in Chapter 3. Synergistic effects between particles and gases in producing irritation were also discussed and we may expect that such synergism plays a role in chronic irritation resulting from smog.

The possibility that lead compounds from the tetraethyl lead in gasoline and admitted to the atmosphere in automobile exhaust can be a health hazard was investigated and dismissed when the use of tetraethyl lead first became popular. (See Chapter 3, p. 184). The early results suggested that most of the lead reacted in the engine with gasoline additives to form lead bromide which deposited in the exhaust system, and eventually sloughed off as large, rapidly settling fragments.

The greatly increased use of automobiles, especially in places subject to smog, has once more raised the question of lead hazards. The potential danger, if any, has not been determined, but some previously held ideas of the nature of atmospheric lead from automobiles have had to be revised.

Mueller et al.[66] used several methods for determining the size of the lead particles emitted by automobiles operating on gasoline containing tetraethyl lead. The results showed that most of the mass of the lead in the exhaust was associated with particles less than one micron in diameter. Robinson et al.[67] investigated the variations of atmospheric lead concentrations in several cities, particularly in the San Francisco Bay region and in the Los Angeles basin. The size distributions of the lead aerosol were found to be much the same at all the locations tested. A typical size distribution had a mass-median diameter of 0.2 micron with quartiles at 0.1 micron and 0.5 micron. These data were obtained with a Goetz "Aerosol Spectrometer"[68] which is based on centrifugal sedimentation, and the sizes quoted are equivalent diameters in that they were calculated by assigning a density of unity to the particles. There is little doubt that the principal source of the lead aerosol in these field sampling tests was automobile exhaust.

Since the toxicity of lead compounds is directly related to their solubility, the fraction of the atmospheric lead aerosol which was composed of water-soluble compounds was determined. The average solubility at room temperature was 9 percent and varied from less than 1 to 18 percent.

These results are significant with respect to toxicity since they suggest that the lead-containing particles in air are too small to settle rapidly and are of such a size that they are readily retained in the respiratory system. Even so, it is questionable whether the concentrations are high enough to constitute a hazard.

Concentrations of lead in the air of 32 cities and 9 nonurban stations have been determined as part of the activities of the National Air sampling network. The arithmetic means of the concentrations in the cities varied from 0.1 to 1.7 µg/cu meter for the years 1957 and 1958. The high value was obtained in Los Angeles. On the other hand, the maximum concentration for 1958 for any of the nonurban stations was 0.1 µg/cu meter.

**Effects on plants.** It has long been recognized that air pollutants can have a devastating effect on plants. Smokes and fumes from factory stacks have often almost completely eliminated vegetation in the vicinity of some industrial operations. In fact, historically, much of the concern with air pollution has centered on the effects of the pollutants on vegetation.

One might expect that the effect of city smog on vegetation would be very much less important than that of the much more concentrated effluents near factories and other industrial operations. While the effects of the concentrated effluents are indeed at times more dramatic, city smog also is capable of producing extensive damage to plants, and the economic loss from this source has undoubtedly amounted to many millions of dollars.

The type of damage produced is greatly influenced by the nature of the smog, and examination of the condition of various types of plants in the vicinity of a city can furnish considerable information concerning the nature and intensity of smog in that city. Photochemical smog is particularly well-known for producing a type of damage sometimes called silver leaf. According to the Air Pollution Manual[32] this type of smog damage has resulted in increasingly serious economic losses since 1944, until by 1960 the estimated yearly loss in the Los Angeles area alone exceeded $5,000,000. This type of damage has also been reported in northern California and in major cities elsewhere in the world, including London, Paris, Sao Paulo, and various parts of the United States.

This type of injury is variously described as a silvering, bronzing, or glazing which almost always first appears on the underside of the leaves. The symptoms have been described in detail by Thomas and Hendricks.[69] Qualitatively, the nature of the damage is quite characterisitc of photochemical smog but the susceptibility varies with type of plant. Spinach is very susceptible. At first the under surface of the leaf assumes an oily appearance which is followed in one or two days by the silvering or bronzing. The spongy cells and lower epidermal cells are collapsed, leaving air spaces below the epidermis and giving the impression that the lower epidermis is detached. The top of the leaf, opposite the silvered region, then becomes light-colored and the collapse extends through the leaf.

When the smog intensity has been light and the chloroplasts are undamaged, the symptoms of injury may disappear and the plants completely recover. Chronic damage is somewhat more severe and is described[69] as the condition when only a limited number of cells are killed, no macroscopic collapse occurs, and the leaves merely lighten in color. The silver-leaf stage is sometimes described as acute injury.

In broad-leaved plants such as spinach the injured region is an irregularly shaped area, but in narrow-leaved plants such as the wild oats of California the damage may produce a banded appearance.

Numerous variations of these symptoms have been described. Thus alfalfa, which has stomata on both sides of the leaves, may exhibit chronic injury on the upper side alone, the lower side alone, or both sides. The lower surfaces of the leaves of table beets may develop a layer of brown cork, while the upper surface may develop a weathered appearance with reddening.[70]

Although thorough studies have been made of the effect on plants of a large number of the components of photochemical smog, the substance or substances responsible for the plant damage remain unknown. Haagen-Smit and co-workers[71] have suggested that the damage is caused by organic peroxides, but laboratory experiments with essentially pure organic peroxides have failed to produce typical lesions.

The responsible substances (phytotoxicants) almost certainly are formed as a result of the photochemical reactions described earlier in this chapter. The irradiation of mixtures of nitrogen dioxide, olefins, and air at concentrations comparable to those found in smog yield products which induce typical plant damage. Similar results have been obtained by irradiating automobile exhaust gases with sunlight.[72]

When ozone and olefins are allowed to react with each other at concentrations comparable to those found in photochemical smog, phytotoxicants result which produce typical damage. With the same mixtures and conditions the eye irritants produced are much less active than those found in smog. It seems likely that the phytotoxicants and the eye irritants are quite different substances or combinations of substances. Photochemical phytotoxicant formation may be a process in which ozone is produced by a series of reactions the first of which is photochemical, followed by the "dark" or "thermal" reaction of ozone with a hydrocarbon or other organic substance.

"PAN" (peroxyacetyl nitrite), a product of photochemical smog reactions mentioned earlier, produces plant effects somewhat like those of photochemical smog, but not identical with them. Apparently ozone-olefin reaction products are restricted in their phytotoxic effects largely to fully expanded leaf tissue, while "PAN" seems to be most toxic to younger plant tissue. Possibly plant damage, like eye irritation, cannot be attributed to a single substance or type of substance.[73]

The phytotoxicants in ozone-olefin reaction products seem to be rather short-lived, the lifetime being a matter of minutes and depending to a considerable extent on the olefin.[74,75] Such instability suggests that either an ozone-olefin addition complex or a zwitter ion into which it decomposes, or both, are responsible for the toxic effect. The "PAN" and presumably also the ozone-olefin reaction products which cause the plant damage are in vapor form.

Little is known about the possible contribution of particulates to this type of phytotoxicant action. Thomas and Hendricks have stated that two types of smog injury to vegetation have been recognized in Los Angeles.[69] One is the type of damage just discussed and the other is due to deposition of fog droplets on the leaves. The latter consists of weathered and spotted effects which may be produced by a combination of heavy smog and dense fog. Such a combination is not at all unusual in Los Angeles. However, it remains to be proved that this type of damage is caused by fog.

Because of the great damage to plants produced by photochemical smog, several studies have been made of the possibility of protecting plants from such damage with chemotherapy. Freebairn[76] found that spraying plants with vitamin C sprays at least partially protected them from damage from photochemical smog. In some cases the protection was complete, but for most plants only partial protection was obtained. Presumably this is because different plants absorb vitamin C at widely different rates. This work was undertaken using various salts of ascorbic acid rather than ascorbic acid (vitamin C) itself.

Vitamin C is an antioxidant under many conditions, so other antioxidants have been examined for chemotherapeutic action. Ordin *et al.*[77] investigated nickel di-N-butyl dithiocarbamate, zinc ethylene bis [dithiocarbamate] and potassium ascorbate dispersed as dusts. The plants were exposed to "natural" smog, ozone, and "PAN." The antioxidants seemed to be at least partially effective against smog and ozone but not against "PAN." The authors concluded that these antioxidants exerted their effect only by coating the leaf surface. In neither of these two studies was any attention given to the effects of particle size or size distribution.

Studies of plant damage in coal-burning communities have been largely restricted to studies of the effects of individual smog components, such as sulfur dioxide, hydrogen sulfide, and ammonia. As mentioned above, the suggestion has been made that the nature of the damage to plants be used to determine the nature and to some extent the intensity of air pollution. Benedict and Breen[78] compiled a list of 15 weeds which occur more or less commonly throughout the United States. This list in turn was submitted to 25 state agricultural stations with the request that they select the ten most common species in their area. Ten weeds were than selected for final study. Specimens of these weeds were fumigated with six common pollutants. Results were recorded as (1) descriptions and photographs of the markings produced on each weed by each fumigant, and (2) relative resistance of the various weeds to each fumigant. This approach to smog monitoring has been reviewed by Darley.[79]

### Prevention or control of particle production

The only method that has been found at all effective in minimizing smog is control at the source. Numerous suggestions, some very intelligent, many naive, and all very imaginative, have been made for dealing with the smog once it has developed. The difficulty with such suggestions is usually the energy or logistic requirements.[80]

Smog control is expensive, and whether the source is industrial, home, automotive, or trash burning, the cost ultimately must be borne by the community. Thus each community, which may even mean each country, that has an air pollution problem must ultimately decide how much it is willing to pay to achieve a given degree of cleanliness. Usually the price for complete restoration to natural conditions is unreasonably large, and compromises have to be made.

The effectiveness of control measures in many cities of the United States is well known, and most persons have seen the "before-and-after" photographs demonstrating its results. In such cities the control is largely a matter of setting limits on factory emissions, as discussed in more detail later. Elimination of backyard burning of trash and of dump burning by "cut-and-fill" methods has also been helpful. Restriction of the grade of coal used in home furnaces has in places considerably decreased the amount of soot in the atmosphere.

Control measures must be quite different in cities where photochemical smog is predominant. Such measures in Los Angeles provide classic examples. The emission of sulfur dioxide from refineries was the first to be controlled. Next came backyard incinerators. Third came a device to be attached to automobile engines to remove much of the hydrocarbons emitted from the crankcase where oil is added, the so-called "blow-by." The fourth measure is the control of hydrocarbons in the automotive exhaust gas.

Several possibilities exist for decreasing the hydrocarbon content of exhaust gases, thus presumably decreasing both the gaseous and particulate components of photochemical smog. The approach emphasized in California is to destroy the hydrocarbons present in the exhaust before they reach the open atmosphere. There are two general methods for doing this, both using afterburners. One general method utilizes the "flame afterburner," which is actually a high-temperature combustion chamber in which the hydrocarbons are burned. The other utilizes "catalytic afterburners" which catalytically oxidize the hydrocarbons at relatively low temperatures.

There are problems common to both types of afterburners. When the carburetor mixtures are rich, there may be too little oxygen in the exhaust to convert the hydrocarbons to carbon dioxide and water. Heat may have to be added to the incoming exhaust, particularly for flame afterburners. The former problem is solved readily by introducing air either with an air pump or a venturi. The extra heat may be provided by a heat exchanger in which the hot, burned exhaust gases provide heat to the cooler incoming gases. An alternative method is to burn supplemental gasoline in the afterburner.

In addition to the problems mentioned above, it may be necessary to remove the excess heat produced by the combustion in the afterburner. Both types of devices remove carbon monoxide as well as hydrocarbons, but they do not destroy the oxides of nitrogen; and unless properly designed and operated, the flame afterburners can actually produce oxides of nitrogen by fixation of atmospheric nitrogen.

Considerations in afterburner design must be cost, size, and servicing requirements. Catalytic afterburners tend to become fouled from the accumulation of fine particles and gummy films on the catalyst surfaces, and the catalyst must be periodically replaced.

## INDUSTRIAL AIR POLLUTION

### Examples of problems

Almost any industrial activity is a potential or actual producer of air pollution. The pollutants may be either solid or gaseous, and some experts even classify industrial noise as a type of air pollution. The pollutants may bother only the workers in the plant or factory, in which case the problem is generally classified as one of industrial hygiene. If the pollutants affect the area outside the immediate factory grounds the problem is considered to be one of air pollution.

Processes carried out in many industries make them particularly subject to air pollution problems. There is no point in attempting to discuss or even to list all such industries, but it is probably worth while to mention a few to indicate the problems involved. Such industries have often been highly successful in overcoming their problems.

A major class of industrial air pollutants consists of fluorine and various gaseous and solid fluorine compounds. The compounds include hydrogen fluoride, aluminum fluoride, sodium fluoride, silicon fluoride, and hydrofluosilicic acid. The fluorides can do considerable damage to plants and to grazing animals such as cattle that feed on the plants. The gaseous fluorides are absorbed by the leaves, but little translocation occurs. Soluble particulate fluorides are also absorbed by plants and cause damage. The types of lesions produced vary markedly and are described in detail in the Air Pollution Manual.[32] Damage to agricultural plants has been a problem in many states, including California, Florida, Idaho, Montana, New Jersey, Oregon, Tennessee, Utah, and Washington.[81]

Probably the greatest economic loss as a result of fluoride ingestion by animals results from the reduced food consumption. There may be loss of weight or a failure to gain weight, decreased milk production, stiffness, and lameness. Perhaps the most characteristic symptom of animals exposed while young to excessive fluoride is a mottled condition of the tooth enamel. Large ingestion of fluoride may result in calcification of the ligaments and in bony overgrowths.

Numerous industrial operations produce fluorides, including the production of ceramics, and certain fertilizers and metals. Aluminum production is an example of such an operation. Aluminum is a very common element in the earth's crust but the only aluminum ore of appreciable commercial significance is bauxite, an impure mixture of hydrated aluminum oxides and hydroxides. It is refined and converted to alumina by various processes including calcining at 2000°F. The resulting alumina is a fine powder; minimizing the losses of dust carried by the effluent gases from the calcining operation is itself a problem in fine particle technology.

The alumina is almost always converted to aluminum by means of the Hall-Heroult process. This is an electrolytic process in which the alumina is dissolved in molten cryolite ($Na_3AlF_6$) and the aluminum liberated by passing a current between carbon electrodes immersed in the melt. The operating temperature is high, usually near 1000°C, and various fluorides are liberated from the bath in the form of a dense white fume. The pots are generally closed, but they must be opened occasionally, liberating fume, and there is some leakage.

The particulate material in the fumes is almost certainly of submicron size when first produced, but it rapidly coagulates to form larger particles which readily settle on vegetation. Individual pots may be exhausted, the effluent gases being scrubbed with sprays of water to remove gaseous and particulate fluorides, or all the gases leaving the rooms housing the pots may have to be treated. Since a large fraction of the fluorides in the fume is soluble, such scrubbers are usually very effective.

The history of the control of fluoride emissions from a particular aluminum plant was described by Ott and Hatchard.[82] This plant utilizes the Soderberg modification of the Hall-Heroult process. The 35-ton anode is composed of an anode paste consisting of pitch and coke baked to form a block of carbon. It is immersed in the electrolyte consisting of a solution of alumina in cryolite with a little calcium fluoride added to lower the melting point. The surface of the electrolyte is covered with a layer of alumina to help confine the fumes.

Prior to building the plant, air and foliage samples in the vicinity were analyzed for fluoride to estimate the background concentrations.

The plans for the plant had to be approved by a local "Authority". The control equipment included a 12,000 ft, 3-exhaust fan to evacuate the fumes produced by the cells through a "multiclone". The effluent gas and dust was then passed through a counterflow spray scrubber tower. Each such control unit served 15 cells. These control units were found to remove at least 95 percent of the fluorides entering them. The individual cells were equipped with vacuum duct systems, but some fume escaped from these systems and was vented from the top of the buildings. Accordingly, spray nozzles were installed at the roof "monitors" to remove the fluorides that escaped the duct systems.

The ferrous metallurgical industry provides one example of an industry which contributes to the particulate pollution of the atmosphere in a number of operations.

The open hearth method of steel-making uses a reverberatory furnace called a regenerative furnace. Gas is used as fuel and each end of the furnace is equipped for the intake and outlet of both gas and air. The process uses either pig iron and fresh ore or pig iron and scrap steel. The major difficulties so far as air pollution is concerned are in controlling gas temperature and volume, and particulate loading and size. Most particulate emissions occur during the first half hour after the addition of hot metal and during the latter part of an 8-12 hour heat cycle.[83] The size distribution of the particles in the fumes of an open hearth effluent are given in Table 4-9.

The fumes consist largely of iron oxides with smaller amounts of zinc, lead, and sulfur oxides. Fluorspar may be added to increase the fluidity of the slag, in which case the fumes will contain fluorides, possibly largely hydrogen fluoride. The ore may also have a high fluoride content, with a similar result. Water scrubbers, electrostatic precipitators, and filters are used to control particulate effluent, and lime has been added to the effluent gas streams prior to particle collection to remove hydrogen fluoride.

TABLE 4-9. SIZE DISTRIBUTION OF
PARTICLES IN THE FUME FROM AN
OPEN HEARTH FURNACE.[84]

| Diameter range (microns) | Weight percent in size fraction |
|---|---|
| 1.0 – 3.0 | 7.3 |
| 0.5 – 1.0 | 28.4 |
| 0.15–0.5 | 49.5 |
| < 0.15 | 14.8 |

The Bessemer process of manufacturing steel involves the oxidation of impurities in the iron by blowing air through the molten iron; the heat of oxidation maintains the temperature above the melting point during the operation. The process is carried out in an egg-shaped "converter" made of steel and lined with silica and clay or dolomite. Iron is introduced and the finished steel poured out of an opening in the upper narrow end. Air is forced in through holes in the bottom called tuyères. The converters are called acid or basic depending upon the nature of the lining.

According to Sheehy and Lindstrom, the Bessemer converter is the most difficult air pollution problem in the steel industry.[83] The blow cycle of an acid converter can be divided into three parts, each lasting a few minutes. Dust concentrations in the exhaust gases of an acid converter have been found to be 0.178, 0.371, and 0.218 pound of dust per 1000 pounds of exhaust gas.[85] The particles are largely iron oxides.

The usual explanation for particle formation in Bessemer converters is that the exothermic reaction of oxygen and iron causes a high temperature at the reaction zone, vaporizing some of the iron. These vapors, mixed with nitrogen and carbon monoxide, condense as they pass through the molten metal to form an aerosol. The aerosol particles oxidize upon coming in contact with the outside air, producing a brown smoke. The addition of steam to the blowing air largely eliminates the formation of such smoke, but the mechanism of the suppression is not well understood.

Another theory of the smoke formation—the iron carbonyl theory—is that ferrous oxide is formed when the air meets the bath surface and that the ferrous oxide reacts with iron carbide to form iron carbonyl. The latter dissociates to carbon monoxide and iron, and the iron oxidizes to form iron oxide.

Flames many feet long are emitted from the mouth of the Bessemer converter. Thus it is understandable that collection of the fumes as an air pollution control measure has not been seriously attempted.

Basic oxygen converters are similar to basic Bessemer converters except that oxygen is forced in through the top instead of air through the bottom. The emissions from the converter can be passed through a waste heat boiler, cooled, and then passed through an electrostatic precipitator or other dust-collection device.

Electric-arc steel furnaces provide a method for making large amounts of high-grade steel with careful control of temperature and freedom from contamination by fuel. Arcing occurs between the electrodes and the melted steel charge. The emitted fume may consist largely of iron or iron oxide, but non-ferrous materials in the melt may also contribute to it. Typically, about 70 percent of the fume particles are less than 5 microns in diameter.[86,87]

According to Adams,[87] the three types of particle-removal equipment usually used in conjunction with electric furnaces are wet dust collectors, bag houses, and electrostatic precipitators. The fumes are emitted at high temperatures, and pre-cooling of the gases is often required.

The blast furnace itself is a well-known producer of particulate pollution. The blast furnace operation involves charging iron ore, coke, and flux (limestone plus dolomite) into the top of the furnace and blowing hot air into the bottom. The oxygen of the air combines with the carbon of the coke to form carbon monoxide, which reduces the ore to iron. This operation produces tremenduous quantities of dust, a large percentage of which is of submicron size. Hemeon[88] states that there are two main types of dust emission incident to the operation of blast furnaces. One is the residual dust in blast furnace gas and the other is the occasional escape of dust-laden gas from the bleeder openings of the furnace. Both types of particle-laden gas are generally largely freed of particles as an air pollution control measure.

The gas cleaning usually occurs in two steps. The first consists of scrubbing with water sprays which remove most of the larger particles. The second step involves passing the gases through cleaners such as electrostatic precipitators and Theissen disintegrators which remove most of the rest of the dust.[89]

The production of coke for blast furnace operation has also involved air pollution problems. Most coke is now produced in the modern by-product coke oven. Hemeon[90] lists four operations that produce visible smoke or other emissions: (a) charging the ovens with coal, (b) leakage during carbonization, (c) pushing the coke from the ovens, and (d) quenching the hot coke. Control of emissions is generally effected by appropriate oven design and in the case of quenching, with water sprays. The particles in the first three types of emissions are largely of submicron size but those in the last type are relatively large, consisting mainly of water droplets and coke particles, and are relatively easily collected.

A third example of an industrial operation which has severe and varied atmospheric pollution problems is the public utility industry. Its problems arise almost entirely from combustion products and from the handling and storage of fuels.[91] The public utility most concerned with air pollution problems is the electricity-generating industry, most of which uses steam for power. Steam is produced in boilers by burning fuel, and the steam is used to drive turbines which in turn drive generators.

The fuels are generally chosen on the basis of availability and cost, and are practically always coal, natural gas, or fuel oil. In 1958 about 78 percent of the electrical energy for the United States was generated with steam turbines, and of this about 68 percent was produced with coal, 24 percent with natural gas, and 8 percent with fuel oil.[91]

Both gaseous and particulate pollutants are produced. The former include sulfur dioxide, nitric oxide, carbon monoxide, and carbon dioxide. Except as they may contribute to chemical reactions producing particles in photochemical smog their control is beyond the scope of this book.

The particles include sulfuric acid droplets (often reported as $SO_3$ and listed as a gas), fly ash, smoke (including carbon particles and gums), and at times small cinders. The sulfuric acid droplets are in the diameter range 0.1 to 1 micron, the fly ash in the range 1 to several hundred microns, and the smoke particles are largely in the range 0.01 to 1 micron. Since an excess of combustion air is usually used, combustible smoke is usually emitted to a very slight extent. The most common forms of ash particles include small ones from burning coal and usually called fly ash, larger particles from coal which are called cinders, and particles from the burning of fuel oil.[91]

When coal is used as the fuel it is crushed or pulverized, suspended in air, and fed into the furnace as a suspension. Few plants use furnaces equipped with grates or beds of fuel. Commercial-grade coals usually contain 5 to 15 percent of incumbustible material which must be removed either in the form of a slag or as fly ash. From an air pollution standpoint, the larger the amount of such material which can be removed as slag, the easier will be the control because of decreased requirements for the capacity of collection equipment or frequency of cleaning. The control can be effected by a combination of mechanical collectors such as cyclones to remove large particles and electrostatic precipitators to remove the smaller ones.

The disposal of the collected fly ash can be a serious problem. A utility system may produce as much as a million tons of fly ash per year.[92] Fortunately, there are a number of industrial uses of fly ash including ready-mixed concrete, building blocks, slag and clay bricks, filtering media and soil conditioning agents.

Steam-electric generating stations using natural gas for fuel discharge relatively little particulate material into the air. Usually they produce no plumes or only faintly visible ones, but when the air is cold or very humid, water vapor produced by the combustion may condense to form a plume of water droplets. By-product gases are sometimes used as fuel, but although they may cause local problems from pollutant gases, they usually are not important sources of atmospheric particulates.

Fuel oils are seldom if ever completely free of non-combustible constituents and consequently produce ash which usually varies in diameter from submicron to about 50 microns. The oils are usually injected into the furnaces as a spray mixed with heated air. Thus the size of the ash particles depends to a considerable extent on the size of the droplets in the spray and the concentration of incombustible material in the oil. Most fuel oils contain less than 0.2 percent of such material, and the amount of ash produced by plants using fuel oil is very much less than the amount produced by plants using coal.

Commercial fuel oils generally contain considerable sulfur, which burns to form sulfur dioxide and trioxide, the latter rapidly combining with water vapor to form a sulfuric acid mist. The sulfuric acid droplets are for the most part much smaller and therefore more difficult to collect than the particles of ash.

The particle removal equipment for fuel oil-burning plants can be similar to that used for coal-burning plants, where mechanical collectors are used to remove larger particles, and filters or electrostatic precipitators are used for the fine particles.

Underwood[93] has reviewed the methods for the removal of submicron-diameter particles from industrial gases, with emphasis on the steel and electricity industries. The basic theory of electrostatic precipitators, fiber and bag filters, and wet scrubbers is included.

## Dispersion and deposition

The degree of unpleasantness produced by any local source of air pollution is markedly influenced by the fate of the pollutants after they enter the atmosphere. Thus the rate of mixing of the pollutants with the surrounding atmosphere, the path that the air masses containing them take as they travel downwind, and the coagulation, sedimentation, and deposition of the particles all play a role in determining the objectional effects of the pollutants. Only the latter are affected by particle size unless the smoke or fume plumes are heavily loaded with particles, in which case a mass subsidence may occur.

The rate of mixing of pollutants with the surrounding atmosphere results from atmospheric turbulence and molecular diffusion. The former, sometimes called turbulent diffusion, is much more important than molecular diffusion when the pollutants consist of particles. Atmospheric turbulence and therefore turbulent diffusion vary greatly with weather conditions.

There are a number of situations involving air pollution where a knowledge of the rate of pollutant dilution may be very important. One such situation is that in which several possible locations for a plant are being considered. In general it is neither possible nor necessarily desirable to choose a location corresponding to the highest rate of dilution. On the other hand, a knowledge of the dilution rates, sedimentation rates, and the direction of the prevailing winds may be important factors in selecting a plant site.

Knowledge of such factors may also be important when an evaluation must be made of possible harmful effects of pollutants from a particular industrial plant. Such knowledge may be particularly helpful in the case of litigation. In such cases a comparison of the actual damage or complaints with estimates of the concentrations of pollutants from the suspected source actually reaching the area in question may help to establish the validity of the complaints or clear the plant of blame. An excellent example of the importance of such a study occurred during the early days of the investigations of Los Angeles smog. Oil refineries in the area were accused in the press, on the radio, and in public meetings of producing effluents which caused the smog. A study of air movements using fluorescent particle tracers by scientists at the University of California at Los Angeles finally demonstrated that the refineries contributed little directly to the smog.

Most industrial air pollution sources can be considered to be continuous point sources, usually stacks or vents, at a low altitude above the ground. The stream of pollutant ejected into the air creates turbulence which tends to cause dilution at a greater rate than would result from natural causes. Reliable data on this initial phase is difficult to obtain, but while the stream of polluted gas moves with respect to the surrounding air the concentration of any given pollutant seems to vary exponentially with distance downwind:

$$C = K/x^p \qquad (4.31)$$

where $C$ is the concentration, $p$ is an exponent varying from 1.5 to 2.0, $x$ is the distance downwind, and $K$ is a constant which depends on the stack concentrations and emission characteristics.[94] This equation usually applies for only a few seconds and a few hundred yards from the source.

Equations have been developed by Sutton[95] and by Bosanquet and Pearson[96] to predict atmospheric turbulence. Sutton's equation in a form applicable to point source emission is

$$c(x, y, z) = \frac{Q}{\pi \bar{u} C_y C_z x^{2-n}} \exp\left(- \frac{y^2}{C_y x^{2-n}} - \frac{z^2}{C_z^2 x^{2-n}}\right) \qquad (4.32)$$

where $c$ is the concentration of a pollutant at a point $(x, y, z)$ downwind of a continuous source of rate $Q$ at the point $(0, 0, 0)$ in free air. The mean wind direction is along the $x$-axis, $y$ is the horizontal axis, $z$ is the vertical axis, $\bar{u}$ is the mean wind speed, $C_y$ and $C_z$ are cross wind and vertical diffusion coefficients, and $n$ is a dimensionless number with a value between 1 and 2. The concentration on the $x$-axis $(x, 0, 0)$ is the coefficient of the exponential term, $Q/\pi \bar{u} C_y C_z x^{2-n}$. This equation is based on the assumption that the plume density is the same as that of the surrounding air.

When the source cannot be considered to be in free air because it is near the ground the following equation applies:

$$c(x, y, z) = \frac{Q}{\pi \bar{u} C_y C_z x^{2-n}} \exp\left(- \frac{y^2}{C_y^2 x^{2-n}}\right)$$
$$\left\{\exp \frac{-(z + h)^2}{C_z^2 x^{2-n}} + \exp \frac{-(z - h)^2}{C_z^2 x^{2-n}}\right\} \qquad (4.33)$$

where $h$ is the source height.

Interest usually centers on the concentration at the surface, where $z = 0$. In this case equation 4.33 becomes

$$c(x, y, 0) = \frac{2Q}{\pi \bar{u} C_y C_z x^{2-n}} \exp\left(- \frac{y^2}{C_y^2 x^{2-n}} - \frac{h^2}{C_z^2 x^{2-n}}\right) \qquad (4.34)$$

The maximum concentration at the ground is given by the equation

$$c_{max}(x_{max}, 0, 0) = \frac{2}{e\pi} \cdot \frac{Q}{\bar{u} h^2} \cdot \frac{C_z}{C_y} \qquad (4.35)$$

and this is located at a distance on the ground from the point directly below the source

$$x_{max} = \left(\frac{h}{C_z}\right)^{2/2-n} \qquad (4.36)$$

The equation of Bosanquet and Pearson corresponding to 4.34, 4.35, and 4.36 are

$$c(x, y, 0) = \frac{Q}{(2\pi)^{1/2} pq\bar{u}x^2} \exp\left(-\frac{y^2}{2q^2 x^2} - \frac{h}{px}\right) \tag{4.37}$$

$$c_{max}(x_{max}, 0, 0) = \left(\frac{8}{\pi e^4}\right)^{1/2} \cdot \frac{Q}{\bar{u}h^2} \cdot \frac{p}{q} \tag{4.38}$$

and

$$c_{max} = \frac{h}{2p} \tag{4.39}$$

where $p$ and $q$ are vertical and horizontal diffusion coefficients.

The equations are dimensional. When concentrations are in mass/cu meter, $Q$ is in mass/second, and wind speed is in meters per second, $C_y$ and $C_z$ have the dimensions meter$^{n/2}$. Position coordinates are of course then in meters. Non-dimensional forms of equations 4.34 and 4.37 can be written:[32]

$$\frac{c}{c_{max}} = \left(\frac{x_{max}}{x}\right)^{2-n} \exp\left\{1 - \left(\frac{x_{max}}{x}\right)^{2-n}\right\} \tag{4.40}$$

and

$$\frac{c}{c_{max}} = \left(\frac{x_{max}}{x}\right)^2 \exp\left\{2 - 2\left(\frac{x_{max}}{x}\right)\right\} \tag{4.41}$$

Some investigators prefer the Sutton to the Basenquet equations since the former have three coefficients and the latter two. This gives the Sutton equations an advantage with respect to fitting the equations to particular meteorological conditions. However, the two sets of equations agree in a number of respects. Nomographs have been devised for the solution of both types of equation.[97,98]

Experimental values of diffusion coefficients for various meteorological conditions have been published by many investigators.[32,98,99] None the less, these equations must be used with considerable caution, and are usually not at all applicable when wind conditions are highly variable. They are most useful for predicting or correlating average or most probable conditions.

The effect of varying atmospheric conditions on the behavior of smoke plumes is demonstrated with a series of photographs of oil plumes taken by the Meteorology Group at the Brookhaven National Laboratory (Figures 4-9 to 4-12).

The theory of turbulent diffusion of emission from continuous and line sources has also been investigated by Calder.[100] His equations are based in part on studies in Germany of turbulent flow over roughened surfaces. Following is the equation for an infinite continuously emitting line source of strength $Q$g/cm sec situated at ground level:

$$c = \frac{Q}{kv_x x} \exp\left(- \frac{\bar{u}z}{kv_x x}\right). \tag{4.42}$$

Figure 4-9. Inversion oil-fog plume—Brookhaven Test Stack. This photograph was taken during an inversion and is typical of stable atmospheric conditions. (*Courtesy Brookhaven National Laboratory*)

Concentrations at ground level are obtained by setting the exponential term equal to unity. Here $k$ is a non-dimensional constant having the value 0.45 which is sometimes referred to in the literature as "Karman's constant." The value of $v_x$ can be obtained by plotting the mean wind velocity $\bar{u}$ against the logarithm of the height; the slope of the resulting straight line is $v_x/k$.

Following is Calder's equation for a continuous point source at ground

Figure 4-10. Lapse oil-fog plume—Brookhaven Test Stack. This photo shows the breakup of an inversion and illustrates both convective and mechanical turbulence. (*Courtesy Brookhaven National Laboratory*)

level having a source strength of $Q$g/sec:

$$c = \frac{Q\bar{u}\left[-\dfrac{\bar{u}}{kv_x x}\left(\dfrac{y}{a} + z\right)\right]}{2k^2 a v_x^2 x^2} \tag{4.43}$$

where $a$ is the ratio of the mean absolute components of crosswind and vertical eddy velocities. Calder points out that this ratio can be found from the records obtained using an instrument such as the Taylor bi-directional wind vane.

These equations were compared with observational data on gas travel obtained in the field, at Porton, England. Quite satisfactory agreement, probably within the limits of experimental error, was obtained.

Figure 4-11. Lapse oil-fog plume—Brookhaven Test Stack. This photo illustrates large instability and is associated with convective turbulence. (*Courtesy Brookhaven National Laboratory*)

When the stack emissions are lighter or heavier than air the above equations do not apply. Thus Sutton[101] and Scorer[102] have considered the importance of gas temperatures and the fact that high temperatures and the resulting buoyancy reduce the concentrations of contaminants at the ground. Bodurtha[103] has discussed the vehavior of dense stack gases and demonstrated that they descend rapidly to the ground. His results showed that such gases should be discharged vertically from a stack with the minimum practical diameter so as to obtain the maximum stack gas velocity for a given volume flow rate.

Scorer[104] has shown that when the primary cause of turbulence in the air is thermal convection over land, both heat and pollutants may be transferred vertically many times more efficiently than momentum.

Particles in a plume can have at least two effects on plume behavior. If

the particles are so fine that to a large extent they remain with the plume
or are present in such high concentrations that in falling they carry the
plume gases with them (mass subsidence), they will produce a dense plume
such as those discussed by Bodurtha[103] and by Scorer.[102]   However, the
more common effect is the sedimentation of particles from the plume, de-
pleting it of comtaminants and depositing them on the ground.

Bosanquet *et al.*[105] developed a theoretical equation for predicting the
average rate of dust deposition by taking into account the terminal velocities of the settling particles as well as the meteorological considerations.
Sedimentation moves the position of maximum deposition closer to the

Figure 4-12. Lapse oil-fog plume—Brookhaven Test Stack.  This photo shows
a very unstable atmospheric condition associated with convective tubulence.
(*Courtesy Brookhaven National Laboratory*)

stack as the terminal velocity of the particles increases. Predicted results were found to agree with observations of the maximan deposition position within a factor of 2. According to Bosanquet *et al*, the average dust deposition rate $F$ over a 45° sector downwind is given by the equation

$$F = 1.27 \frac{Wbp^2}{H^2} \frac{(v/p\bar{u})(H/px)^{2+v/p\bar{u}}\exp(-H/px)}{\Gamma(1 + v/p\bar{u})} \qquad (4.44)$$

where $W$ is the emission rate of the dust from a stack of effective height $H$, $b$ is the fraction of time the wind blows toward the 45° sector, and $v$ is the terminal falling velocity of the dust particles. Tables of gamma functions can be used to evaluate the denominator of 4.44. The effective height is greater than the actual stack height due to the velocity of the stack gases and any elevation of stack gas temperature. Equations for calculating the effective height were proposed by Bosanquet *et al.* and the subject was reviewed by Gosline, Falk, and Helmers.[106]

Equation 4.44 is for a plume containing particles of a single size. In any actual situation where the particle sizes have a wide range, this equation would have to be solved for a number of size ranges and the results combined.

The dimensions of 4.44 are such that if $v$ and $\bar{u}$ are in consistent units, and $H$ and $x$ are in feet, $F$ is in units of $W/\text{ft}^2$.

According to Hawkins and Nonhebel,[107] when particles have a free-falling diameter of 20 microns or less, the settling rate is so low compared with the wind speed that the particles diffuse with the gas stream, and the Bosanquet equation may be used in its original form to determine the maximum concentrations at ground level. For such particles, the following equation may be used to calculate the maximum rate of deposition of the dust in tons per square mile per year:

$$t = 57 \times 10^9 \frac{W}{uH^2} \frac{bv}{6.7} \qquad (4.45)$$

where $W$ is in tons/hr, $\bar{u}$ is ft/sec, $H$ is in ft, $b$ again is the proportion of the year that the wind is within $\pm 22.5°$ of the prevailing direction, and $v$ is in ft/sec.

When the particles are larger, an equation such as 4.44 must be used. Deposition rates for various sizes of particles as calculated by Bosanquet *et al.* are shown in Figure 4-13.

Baron, Gerhard, and Johnstone[108] developed an approximate method for estimating deposition of aerosol particles from point sources based on the Sutton statistical methods.[108] They assumed that concentration profiles above the ground can be expressed as the sum of two profiles,

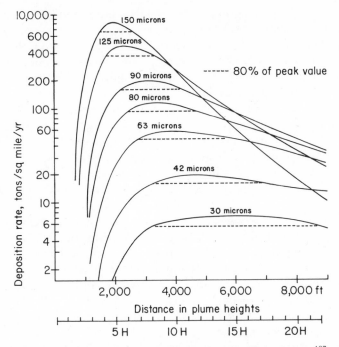

Figure 4-13. Deposition rates of particles of different diameters.[107] Effective height = 400 ft. Rate of emission of each size of particle = 0.1 tn./h. Wind speed = 20 ft/sec. Wind directional frequency, $b = 0.2$. (*Courtesy of the Institute of Fuel*)

one resulting from diffusion from the source and the other from an image of the source below the ground. They also assumed that the rate of deposition is controlled by the concentration near the ground and by the "true" settling rate through the stagnant layer. Their equations are rather complicated, but solutions are given for various conditions.

A modified Sutton equation has also been suggested in a U.S. Atomic Energy Commission report.[109, 110] This equation was derived by reducing the distance between the ground and the axis of the plume to take into account the effect of the settling rates of the particles. This is accomplished by replacing $h$ in equation 4.34 with $h - vx/\bar{u}$ and omitting the factor 2, since there is no ground reflection of individual particles. The deposition rate $F$ (mg/cm$^2$ month) is then found by multiplying the ground level concentration by the settling velocity:

$$F = \frac{263 Q v}{C_y C_x \bar{u} x^{2-n}} \exp\left[-\frac{1}{x^{2-n}}\left(\frac{y^2}{C_y^2} + \frac{(h - xv/\bar{u})^2}{C_x^2}\right)\right] \qquad (4.46)$$

$C_y$ and $C_x$ have the dimensions $m^{n/2}$, velocities are in m/sec, distances in meters, and particulate emission rate in mg/sec.

Useful as such equations are for correlation and prediction, they cannot replace actual determination of concentration and deposition patterns for evaluating the contribution of individual plants to a given air pollution problem. Sometimes the pollutant emitted by a plant is so unique that the pollutant itself can be used as a tracer to investigate the dispersion and turbulent diffusion of the plume. However, this is not practical when, as in the case of fluorides, there may be a natural source, or when there is more than one man-made source. In such cases it is usually necessary to incorporate some tracer in the stack gases which can be collected at sampling stations located at various distances and directions from the source.

The tracers that have been used have almost always been particles. They must be small enough that they do not settle out of the plume to an appreciable extent before they reach the sampling station. If the particles are to be collected on membrane filters and counted, concentrations must not be so high that appreciable agglomeration occurs. Furthermore, the particles must be large enough so that they will not be overlooked during the counting operation. The diameter range 0.5 to 5 microns is especially appropriate.

Numerous tracers have been suggested and employed. Perhaps the most widely used have been insoluble fluorescent substances such as zinc sulfide, zinc silicate, and zinc cadmium sulfide, especially the latter. Water-soluble fluorescent dyes such as uranine, radioactive particles, and antimony oxide have also been used.

The insoluble fluorescent particle technique offers the following advantages:[111]

(a) The particles are easily distinguished from naturally occurring fluorescent particles by color and brightness.

(b) They are commercially available in powdered form having the desired size range.

(c) They can be collected quantitatively on membrane filters which retain the particles on the surface with little penetration, where they can be detected and counted using a microscope and ultraviolet illumination.

(d) Fluorescent particle concentrations as low as one particle in ten ft$^3$ of air can be measured using a sample size of about 500 ft.$^3$

Not only must the particles in the powder be of the proper size, they must be dispersed in air as discrete particles. There must also be uniform distribution in the conveying stream of air. Several methods for accomplishing this dispersion have been described.[112, 113] One technique uses a centrifugal blower fed from a hopper by means of a rotating gear mechanism. Another method erodes solid pellets of the compressed tracer with jets of compressed air.

Sampling of insoluble fluorescent particles is usually accomplished with a membrane filter on an intermittent basis, although the sampling can also be done continuously by impaction on tape. If the latter method is used, the sampling rate must be such that there is no piling up of particles.

Holden, Dresch, and Cadle[111] have described statistical methods for counting particles which permit quite accurate control of the probable error for each sample. The method involves a rapid preliminary count of the particle density on each filter to provide data for estimating the number of fields to be counted to obtain the desired accuracy. A technician training program is also described.

Particle counting is both tedious and expensive, and the proper dispersion of insoluble powders is difficult. A method which avoids these problems involves the use of water-soluble fluorescent dyes such as uranine (the sodium salt of fluorescein).[114] Aqueous solutions of the dye are dispersed in the stack gases by aspirating-type aerosol generators, and evaporation of the droplets yields the desired particles. These are collected at the sampling stations on filters, which need not be of the membrane type. The filters are extracted with water and the dye contents of the resulting solutions are determined with a fluorescence photometer. The main disadvantage of this technique is that most desirable water-soluble dyes are sensitive to the high temperatures often encountered in stack gases.

Tracer studies lose much of their value unless meteorological information is obtained at each sampling station as the samples are collected. The minimum information which should be obtained concerns wind speed and direction. Some estimate of atmospheric stability is also important, and is usually achieved by measuring the rate of change of temperature with height. In particular it is important to differentiate between a temperature lapse and inversion and this can be achieved by measuring two temperatures from some vertical structure using a minimum height separation of 150 ft.

### Monitoring industrial particulate effluents

An important aspect of controlling industrial pollutants is determining the emission rate of the pollutants at or near the source. This is important to the plant operator who needs to monitor his stack gases to ensure that he is not contaminating the nearby landscape and to the law enforcement official, who may be called a "smoke inspector," to ascertain that the plant is complying with local ordinances. Such monitoring is also required to determine the effectiveness of newly installed particle-collecting equipment.

The monitoring may be accomplished at three general locations: (a) within stacks or ducts, (b) in the plumes immediately after they leave the stacks, and (c) near the ground at some distance from the plant. The first of these is particularly appropriate for plant management and the second for inspection officials. The third is more cumbersome than the other two, since it requires a network of sampling stations and is generally used to assess potential damage by the effluents.

Determining the concentrations and size distributions of particles passing through a duct or stack is simple in principle but is subject to a number of pitfalls. If the particles are actually to be collected, the design of the sampling probe may be very important. For example, if the particles are larger than a few microns in diameter it will be important to sample isokinetically. A number of probes have been designed to permit such sampling. A sampler developed by Lapple[115] uses a two-liquid "null-point" differential manometer to achieve automatic velocity balancing. The flow of gas through the sampling line is adjusted so as to maintain the interface in the manometer at a zero point, which represents equal sampling and stack velocities. A stack sampler designed by the Environmental Research Laboratory of the University of Washington[116] uses a Pitot tube to measure the flue velocity and an orifice flow meter to adjust the sampling flow rate so that it matches the flue velocity.

The velocity in a stack varies with distance from the wall, and accurate sampling requires the accumulation of samples from several different positions.

The tube leading from the probe to the collecting device should be as large as reasonable, as short as possible, and contain no sharp bends. Settling and impaction of particles onto the walls of tubes can be a serious source of error, especially for particles or aggregates of particles more than a micron in size. The error to be expected from a given set of conditions can be calculated from the equations in Chapter II.

The usual method for collecting the particles from the gas-stream flowing from the line from the probe is to draw the entire stream through a filter which is often in the form of a thimble. The thimble is then weighed to provide the desired mass concentration.

Often the particle size distribution is required in addition to the mass concentration. This may be obtained by conventional optical or electron microscope techniques. Such a procedure furnishes useful results only if one is interested in the "ultimate" particle size, since any aggregates which may exist when the particles are gas-borne lose their identity when added to the bulk material. However, the size distribution of the aggregates is often desired since it is the size and density of these that control the rate at which the particulate material settles from the plume. Thus, if particle size information is desired, a collection mechanism which causes neither a piling up nor a break up of the aggregates is highly desirable. Such collection can be achieved with small electrostatic precipitators, thermal precipitators, or even sedimentation boxes. The choice depends somewhat on particle size, sedimentation being especially appropriate for particles larger than one or two microns. Commercial aerosol sampling instruments of various kinds are listed in references 116 and 117.

Light-scattering techniques can be used to continuously monitor the particulate concentrations in stacks. A beam of light passed through the stack impinges upon a detector such as a bolometer. The output from the detector operates a recorder. One commercial device of this type utilizes a 200-watt sealed-beam spotlight and a temperature compensator for the bolometer. A slotted pipe provides a fixed light path length and rigid alignment between the source and the detector. Smoke passes through the slots in the pipe, and the decrease in transmittance is a measure of the smoke concentration. Photocells are used as detectors in other commercially available devices.

Mitchell and Engdahl[118] have surveyed methods for the measurement of particulate concentration in flowing gas streams. In addition to the methods just mentioned, they describe the use of certain physical characteristics of the dust particles, such as radioactivity, dielectric constant, and ability to acquire a charge in an ion atmosphere, which can be related to the mass concentrations of the particles. The attenuation of sound or of nuclear radiation can be substituted for the attenuation of light. They point out that principles which appear promising at very high dust loadings may not be applicable at low dust loadings, and vice versa. The problem is also complicated by factors such as variable particle size distribution, variable gas velocity, and variable gas humidity and temperature.

A method which has been employed for many years for measuring the density of plumes after they have formed beyond the top of stacks or other vents involves the use of the Ringelmann charts. These charts consist of graduated scales of gray which vary by five equal steps between black and white. They are produced as rectangular grills of black lines of definite width and spacing on a white background. This arrangement permits accurate reproduction, and the charts actually appear to be gray when placed at some distance from the observer.[119]

The chart is used by hanging it level with the eye about 50 ft from the observer and nearly in line with the chimney. The observer compares the smoke as it issues from the chimney with the charts and selects the chart which most nearly corresponds to the shade of the smoke. The chart number is the measure of smoke darkness. Once an observer has obtained considerable experience he no longer has to refer to the charts. In spite of the many objections to such a system, it has been found to be very useful in establishing legal codes and has played a major role in decreasing air pollution in many cities of the United States.

One drawback to the Ringelmann system is that the plumes from many stacks that are emitting large amounts of pollutants are very light-colored or even white. Attempts are being made by some air pollution control districts, with claimed success, to estimate the densities of such fumes, assigning them numbers corresponding to the numbers on Ringelmann charts. An obvious difficulty with this approach is that the optical density of plumes consisting of water droplets or hygroscopic particles will vary markedly with the relative humidity and temperature of the ambient air.

Various modifications of the Ringlemann charts have been suggested. Small cards replace the charts in one modification. Another consists of photographs of plumes of varying optical density or reflectance. A third consists of translucent reference slides which are viewed against the sky.

A number of instruments have been developed for estimating the densities of plumes in the hope that more objective values might be obtained than is possible simply by visual comparison with the Ringelmann charts. Rose, Nader, and Drinker[120] describe a "smoke inspection guide" which makes use of a very sensitive photometer equipped with a collimating tube to limit the light reaching the photometer to that from the specific areas under observation. A sighting tube is used to select the areas to be scanned. The instrument was standardized using a Ringelmann chart, a standard smoke cell, and a "film guide" consisting of small strips of film "of the same neutral coloration as the standard smoke." The film guide was mounted 1 in. from the end of the collimator. The photometer and film guide were tested for two types of use, (a) an indirect comparison of guide blackness relative to the sky background to that of the smoke plume relative to the sky background, and (b) a direct comparison of the darkness of the guide with that of the smoke plume. These authors concluded that this device provides a better, more reproducible method for smoke inspection than the printed Ringelmann chart.

Numerous methods have been used for monitoring the particles in the air in the vicinity of some industrial operation. Often the best way of doing this is an indirect method, calculating particle concentrations and size distributions from a combination of stack gas analysis, tracer study, and analysis of meteorological conditions. However, sometimes this approach is not appropriate or must be supplemented, for example, if litigation is involved. In such cases, the particles must be monitored directly.

Particle monitoring in the vicinity of a single source such as a stack usually falls into one of two categories, namely (a) that in which the determination of mass or number concentrations furnishes all the needed data, and (b) that in which particle size distributions as well as mass or number concentrations are required.

Many techniques and instruments are available for determining mass or number concentrations. Usually the particles are removed from suspension by filtration, electrostatic precipitation, thermal precipitation, or impaction. The collected particles may be counted or weighed, or the particle concentration estimated from the "darkness" or degree of reflectance of the surface on which the particles are collected. The latter technique is the basis of several automatic sampling devices.[121]

Since we are concerned especially with the importance of particle size, monitoring methods which permit measurements of both size distribution and concentrations will be described in a little more detail. One such technique involves the use of membrane filters in much the same way that they are used for tracer studies, except that the particles are illuminated with visible instead of ultraviolet light, and are measured as well as counted. This is the basis of a recommended method of the Air Pollution Control Association.[121] The method (APM2.3) takes advantage of the fact that membrane filters are rendered transparent when a little oil is added to them which has a refractive index about that of the filter material (about 1.50 for daylight at room temperature). This permits microscopic examination with transmitted as well as reflected illumination. One ft$^3$ of air is aspirated through a one-inch diameter membrane filter, using a critical orifice that controls the sampling rate at 4.91/min and sampling for five minutes and 45 seconds. The filter is placed on a microscope slide, a drop of immersion oil* is added, and particles are counted using an oil immersion (97 ×) objective and a 10 × ocular. The particles in from 12 to 49 fields are counted, using a calibrated Whipple disc, until at least 500 particles are counted.

*Cargille's (formerly Shillaber's) non-drying immersion oil is recommended.

The number concentration of particles in millions of particles per ft$^3$ can be calculated using the equation

$$\text{MPPCF} = \frac{\begin{array}{c}\text{Total count} \times \text{ effective}\\ \text{area of filter paper}\end{array}}{\begin{array}{c}\text{Number of fields} \times \text{ area}\\ \text{of field} \times \text{ cubic feet}\\ \text{sampled} \times 10^6\end{array}} \tag{4.47}$$

The particle size distributions can of course be determined using these same filters. APM-2.3 recommends calibrating an ocular micrometer with a stage micrometer and measuring the size of the particles, defining size as "the distance between the extreme points of the dust particle when measured in a horizontal direction." At least 500 particles are measured and a size distribution plotted. An alternative method is described using a microprojector. Although not mentioned in APM-2.3, membrane filters can also be used to collect particles to be counted and measured with an electron microscope, using preparative methods previously reviewed by the author.[122]

When very large particles are to be collected and measured, sedimentation techniques are sometimes useful. One of the simplest and commonest ways of doing this is to coat slides with a thin, uniform layer of grease and set several of them in a horizontal position at each sampling station. Concentrations and size distributions are determined at the end of some predetermined time. The results are difficult to interpret since the particles do not all come from the same pocket of air.

A method that the author has found to yield much more meaningful results involves the use of a box equipped with two trap doors at opposite ends. Slides, which may be coated with grease, are placed on the bottom of the box which is then kept closed until the time of use. Sampling is achieved by placing the box on a platform so that the axis through the centers of the two doors is parallel to the wind direction. The doors are opened and then closed again simultaneously after the air in the box has been replaced by the air to be sampled.

Usually rather simple, inexpensive methods are preferred to expensive instrumentation, since a number of sampling stations are operated simultaneously. However, sometimes continuous monitoring for long periods of time is desired. In such cases an automatic particle counter and sizer is often useful, such as those based on the intensity of light scattered by individual particles.[123,124] At least two versions are commercially available.

Sometimes it is advantageous or necessary to determine the concentration and size distribution of particles without removing them from the air or interfering with their normal air movement. This requirement is rather rare but has occurred in studies of individual contributions to arctic "ice fog" in the vicinity of airports, and the concentrations and size distributions of evaporating droplets. In such cases a combination of microscopy and high-speed photography may be desirable.

For such a system to be useful it is necessary to take into account the particle size range and concentration range of interest, the speed and resolving power of the film, the relationship between the volume in focus and the resolving power of the objective lens, and the flash duration and intensity. The requirements for direct photomicrography of airborne particles include those for photomicrography of particles collected on microscope slides, namely, a microscope, a camera body and film holder, and a light source. However, there are characteristics of airborne particles which add complications. As the particles are in motion, the exposure time must be short enough to "stop" the particles; the light intensity and film speed must be large enough to produce satisfactory images. If a high-resolution objective is used, the number of particles in focus at any given time is very small. The higher the resolution of an objective, the smaller is the volume in focus. Therefore, an instrument developed for one situation may not be at all satisfactory for another.

The theoretical limit of resolution of an objective, the depth of field, and the total volume in focus can all be calculated from the numerical aperture of the objective, as shown in Table 4-10. The equations used

TABLE 4-10. PROPERTIES OF OBJECTIVES[125]

| Numerical Aperture (N. A.) of Objective | Theoretical Limit of Resolution,* $\mu$ | Depth of Field,† $\mu$ | Volume in Focus,‡ Mm.³ | Flashes Required to Obtain Images of 100 Particles.§ No. |
|---|---|---|---|---|
| 0.10 | 2.8 | 28 | 0.99 | 10 |
| 0.15 | 1.8 | 12 | 0.19 | 53 |
| 0.25 | 1.1 | 4.2 | 0.024 | 420 |
| 0.50 | 0.6 | 1.0 | 0.0014 | 7,100 |
| 0.85 | 0.3 | 0.2 | 0.0001 | 100,000 |

*Calculated from the formula $\lambda/2$ N.A., where $\lambda$ is the wave length of the illumination and is assumed to be 0.55 $\mu$.

†Calculated from the formula $c/\tan$ (A.A./2), where $c$ is the diameter of the "circle of confusion" which one is willing to accept and has been chosen to equal the limit of resolution, and A.A. is the angular aperture. The angular aperture can be calculated from the numerical aperture using the formula $2 \sin^{-1}$ N.A.

‡Calculated on the assumption that 5 by 7 in. film is used and that the magnification is × 250 N.A.

§Calculated on the assumption that the aerosol concentration is $10^4$ particles per cubic centimeter.

for making the calculations are included in the table. One method of counteracting the small volume in focus when high-resolution objectives are used to photograph small particles is to provide darkfield illumination with a flash tube and suitable illumination. A large number of flashes is used to expose each frame of film, so that a number of images of particles are obtained on each negative, as shown in Table 4-10.

An instrument based on this principle, designed primarily to photograph particles of ice fog in Alaska, is shown in Figure 4-14, and a general-purpose instrument with built-in timer and film advance mechanism is shown in Figure 4-15. A hollow ball painted black on the inside and having a hole facing the objective is mounted on each instrument to prevent unwanted light from entering the objective when the shutter is open. The rod in front of the objective in Figure 4-11 is used for focusing.[125]

Another variation was used to photograph highly volatile droplets formed by an explosion. The droplets were quite large, about 20-30

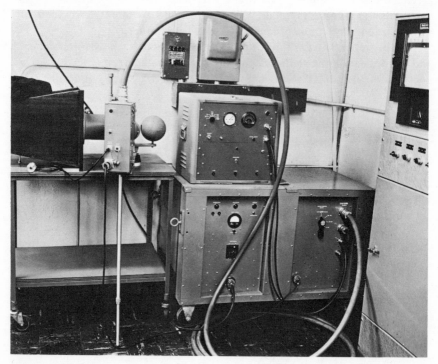

Figure 4-14. Equipment designed for *in situ* photomicrography of ice fog in Alaska.

Figure 4-15. General-purpose instrument for *in situ* aerosol photomicrography.

microns diameter, so a low resolution lens having a relatively large volume in focus could be employed. Transmitted rather than dark-field illumination was used, and a single exposure was made, firing the flash tube milliseconds after the explosion with a time-delay mechanism. Since only a single flash was used, power requirements were modest and were fulfilled with three 300-volt batteries and a capacitor.

High-speed Polaroid film was used and was found to be particularly useful for field operations.

### Control of industrial particulate effluents

Industrial particulate effluents can sometimes be controlled by preventing or limiting their formation. An example is burning coal at high temperatures so that little soot is produced. Often this approach is not possible or is excessively costly. In such cases the particles produced by the industrial operation may have to be removed before they escape from the plant or factory.

Commercially available equipment for removing such particles can be classified as follows: (a) settling chambers, (b) cyclones and inertial separators, (c) wet scrubbers, (d) filters, (e) electrostatic precipitators, and (f) sonic precipitators. Like most such classifications, this is somewhat artificial, since combinations of collection principles are often used.

The basic theory on which the operation of industrial air cleaning equipment is based is discussed in various sections of Chapter 2. While theoretical considerations are indispensable in the design of such equipment and useful in the selection of equipment for specific purposes, its design remains something of an art, since many variables are involved. Equipment selection for a particular plant or industry depends on the particle size distribution, physical and chemical nature of the particulate material (solid, liquid, "tarry," corrosive, etc.), rate at which gas is to be treated, gas temperature, particle concentration, and the removal efficiency required. Various aspects of control methods and equipment have been reviewed in a series of articles in Volume II of Stern's "Air Pollution."[126]

*Settling chambers.* When the particles to be removed are very large, that is, more than about 50 microns in diameter, it may be feasible to remove then in sedimentation chambers. Such chambers are the simplest of collectors and may be only an enlargement of a duct or flue such that the gas velocity is reduced, allowing the larger particles to settle out. This arrangement is particularly useful to prevent overloading equipment for removing fine particles. A common settling chamber consists of a horizontal box, the length of which must be such that the smallest particle to be collected will settle from the top to the bottom of the chamber in less time than required for a particle to traverse the chamber lengthwise. However, turbulence of air in the box will considerably decrease its collection efficiency, and it is conventional to increase its length considerably over that calculated from terminal velocity, usually about two-fold. Various objects may be suspended in the chamber to serve as baffles and decrease turbulence. These include curtains, rods, and screens, but they must not materially change the air velocity in different parts of the chamber or they may actually increase turbulence.

The efficiency of such a chamber can be increased by equipping it with several parallel floors located one above the other. This decreases the distance the particles must fall.

Gas velocities through a settling chamber must be sufficiently low to avoid re-entrainment.

*Inertial separators.* Cyclone separators and various "inertial separators" depend primarily on inertial forces to separate particles from gases. A cyclone separator or collector is a device without moving parts, the main feature of which is a chamber in which the gas stream velocity is converted to a swirling motion of the gas. Centrifugal forces move the suspended particles to the wall.

The most common type of cyclone has a tangential inlet near the top of a vertical cylindrical chamber, and a gas outlet which consists of a cylinder about half the diameter of the chamber, mounted concentrically in the top of the chamber, and extending about one-third of the way down. A cone-shaped extension of the cylindrical chamber leads the collected particles down to an axial discharge port (Figure 4-16). The

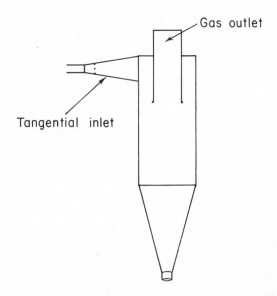

Figure 4-16. Schematic diagram of common cyclone collector.

entering gas creates a spiral flow downward which continues below the gas outlet. Near the bottom of the cone the spiral reverses direction of travel, forming an inner vortex which is usually smaller in diameter than the gas outlet.

The centrifugal force results in a layer of gas rich in dust next to the walls which spirals down the walls to the discharge port. Re-entrainment into the main gas stream at the base of the vortex may be a serious problem and must be considered in the design of the cyclone.

Cyclone separators do not effect a sharp cut in size between particles collected and those allowed to escape, both because of entrainment and because the spiraling gas has a finite thickness. The following equation by Lapple[127] is one of several which have been suggested for estimating the relationship between particle size and other cyclone characteristics:

$$D_{cp} = \sqrt{\frac{9\eta W_1}{2\pi N_p V_i (\rho - \rho')}} \tag{4.48}$$

where $D_{cp}$ is the diameter of particles collected with 50 percent efficiency, $\eta$ is the gas viscosity in lb/ft sec, $W_1$ is inlet width in ft, $N_p$ is the effective number of turns in the cyclone, $V_i$ is the gas inlet velocity in ft/sec, and $\rho$ and $\rho'$ are particle and gas densities in lb/ft$^3$. $D_{cp}$ is about 5 microns for conventional cyclones, but this can be reduced by using smaller, higher-speed cyclones. When particles are larger than 200 microns diameter, settling chambers are probably more appropriate than cyclones since they are more resistant to abrasion.

Several other cyclone designs are commercially available. For example, swirl vanes may be used in place of the tangential inlet to create the vortex action, and the discharge may be peripheral instead of using the cone arrangement. Banks of small cyclones may be used instead of a single large one, or cyclones may be arranged in series. The former usually consist of parallel, small, high-efficiency cyclones operated in banks to provide a practical volume flow rate. Cyclones are often operated in series to partially avoid the problems of re-entrainment.

"Inertial separators" differ from cyclones in that they produce sudden rather than continuous changes in the direction of the gas stream. The theory of such separators is discussed in Chapter 2 (p. 87). The simplest inertial separators are baffle chambers, in which staggered plates or other objects are placed in the gas stream. Such collectors are usually satisfactory for particles 20 microns in diameter or larger. An example of such a device is the Riley flue-gas scrubber in which the ash particles impinge on vertical carbon plates. Water flows over the surfaces of the plates to remove the particles. Gas velocity is about 1000 ft/min. Another commercially available device collects mist droplets by impaction on metal mesh which may be installed in a tower or stack. Some of the most efficient inertial collectors have about 50 percent efficiency for particles as small as 3 microns diameter.

**Wet scrubbers.** Wet scrubbers, in which the particles are collected by impingement with droplets of water or solutions, are widely used in industry. Oils are sometimes sprayed to remove particles not readily wetted by water. A simple type of wet scrubber is merely a tower into the top of which the liquid is sprayed. The gases bearing the particles pass upward through the tower countercurrently. Such scrubbers are only useful for the removal of very coarse particles such as fly ash.

A well-known scrubber which is much more efficient for collecting small particles is the Pease-Anthony, which is actually a combination of scrubber and cyclone. The gas enters tangentially at the bottom of a cylindrical vessel rather than at the top, as in the conventional cyclone (Figure 4-17).

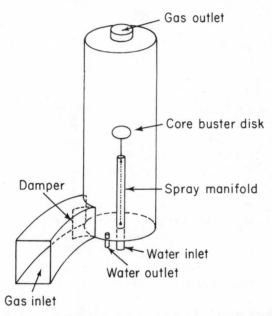

Figure 4-17. Schematic drawing of Pease-Anthony scrubber.

The scrubbing liquid is sprayed out horizontally into the whirling gas stream through an axial manifold entering the bottom of the vessel. The droplets impinge on the particles and carry them to the walls by centrifugal action. Water and particles drain through the bottom. Efficiencies for particles as small as 1 micron diameter may exceed 95 percent.

As discussed in Chapter 2, decreasing the droplet size and increasing the droplet velocity in such a device should increase the collection efficiency. This is borne out by experience and various scrubbers have been designed with this principle in mind. One of these is the venturi scrubber. Dust-laden air is drawn through a cylindrical pipe containing a constriction, the venturi throat. The drop in pressure at the venturi throat draws water through nozzles located about the circumference of the throat. The action is very similar to that of the aspirating type of nebulizer. Very fine droplets are formed and the gas in the throat is in a condition of violent turbulence which contributes to collection efficiency. The spray and gases then pass into a cyclone where the droplets and collected particles are removed from the gas stream. The efficiency of such a scrubber increases with increasing over-all pressure drop. Collection efficiencies exceeding 95 percent have been achieved for submicron size particles.

Small venturi scrubbers have been used for field sampling of airborne particles. They can be used for collecting gases as well as particles by employing the proper solutions.

Scrubbers are also commercially available in which the liquid is sprayed onto a rotating blade or disc, which breaks up the drops and imparts a high velocity to the resulting droplets.

**Filters.** Commercial filters generally operate by either of two mechanisms: one involves collection of the particles on a fiber filter; the other involves building up a thin mat of particles in and on some sort of coarse filter, after which this mat serves as the filtering medium. The latter type is by far the more common for industrial air pollution control because of its much greater capacity per unit area. The well-known cloth collectors or bag filters are in this category, a woven fabric serving as the backing filter. The collection efficiency for small particles is very low at first, since the sizes of the openings are much greater than the size of the particles. Thus at first the particles are collected largely by inertial and diffusional processes. However, the mat usually builds up in a matter of minutes or seconds, and the collection efficiency for small particles increases markedly.

In spite of the claims of very high collection efficiencies for cloth filters, little is known about the effect of particle size on their efficiency. This is not surprising since an extremely long time is required to build up a bed or mat of submicron size particles. When the particle size distribution is large, so that the aerosol contains both submicron and large particles, the mat builds up rapidly. However, in the latter case efficiencies are usually determined on the basis of mass of material collecting (or penetrating) and very small particles may contribute very little to the mass. Nevertheless, cloth filters may be very efficient for very small particles in the presence of large ones, since the former will accumulate in the interstices of the large particles and filter with very high efficiency.

In simplest form, the filters consist of bags of the backing fabric which typically are 1.5 ft in diameter and 30 ft long. They are mounted in a "baghouse" and hang down over a dust-receiving hopper. Dust-laden gas passes through the bags and is discharged directly to the atmosphere. More modern arrangements involve mechanical filters. The dirty gas is passed up through the bags to remove the particles, and the bags are mechanically shaken periodically to discharge the collected particles into a hopper. Numerous modifications are commercially available.

Most of the filter fabrics are cotton sateens, but other materials such as glass or asbestos are used when heat resistance is required.

**Electrostatic precipitators.** Electrostatic precipitators are very efficient for collecting submicron size particles as well as larger ones as discussed in Chapter 2, and the pressure drop through them is of course very small. The latter characteristic gives them decided advantages over baghouses for many purposes. Industrial electrostatic precipitators must fulfill several functions. The first is to produce free electrons and ions which charge the particles. Second is the production of an electrostatic field to induce migration of the charged particles. Third, the dimensions and rate of gas flow must be such that the particles have time to reach the collecting surface. Fourth, reentrainment must be prevented. And fifth, some means must be provided for removal of the collected particles.

Rose and Wood[128] have suggested the equation

$$E = 100[1 - \exp(-Av/V)] \tag{4.49}$$

for the collection efficiency of an industrial precipitator, where $E$ is the efficiency in percent, $A$ is the total electrode collecting surface in meters$^2$, $v$ is the particle drift velocity in meters/sec, and $V$ is the volumetric flow rate in meters$^3$/sec. Gottschlich[129] has suggested that the following equation can be used to calculate $v$ in equation 4.49:

$$v = \frac{3f}{f + 2} \frac{dB^2}{36 \times 10^7 \pi \eta} \left(I + \frac{J\lambda}{d}\right) \tag{4.50}$$

where $f$ is the dielectric constant in electrostatic cgs units, $d$ is the particle diameter, $B$ is the electrical field strength in volts/meter, $\eta$ is the absolute viscosity in poises, $J = 1.764 + 0.562 \exp(-0.785d/\lambda)$, and $\lambda$ is the mean free path of the gas molecules in meters. This equation is based on the assumptions that (a) the charge accumulated by a particle quickly reaches a limiting value, (b) the Stokes-Cunningham law holds, and (c) the terminal velocity of the particle moving to the collecting electrode is rapidly attained. If the electrostatic precipitator is of the wire and plate type the field can be calculated using the equation

$$B = \frac{2ix}{\pi K_0 Kh} \tag{4.51}$$

where $i$ is the electric current per unit length of the discharge electrode in amperes/meter, $x$ is the spacing between the discharge and plate electrodes in meters, $K_0$ is the dielectric constant of a vacuum, $8.8543 \times 10^{-12}$ coulombs/joule-meter, $K$ is the ion mobility in meters$^2$/volt-sec, and $h$ is the average spacing between discharge electrodes in meters.

Most industrial electrostatic precipitators fall into one of two classes, (a) single-stage devices which combine all the functions described above, and (b) two-stage precipitators in which the particles are charged in one stage and collected in the other. Single-stage precipitators, often called Cottrell precipitators, are usually of two types, namely, plate and pipe. The collecting electrodes of the former are parallel plates or screens, or an array of rods, chains, or other elongated objects. The discharge electrodes, which are usually rods or wires, are placed between the collecting electrodes. The collecting electrodes of the latter type are banks of parallel pipes, and the discharge electrodes are located inside and along the axis of the pipes. Plate precipitators are usually used for collecting dusts and pipe precipitators for collecting droplets.[130] Particles may be removed from the electrode surface by mechanical scraping or rapping, or by circulating a liquid over the electrode surface.

The electrodes in the first stage of a two-stage precipitator usually are discharge electrodes consisting of fine wires and collecting electrodes consisting of rods. The voltage between the two sets of electrodes must be high enough to produce a corona discharge.

The second stage produces an electric field with electrodes consisting of parallel plates or concentric cylinders. Generally the voltage across the electrodes is lower than across the electrodes in the first stage, since a corona discharge need not be produced and sparking must be avoided.

According to Lapple,[130] two-stage precipitators have a large cost advantage over Cottrell precipitators since the former can be made smaller as the result of close plate spacing, have a lower power consumption, and can be mass-produced as standardized units. Close plate spacing cannot be used where large amounts of dust are to be collected, as in certain process applications.

Large-scale electrostatic precipitators such as those used for air pollution control are generally powered by rectified alternating current. Small electrostatic precipitators such as those used for sampling are often powered by alternating current, the precipitators themselves acting as rectifiers.

*Sonic precipitators.* The possibility of using acoustic energy for agglomeration in gases, as in the prevention of air pollution, was mentioned in Chapter 2. However, the production of large amounts of ultrasonic energy is expensive and the method has not been popular. Gas-siren generators have been developed which convert compressed gas energy into acoustic energy at 50 to 70 percent efficiency in units that develop up to 100 kw of acoustic energy.[131] A few sonic agglomerators have been used in series with cyclone collectors to recover materials such as carbon black, soda ash, and sulfuric acid droplets.[129]

This brief discussion of devices for the control of industrial air pollution has emphasized the collection efficiency as a function of particle size for several types of collectors. It is important to keep in mind that many other factors such as pressure drop, energy requirements, initial cost, rate of depreciation, and physical state of the material to be removed must be considered in selecting control equipment. Such factors are discussed in detail in many of the references listed.

### REFERENCES

1. Bartel, A. W., and J. W. Temple, *Ind. Eng. Chem.*, **44,** 857 (1952).
2. Stanford Research Institute, "The Smog Problem in Los Angeles County," Menlo Park, Calif., 1954.
3. Magill, P. L., D. H. Hutchison, and J. M. Stormes, in "Proceedings of the Second National Air Pollution Symposium," Stanford Research Institute, ed., Menlo Park, Calif., 1952.
4. Haagen-Smit, A. J., C. E. Bradley, and M. M. Fox, *Ind. Eng. Chem.*, **45,** 2086 (1953).
5. Hanst, P. L., and J. G. Calvert, *J. Phys. Chem.*, **63,** 71, 2071 (1959).
6. Leighton, P. A., "Photochemistry of Air Pollution," Academic Press, New York, 1961.
7. Cadle, R. D., in "Conference on Chemical Reactions in Urban Atmospheres," Report No. 15, Air Pollution Foundation, November, 1956.
8. Stephens, E. R., W. E. Scott, P. L. Hanst, and R. C. Doerr, *J. Air Pollution Control Assoc.*, **6,** 159 (1956); *Proc. Am. Petrol. Inst.*, **36,** III, 288 (1956).
9. Stephens, E. R., E. F. Darley, O. C. Taylor, and W. E. Scott, *Int. J. Air & Water Pollution*, **4,** 79 (1961).
10. Cadle, R. D., and C. Schadt, *J. Am. Chem. Soc.*, **74,** 6002 (1952).
11. Vrbǎski, T., and R. J. Cvetanović, *Can. J. Chem.*, **38,** 1053, 1063 (1960).
12. Darley, E. F., E. R. Stephens, J. T. Middleton, and P. L. Hanst, *Intern. J. Air Pollution*, **1,** 155 (1959).
13. Eastman, R. H., and R. M. Silverstein, *J. Am. Chem. Soc.*, **75,** 1493 (1953).
14. Cadle, R. D., and P. L. Magill, *AMA Arch. Ind. Hyg. Occ. Med.*, **4,** 74 (1951).
15. Renzetti, N. A., and G. J. Doyle, *J. Air Pollution Control Assoc.*, **8,** 293 (1959); *Intern. J. Air Pollution*, **2,** 327 (1960).
16. Schuck, E. A., and G. J. Doyle, "Photooxidation of Hydrocarbons in Mixtures Containing Oxides of Nitrogen and Sulfur Dioxide," Rept. No. 29. Air Pollution Foundation, San Marino, Calif., 1959.
17. Hanst, P. L., E. R. Stephens, W. E. Scott, and R. C. Doerr, "Atmospheric Ozone-Olefin Reactions," The Franklin Institute, Philadelphia, 1958.

18. Salzman, B. E., *Ind. Eng. Chem.*, **50**, 677 (1958).
19. Criegee, R., G. Bust, and H. Zinke, *Chem. Ber.*, **87**, 766 (1954).
20. Schuck, E. H., H. W. Ford, and E. R. Stephens, "Air Pollution Effects of Irradiated Automobile Exhaust as Related to Fuel Composition," Rept. No. 26, Air Pollution Foundation, San Marino, California, 1958.
21. Endow, N., G. J. Doyle, and J. L. Jones, *J. Air Pollution Control Assoc.*, **13**, 141 (1963).
22. Cadle, R. D., *Anal. Chem.*, **23**, 196 (1951).
23. Cadle, R. D., S. Rubin, C. I. Glassbrook, and P. L. Magill, *Arch. Ind. Hyg. Occ. Med.*, **2**, 698 (1950).
24. Cadle, R. D., in "Atmospheric Chemistry of Chlorine and Sulfur Compounds," Monograph No. 3, American Geophysical Union, 1959.
25. Titus, R. N., and H. L. Gray, *Ind. Eng. Chem., Anal. Ed.*, **2**, 368 (1930).
26. Benedetti-Pichler, A. A., and J. R. Rachele, *Ind. Eng. Chem., Anal. Ed.*, **12**, 233 (1940).
27. Kirk, P. L., "Quantitative Ultramicro-Analysis," Wiley, New York, 1950.
28. Chamot, E. M., and C. W. Mason, "Handbook of Chemical Microscopy," 2nd ed., Wiley, New York, 1946 and vol. 1, 3rd ed., Wiley, New York, 1958.
29. Sumi, L., A. Corkery, and J. L. Monkman, in "Atmospheric Chemistry of Chlorine and Sulfur Compounds," Monograph No. 3, American Geophysical Union, 1959.
30. Public Health Service Publication No. 637. GPO, "Air Pollution Measurements of the National Air Sampling Network," Superintendent of Documents, Washington 25, D.C., 1958.
31. Zimmer, C. E., E. C. Tabor, and A. C. Stern, *J. Air Poll. Control Assoc.*, **9**, 136 (1959).
32. Am. Ind. Hyg. Assoc., "Air Pollution Manual, Part 1.... Evaluation," Detroit, 1960.
33. McCullough, S., and P. J. Perkins, "Flight Camera for Photographing Cloud Droplets in Natural Suspension in the Atmosphere," N.A.C.A. Res. Memo. E50K01, 1951.
34. Nader, J. S., G. C. Ortman, and M. T. Massey, *Am. Ind. Hyg. Assoc. J.*, **22**, 42 (1961).
35. Rupp, W. H., in "Air Pollution Handbook," P. L. Magill, F. R. Holden, and C. Ackley, eds., McGraw-Hill, New York, 1956.
36. McCrone, W. C., and M. A. Salzenstein, *J. Air Poll. Control Assoc.*, **12**, 195 (1962).
37. Lapple, C. E., *S.R.I. Journal*, **5**, 95, Stanford Research Institute, Menlo Park, Calif., 1961.
38. Gas Appliance Manufacturers Assoc., Inc., "GAMA Statistical Highlights, Ten Year Summary, 1950–1959," New York, 1960; Schueneman, J., *J. Air Poll. Control Assoc.*, **13**, 116 (1963).
39. Middleton, J. T., and A. J. Haagensmit, "The Occurrence Distribution and Significance of Photochemical Air Pollution in the United States and Canada," present at 53rd Assoc. Meeting, Air Poll. Control Assoc., Cincinnati, Ohio, May, 1960.
40. Niemeyer, L. E., *J. Air Poll. Control Assoc.*, **13**, 381 (1963).
41. Robinson, E., in "Air Pollution," **1**, A. C. Stern, ed., Academic Press, New York, 1962.

42. "Manual of Surface Observations" (WBAN), Circular N, 7th ed. USGPO, Washington, D.C., 1955.
43. Steffens, C., and S. Rubin, in "Proceedings of the First National Air Pollution Symposium," Stanford Research Institute, Menlo Park, Calif., 1949.
44. Steffens, C., in "Air Pollution Handbook," P. L. Magill, F. R. Holden, and C. Ackley, eds., McGraw-Hill, New York, 1956.
45. Steffens, C., *Ind. Eng. Chem.*, **41**, 2396 (1949).
46. Marynowski, C. W., and F. E. Littman, Proc. Air Pollution Control Assoc. for 1953, p. 45 (pub. 1954).
47. Bradbury, N. E., and E. M. Fryer, *Bull. Am. Meteorol Soc.*, **21**, 391 (1940).
48. Middleton, W. E. K., "Vision Through the Atmosphere," Univ. of Toronto Press, Toronto, Ontario, 1952.
49. van de Hulst, H. C., "Light Scattering by Small Particles," Wiley, New York, 1957.
50. Goldsmith, J. R., in "Air Pollution," **1**, A. C. Stern, ed., Academic Press, New York, 1962.
51. Lawther, P. J., in "Proceedings of the Third National Air Pollution Symposium," Stanford Research Institute, Menlo Park, Calif., 1955.
52. Lawther, P. J., in "Atmospheric Chemistry of Chlorine and Sulfur Compounds," Monograph No. 3, American Geophysical Union, 1959.
53. Johnstone, H. F., and D. R. Coughanowr, *Ind. Eng. Chem.*, **50**, 1169 (1958).
54. Stokinger, H. E., in "Air Pollution," **1**, A. C. Stern, ed. Academic Press, New York, 1962.
55. Clamann, H. G., and R. W. Bancroft, "Advances in Chemistry," *No. 21*, 352 (1959); Clamann, H. G., in "Proc. Intern. Symposium Phys. Med. Atmosphere Space," 2nd, San Antonio, 1960.
56. Mittler, S., *Ind. Med & Surg.*, **27**, 43 (1958).
57. Wagner, W. D., O. J. Dobrogorski, and H. E. Stokinger, *Arch. Envir. Health*, **2**, 534 (1961).
58. Cadle, R. D., and P. L. Magill, *AMA Arch. Ind. Hyg. Occ. Med.*, **4**, 74 (1951).
59. Buchberg, H., K. W. Wilson, M. H. Jones, and K. G. Lindh., *Int. J. Air Water Poll.*, **7**, 257 (1963).
60. Renzetti, N. A., and E. A. Schuck, *J. Air Poll. Control Assoc.*, **11**, 12, (1961).
61. Cadle, R. D., and H. S. Johnston, in "Proceedings of the Second National Air Pollution Symposium," Stanford Research Institute, Menlo Park, Calif., 1952.
62. Prindle, R. A., *J. Air Poll. Control Assoc.*, **9**, 12 (1959).
63. Kotin, P., and H. L. Falk, in "Proceedings of the Third National Air Pollution Symposium," Stanford Research Institute, Menlo Park, Calif., 1955.
64. Sawicki, E., W. C. Elbert, T. R. Hauser, F. T. Fox, and T. W. Stanley, *Am. Ind. Hyg. Assoc. J.*, **21**, 443 (1960).
65. Stokinger, H. E., W. D. Wagner, and O. J. Dobrogorski, *AMA Arch. Ind. Health*, **16**, 514 (1957).
66. Mueller, P. K., H. L. Helwig, A. E. Alcocer, W. K. Gong, and E. E. Jones. Concentration of fine particles and lead in auto exhaust. Preprint

of paper presented to Am. Soc. for Testing Materials, Los Angeles, Calif., Oct. 1962.

67. Robinson, E., F. L. Ludwig, J. E. De Vries, and R. E. Hopkins, "Variations of Atmospheric Lead Concentrations and Type with Particle Size," Stanford Research Institute, Menlo Park, Calif., 1963.

68. Goetz, A., H. J. R. Stevenson, and O. Preining, *J. Air Poll. Control Assoc.*, **10,** 378 (1960).

69. Thomas, M. D., and R. H. Hendricks, in "Air Pollution Handbook," P. L. Magill, F. R. Holden, and C. Ackley, ed., McGraw-Hill, New York, 1956.

70. Bobrov, R. A., in "Proceedings of the Third National Air Pollution Symposium," Stanford Research Institute, Menlo Park, Calif., 1955.

71. Haagen-Smit, A. J., E. F. Durley, M. Zailtin, H. Hull, and W. Noble, *Plant Physiol.*, **27,** 18 (1952).

72. Cann, G. R., W. M. Noble, and G. P. Larson, *Air Repair*, **4,** 83 (1954).

73. Richards, B. L., and O. C. Taylor, *J. Air Poll. Control Assoc.*, **11,** 125 (1961).

74. Arnold, W. N., *Int. J. Air Poll.*, **2,** 167 (1959).

75. Darley, E. F., E. R. Stephens, J. T. Middleton, and P. L. Hanst, *Int. J. Air Poll.*, **1,** 155 (1959).

76. Freebairn, H. T., *J. Air Poll. Control Assoc.*, **10,** 314 (1960).

77. Ordin, L., O. C. Taylor, B. E. Propst, and E. A. Cardiff, *Int. J. Air and Water Poll.*, **6,** 223 (1962).

78. Benedict, H. M., and W. H. Breen, in "Proceedings of the Third National Air Pollution Symposium," Stanford Research Institute, Menlo Park, Calif., 1952.

79. Darley, E. F., *J. Air Poll. Cont. Assoc.*, **10,** 198 (1960).

80. Cadle, R. D., and H. C. Wohlers, *Air Repair* (Now *J. Air Poll. Control Assoc.*), **1,** No. 4, 30 (1952).

81. Middleton, J. T., E. F. Darley, F. Ellis, R. F. Bremer, *J. Air Poll. Cont. Assoc.*, **8,** 9 (1958).

82. Ott, R. R., and R. E. Hatchard, *J. Air Poll. Cont. Assoc.*, **13,** 437 (1963).

83. Sheehy, J. P., and C. A. Lindstrom, in "Air Pollution," **2,** A. E. Stern, ed., Academic Press, New York, 1962.

84. Allen, G. L., F. H. Viets, and L. C. McCabe, U.S. Bureau of Mines Inform. Circ. 7627 (1952).

85. Orban, A., J. Hummell, and G. Cooks, *J. Air Poll. Control Assoc.*, **11,** 103 (1961).

86. Brief, R. S., A. Rose, and D. Stephan, *J. Air Poll. Control Assoc.*, **6,** No. 4, 1 (1957).

87. Adams, R. L., *J. Air Poll. Control Assoc.*, **14,** 299 (1964).

88. Hemeon, W. C. L., *J. Air Poll. Control Assoc.*, **7,** 62 (1957).

89. Howell, G. A., *Air Repair*, **3,** 163 (1954).

90. Hemeon, W. C. L., *J. Air Poll. Control Assoc.*, **10,** 208 (1960).

91. Committee T1-5, *J. Air Poll. Control Assoc.*, **10,** 292 (1960).

92. Russell, H. H., *J. Air Poll. Control Assoc.*, **7,** 46 (1957).

93. Underwood, G., *Int. J. Air and Water Poll.*, **6,** 229 (1962).

94. Smith, M. E., in "Chemical Reactions in the Lower and Upper Atmosphere," Stanford Research Institute, ed., Interscience, New York, 1961.

95. Sutton, O. G., *Quart. J. Roy. Meteorol. Soc.*, **73,** 257, 426 (1947).

96. Bosanquet, C. H., and J. L. Pearson, *Trans. Faraday Soc.*, **32**, 1249 (1936).
97. U.S. Weather Bureau, "Meteorology and Atomic Energy," prepared for the U.S. Atomic Energy Commission, 1959.
98. Falk, L. L., W. R. Chalker, J. A. Greene, C. B. Cave, and C. W. Thorngate, *Air Repair*, **4**, 35 (1954).
99. Sutton, O. G., "Micrometeorology; A Study of Physical Processes in the Lowest Layers of the Earth's Atmosphere," McGraw-Hill, New York, 1953.
100. Calder, K. R., in "Air Pollution," L. C. McCabe, ed., McGraw-Hill, New York, 1952.
101. Sutton, O. G., *Brit. Chem. Eng.*, **1**, 202 (August, 1956).
102. Scorer, R. S., *Int. J. Air Poll.*, **1**, 198 (1959).
103. Bodurtha, Jr., F. T., *J. Air Poll. Control Assoc.*, **11**, 431 (1961).
104. Scorer, R. S., *Int. J. Air Poll.*, **6**, 101 (1962).
105. Bosanquet, C. H., W. F. Carey, and E. M. Halton, *Proc. Inst. Mech. Engrs. (London)*, **162**, 355 (1950).
106. Gosline, C. A., T. L. Falks, and E. N. Helmers, in "Air Pollution Handbook," P. L. Magill, F. R. Holden, and C. Ackley, eds., McGraw-Hill, New York, 1957.
107. Hawkins, J. E., and G. Nonhebel, *J. Inst. Fuel*, **28**, 530 (1955).
108. Baron, T., E. R. Gerhard, and H. F. Johnstone, *Ind. Eng. Chem.*, **41**, 2403 (1949).
109. "Meteorology and Atomic Energy," U. S. Atomic Energy Commission Report AECU-3066 (1955).
110. Strom, G. H., in "Air Pollution," **1**, A. C. Stern, ed., Academic Press, New York, 1962.
111. Holden, F. R., F. W. Dresch, and R. D. Cadle, *A.M.A. Arch. Ind. Hyg. Occ. Med.*, **9**, 291 (1954).
112. Perkins, W. A., P. A. Leighton, S. W. Grinnel, and F. X. Webster, in "Proceedings of the Second National Air Pollution Symposium," Stanford Research Institute, Menlo Park, Calif., 1952.
113. R. R. Braham, B. K. Seely, and W. D. Crozier, *Tr. Am. Geophys. Union*, **33**, 825 (1952).
114. Robinson, E., J. A. MacLeod, and C. E. Lapple, *J. Meteorol.*, **16**, 63 (1959).
115. Lapple, C. E., *Heating, Piping, Air Conditioning*, (July, August, October, November 1944; December 1945; February, 1946).
116. Yaffee, C. D., D. H. Byers, and A. D. Hosey, eds., "Encyclopedia of Instrumentation for Industrial Hygiene," University of Michigan, Ann Arbor, Mich., 1956.
117. American Conference of Governmental Industrial Hygienists, "Air Sampling Instruments for Evaluation of Atmospheric Contaminants," 1014 Broadway, Cincinnati, Ohio, 1962.
118. Mitchell, R. I., and R. B. Engdahl, *J. Air Poll. Control Assoc.*, **13**, 558 (1963).
119. Kudlich, R., "Ringelman Smoke Chart," U.S. Bureau of Mines, Inform. Circ. 6888, revised 1941.
120. Rose, A. H., J. S. Nader, and P. A. Drinker, *J. Air Poll. Control Assoc.*, **8**, 112 (1958).
121. Air Pollution Measurements Committee, *J. Air Poll. Control Assoc.*, **13**, 397 (1963).
122. Cadle, R. D., "Particle Size Determination," Interscience, New York, 1955.

123. Gucker, F. T., Jr., in L. McCabe, ed., "Air Pollution," McGraw-Hill, New York, 1952.
124. Gucker, F. T., Jr., and D. G. Rose, *Brit. J. Appl. Phys.*, Suppl. 3, 138 (1954).
125. Cadle, R. D., and E. J. Wiggins, *Arch. Ind. Hyg. Occ. Med.*, **12,** 584 (1955).
126. Stern, A. C., "Air Pollution," **2,** Academic Press, New York, 1962.
127. Lapple, C. E., *Ind. Hyg. Quart.*, **5,** No. 11, 40 (1950).
128. Rose, H. E., and A. J. Wood, "An Introduction to Electrostatic Precipitation in Theory and Practice," Constable, London, 1956.
129. Gottschlich, C. F., in "Air Pollution," **2,** A. C. Stern, ed., Academic Press, New York, 1962.
130. Lapple, C. E., in "Chemical Engineers' Handbook," 3rd. ed., J. A. Perry, ed., McGraw-Hill, New York, 1950.
131. Heuter, T. F., and R. H. Bolt, "Sonics," Wiley, New York, 1954.

# Chapter 5

# Clean Rooms

## THE NEED FOR CLEAN ROOMS

### Definitions

A clean room, also often referred to as a white room, can be loosely defined as any room maintained relatively free of dust in order to conduct some operation more advantageously. The two terms are usually used in this manner. Clean rooms are becoming so important and so widely used that it has become necessary to establish standards for such rooms and highly specific definitions. Federal Standard No 209 defines clean rooms as follows.[1]

"A clean room is an enclosed area employing control over the particulate matter in air with temperature, humidity and pressure as required. To meet the requirements of a clean room as defined by this standard, all clean rooms must maintain a particulate count as specified in clean room classes, 5.1"

Particle count and size specifications such as this one are discussed later in this chapter.

A work station is defined as "... a work bench or similar working enclosure characterized by having its own filtered air or gas supply."

The Air Force definitions, as stated in Technical Order 00-25-203, are slightly different:[2]

"An AF standard Clean Room (AFSCR) is a work space currently called a room, shop, or facility in which environmental conditions are positively controlled. A clean room requires high standards· of environmental control and cleanliness in order to meet exacting operations and tolerances during the repair, assembly, and test of presicion instruments, electromechanical devices, and other items requiring environmental control."

The Air Force Technical Order continues with the definition of two related types of facilities.

"An AF Clean Work Station (AFCWS) is a contamination controlled work space used to insure a high degree of cleanliness about a work piece. The clean work station contains a surrounding atmosphere of extremely low airborne contamination."

"A Controlled Area is a work space currently called a room, shop, or facility in which better than normal housekeeping is necessary. It is not to be classified as a clean room. Such an area is required for overhaul of electromechanical devices and other items which do not require the strict environmental controls of a clean room, but which should be segregated from excessive dirt-generating operations. This area will be temperature controlled so that the maximum temperature will not exceed 80°F."

### Types of operation

The need to conduct many manufacturing and assembly operations in clean rooms has developed almost entirely since World War II. A large percentage of clean-room operations have been military and "space" developments and have reflected the increasing need for precision and reliability. In particular, the need for dust-free manufacturing conditions has increased as tolerances have decreased.

During World War II, clean rooms were used for the development of the Norden bombsight and the first navigational gyroscopes, although these rooms were essentially normal manufacturing areas equipped with air conditioning.[3] The manufacture of photographic film has long required a high degree of cleanliness to prevent the deposition of dust on the film. Today's highly sophisticated electronic, hydraulic, electromechanical, and electro-optical systems require such extreme precision that the presence of microscopic particles of dust usually found in nominally clean room air is not tolerated. This has led to the development of the clean rooms defined above.

The industries which utilize clean rooms include electronics, pharmaceutical manufacture, photography, rocket and missile component manufacture, instrument manufacturing, electromechanical control mechanisms, the manufacture of solid-state devices, electronic data processing, and nuclear energy. Clean rooms are being used in various laboratories and for special purposes such as the laboratory-scale manufacture of organic-fiber filter paper for stratospheric sampling.

In many cases the need for clean rooms is obvious. Holes in thin-film components of solid-state devices or dust spots on photographic film can be seen. When very close spacings between moving parts must be maintained, particles can jam into these spacings. Hard, sharp particles on bearings can cause wear. On relay or switch surfaces they may result in poor contact or no contact at all. When improved reliability or precision is the aim of using a clean room, the evidence of the advantages to be gained is often circumstantial or non-existent. The circumstantial evidence is often highly compelling but too few data are available to indicate the degree of cleanliness required to achieve the desired results. Not only are safe particle "loadings" (weight of particles per unit volume of air) not known, but very little is known in such cases concerning the importance of particle size. Particle material may also be of considerable importance. A highly abrasive dust may be more harmful in some devices than a dust composed of some soft material, and a corrosive dust may be more harmful than one whose particles are inert.

The Air Force standard clean room is to have a particle concentration of no more than 20,000 particles per cu ft that are 0.5 micron diameter and larger, and no more than 4000 particles per cu ft that are 1.0 micron and larger. The Air Force clean work station is to have a particle concentration of no more than 100 particles per cu ft that are 0.5 micron diameter and larger, a condition that is to be met throughout the entire work station upstream of the work piece. The technical order suggests that items which have clearances in the range from 100 to 1000 millionths of an inch or are affected by particle diameters from 2.5 to 25 microns will require environmental control and should be overhauled in a standard clean room or better. When the clearances are less than 100 millionths of an inch (2.5 microns) a clean work station is required.

Federal Standard 209 defines various classes of rooms, designated class 100, class 10,000, and class 100,000. These classes are based on particle number concentrations with a maximum number of particles permissible for 0.5 micron diameter and 5.0 microns diameter and larger. The class designation refers to the maximum number of particles per cu ft that are 0.5 micron or larger. In addition, the air in clean rooms of classes 10,000 and 100,000 must contain no more than 65 and 700 particles per cu ft, respectively, that are 5 microns in diameter or larger. No attempt is made in this document to indicate the appropriate application of these different classes of clean rooms. It is interesting to note that even the least stringent of the requirements cannot be met by natural air at any location over the continents and other large land masses with the possible exception of the poles and Greenland.[4]

Federal Standard 209 also specifies that all clean rooms shall maintain an air pressure above that of surrounding areas to assure that leakage will be outward and prevent particles from being drawn into the room from outside. Any temperature controls shall be able to maintain a specified temperature within a range of 67° to 77°F within ±0.5°F in areas where highly temperature-sensitive applications are to be undertaken. This standard also specifies that the maximum relative humidity shall be 45 percent and that humidity controls shall be capable of holding a specified relative humidity within ±10 percent for general applications and within ±5 percent for humidity-sensitive applications.

Such specifications are subject to frequent change. Their inclusion here is intended merely to indicate the type and degree of control that seems to be required.

## DESIGN OF CLEAN ROOMS

### Air distribution system

A clean room is much more than a chamber containing filtered air. The particles already in the outside air must be removed as the air is drawn into the room, but equally important is the contamination of the air by particles after it enters the room. In-coming workers unavoidably bring some fine particles on shoes and other items of clothing and even as dandruff and sloughing skin. In addition, the activities of workers produce airborne particles; for example, rubbing clothing over various surfaces will produce airborne lint. Materials and subparts brought into the area may serve to introduce traces of dust, and of course the assembly or manufacturing operations conducted in the room may themselves generate fine particles.

It is important to minimize the contamination rate from these sources, and much of the design of a clean room and its auxiliary equipment is based on this requirement. However, the rate always remains finite, and the air flow through the room must be such that the more-or-less steady state concentration of particles in the room air is always less than the desired upper limit.

Two general types of air distribution systems are being used: laminar-flow systems and nonlaminar-flow or turbulent systems. In clean rooms using laminar-flow distribution systems, the air enters the room through a wall of filters or a ceiling of filters and leaves through the opposite wall or floor, the flow being laminar, that is, without turbulence.

The use of laminar flow in clean rooms was proposed by W. J. Whitfield of the Sandia Corporation in 1961[5,6,7] and two laminar-flow clean rooms were designed and built for this company. Air flowing in a laminar manner across a room rinses the dust in a very efficient manner from the room, as illustrated by Figure 5-1. Dust particles produced in the room are removed almost as soon as they become airborne and do not accumu-

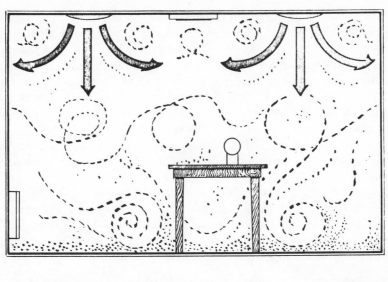

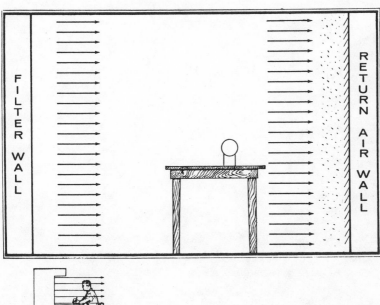

Figure 5-1. Turbulent flow and laminar flow clean rooms. Top—Turbulent flow. Bottom—Laminar flow. (*Courtesy of Agnew-Higgins, Inc.*)

late as a result of eddying and of dead spaces in the air to the extent that is possible when the air is highly turbulent. The flow is not entirely laminar so long as there are objects, especially moving objects, in the room, but a close approximation of such flow is highly effective.

The design and performance of typical laminar flow clean rooms have been described by Bragg.[8] One of these was relatively small, only 10 by 10 ft (Figure 5-2). It consisted of four basic elements, the work-room enclosure, the vertical blower-filter modules, the vertical return damper modules, and the return air duct. The last two constituted two opposite ends of the room. Plenum chambers behind each set of modules were connected by a large return air duct to make a closed circulation loop. The air constantly emerged from the blower-filter modules to produce the laminar air stream across the room. Air reaching the far side of the room was collected into the baffled return damper modules. The purpose of the modules was to produce a uniform velocity distribution at right angles to the direction of air flow.

Figure 5-2. Small laminar clean room built by Parker aircraft.[8]

Since the flow is laminar, the first complete pass of air through such a room removes the particles which have accumulated in the air of the room. No filters are completely effective in removing fine particles from the air, but after the initially present particles are removed from the room, almost all the particles in the air are generated in the room as described above. However, as Bragg points out, these are usually of such low specific gravity and momentum, since the air velocity is low, that they flow around objects in their path and do not settle out before being carried out of the room with the air. However, the airflow rates are so slow that they are not obvious to people in the room. The rate of airflow is set by Federal Standard 209 at 90 fpm ±20 fpm.

When the airflow is horizontal, workers are located in the room so that they are downstream or to one side of the work area. This minimizes deposition on the objects being manufactured of dust generated by the workers themselves. Thus cleanliness is much easier to achieve in a laminar-flow clean room than in one containing turbulent air, since dust generated at one place in the latter may become rather uniformly distributed throughout the room. This feature of laminar-flow rooms is particularly important where the manufacturing operation unavoidably generates considerable dust.

The filter-blower and return damper modules for the 10 ft square room were manufactured by Agnew-Higgins, and were supplied in standard 2-ft sections so that any width of room could be equipped. Such supply air modules are made up of plenum chambers, blower and motor units, and prefilter and final filter units.

It is important that the equipment have a low noise level while operating, essentially no filter by-pass, and that the filters are easy to service or replace. The plenum chamber in the Agnew-Higgins modules produces a uniform outward flow of air. The equipment for this room conformed to Federal Standard 209, which specifies that the incoming air filter bank cover either one entire wall or the entire ceiling.

Two sets of filters are used in the incoming air filter bank. The final filters are of the "HEPA" type ("high efficiency, particulate, air") which were developed by the Atomic Energy Commission and have an efficiency of 99.97 percent or more for aerosol particles 0.3 micron in diameter or larger as determined using dioctyl phthalate.[5] These filters, which constitute the top or rear surface of the enclosure, are flush with the containment surfaces. The mounting arrangement should be such that these filters can be replaced through the rear of the plenum chamber without disturbing the remaining filters and such that a positive seal is readily re-established between the filter and its housing.

The final filters, as specified in Standard 209, were preceded by pre-filters to prolong the life of the HEPA filters. The only requirement for these filters specified by this Standard is that their efficiency should be "...tailored to the anticipated contamination load and the desired life of the HEPA filters." Those used in the 10 ft square room, judging from the manufacturers' literature, were at least "...63% effective on atmospheric dust as measured by the National Bureau of Standards dust spot test."

The blowers used in this room were capable of maintaining the specified flow rate across the room even when there was an increase in pressure of 0.5 in of water across the filters. Obviously the motors must be capable of continuous operation and should be permanently lubricated for the life of the bearing. The fan used by Bragg was a low-speed squirrel-cage type blower, dynamically balanced for quiet operation. The motor was separated from the stream of clean air by a metal partition.

The prefilters were vacuum-cleaned once a month, and although the prefilters were washable, it was not found necessary to wash them during 18 months of operation. The final filters were estimated to last for about ten years before the pressure drop across them would be unreasonable to overcome. The HEPA filters were protected on the clean room side by a perforated metal screen.

The return air wall was made up of adjustable, louvered dampers. The louvers could be adjusted with a key or wrench.

The air conditioning for this small room was accomplished with a small-room unit which discharged cooled air into the return air plenum. It was controlled with a thermostat within the room. Relative humidity was roughly controlled by taking all the make-up air from inside the laboratory, which was separately controlled.

The required slight positive pressure was maintained with a vestibule entry such as that described later.

A second laminar-flow clean room was constructed as the work-load increased (Figure 5-3). It was a wall-to-wall laminar flow room 10 ft wide and 60 ft long. The filter and return modules were on the walls which were 10 ft wide. The work done in this rom was such that the workers rather than the operation they were performing were believed to be the main source of airborne dust. Therefore, the work stations were located along the walls the length of the room, providing an aisle down the center. This put the workers to the side of the work so that particles generated by them would not settle or impinge on the parts being handled. Work stations used for assembly were placed near the wall equipped with filters, and the benches staggered in height, the height increasing with increasing distance downstream. This arrangement permitted the particu-

Figure 5-3. Large laminar clean room built by Parker aircraft.[8]

late material generated at one table to pass under the adjacent down-stream table.

In order to make full use of the walls, entry in the large room was at the return end, through a dressing room downstream of the return damper modules. These were installed in two sets staggered by 4 ft and the door was between them and parallel to the length of the room. This arrangement had the advantage that personnel could enter or leave with relatively little disturbance of the air flow.

The filter modules were the same as those used in the smaller room except that they were free-standing units. The ends of the walls of the room formed the plenum, so they were not equipped with built-in plenum units.

In order to keep the flow in the room as nearly laminar as possible, equipment was kept outside the room to the greatest extent possible, and if this was impossible, mounted flush on the walls. Large items such as ultrasonic cleaning tanks, rinse sink, and fume hoods, were located as far downstream as possible so as to interfere least with laminar flow.

Temperature and humidity were controlled with a 15-ton conventional air-conditioning system. Pressure in the room was maintained about 0.3 in of water greater than that outside.

Another example of laminar-flow clean room is shown in Figures 5-4 and 5-5. Figure 5-6 demonstrates one system of air circulation in such a room.

Most of the above discussion has related to horizontal laminar-flow clean rooms. Rooms having the filters in the ceiling and grating floors have advantages for many applications. An obvious advantage is that the air is moving in the same direction as the air-borne particles are settling. Thus there is no question of particles settling out of the air stream before they are carried out of the room, as there may be for horizontal flow. With such an arrangement it is important that no particle generator, such as a worker's head, be directly above the working area. Such a clean room has been described by Whitfield *et al.*[9] They emphasize that an important consideration in the design of the ceiling plenum is the plenum depth, which is the distance above the filter bank. If the ratio of width to depth does not exceed 4 when air is brought into the plenum from one side at a velocity not exceeding 800 ft per min, the desired uniformity of

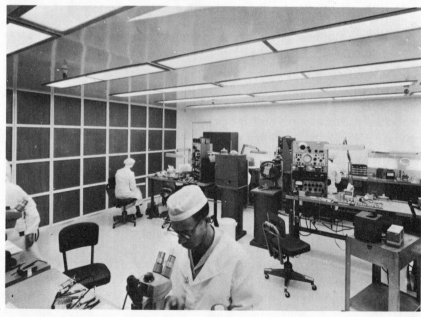

Figure 5-4. This room incorporates Agnew-Higgins model V8 blower-filter modules which are shown in the left hand wall. The floor is vinyl asbestos tile. The walls and ceiling are gypsum board. Translucent plastic panels are mounted in the ceiling and admit light from commercial fixtures suspended in the attic above them. (*Courtesy of The Austin Company*)

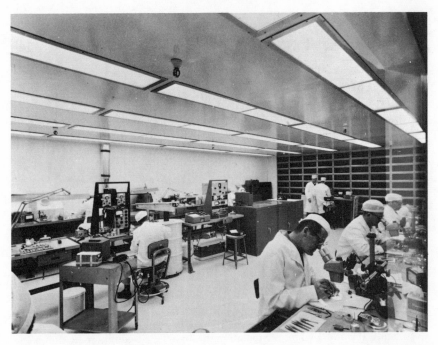

Figure 5-5. This shows the return end of the room shown in Figure 5-4. Note the sprinkler heads in the drop ceiling. The need for these is eliminated if a translucent luminous ceiling is used. If a luminous ceiling is used a foam type weatherstripping tape is applied to the edges of the acrylic plastic pans before they are set in the T-bar frames. Wire spring clips then are placed over the upright leg of the tees to hold the plastic panels against this gasket so that the ceiling is tight. These ceilings pass fire underwriters' code with sprinklers mounted in the roof overhead since they will drop out of their frames at a heat lower then the heat required to actuate the sprinklers. (*Courtesy of The Austin Company*)

air flow into the clean room will be achieved. Plenums with greater width-to-depth ratios can be used successfully, and the ratio can be increased to 8 by bringing air in from both sides of the plenum.

The return-air plenum is below the grating floor, and the collected air as usual is returned to the inlet of the blower system. The floor plenum design should be essentially the same as that for the ceiling plenum. The design Whitfield *et al.* included lining the entire air distribution system with sound-absorbing material to reduce clean-room sound levels.

Prefilters can be located below the grating floor or upstream from the final filters. The prefilter medium can be in sheet form if placed immediately above the filter bank but is preferably pleated when in other parts

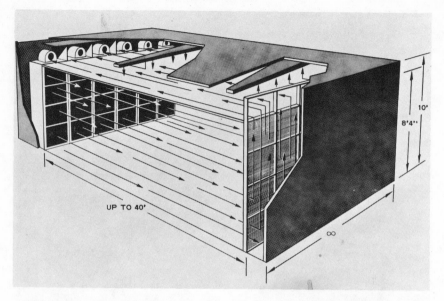

Figure 5-6. Schematic of a closed-loop type recirculating clean room. The tapered ducts in the double-ceiling plenum show how air is delivered to the return air stream and withdrawn for recirculation through the air-conditioning unit. The amount of air in this by-pass is regulated by the amount of cooling or de-humidification required to maintain desired conditions within the clean room. Fresh air is added to the return air duct leading to the air-conditioning system. A rough filter is usually installed in this fresh-air intake. This room will produce conditions several times better than Class 10,000 of the Federal Standard 209 anywhere in the room during conditions of occupancy and in addition will give Class 100 conditions at any point upstream of personnel or work activity. Rooms like this have been built in lengths up to 60 ft and in widths up to 112 ft. (*Courtesy of Agnew-Higgins, Inc.*)

of the system. This permits the use of smaller prefilter dimensions since airflow rates through pleated filters are much higher than through plane filters.

The final filter mounting must be somewhat more rugged for ceiling filters than for wall filters in order to support the filter weight as well as to withstand vibration and air pressure. Whitfield *et al.* recommend that the filter-mounting assembly be equipped with a simple spring mechanism to maintain a force on the filter to compensate for filter-seal fatigue.

Laminar-flow work stations can be used to provide a small working region of particularly clean air when this is more economical than providing a clean room having very high standards of cleanliness, for ex-

Figure 5-7. Console model work station with a 6-ft work chamber. This provides room for two workers or for one worker with an extensive array of parts and equipment. Two rough filters are located in the intake grilles below the counter. Casters can be substituted for the leveling feet provided. Side panels can be removed and units aligned side by side to form continuous work surfaces of any length. (*Courtesy of Agnew-Higgins, Inc.*)

ample, of class 100 (Figure 5-7). Such work stations are generally placed in clean rooms having lower standards than those provided by the work stations. Federal Standard 209 specifications for laminar-flow work stations are very similar to those for laminar-flow clean rooms. For example, the airflow velocity from the air exit of an unobstructed work station should be maintained at 90 ± 20 ft per min across the entire area of the exit to within one inch of the containment surfaces. Outside air should not be drawn into the work area.

Laminar-flow work stations are commercially available in modular form so that a very large size range is possible.* For example, one

*Examples of manufacturers of such equipment are:
(1) Agnew-Higgins, Inc., 7532 Anthony Ave., Garden Grove, Calif.
(2) Air Control, Inc., 450 Narberth Ave., Narberth, Penn.
(3) Edcraft Industries, Inc., 22 Nesbitt St., Newark, N.J.
(4) Pure Air Corporation of America, 317 N. Brea Ave., Los Angeles, Calif.

manufacturer sells both bench type laminar-flow clean work stations and floor-to-ceiling work stations. The former consist of a chamber bounded by a counter, a parapet which may contain lighting, and side walls which are usually transparent. The manufacturer[5] suggests that such work stations can be used to convert ordinary rooms to clean rooms as a result of cleaning the air in the entire room by the filtering action of the stations, and that the number of work stations, $N$, required to produce an air recycling rate of 100 per hour for any room is given by the equation

$$N = V/240F \qquad (5.1)$$

where $F$ is the number of 2 ft $\times$ 2 ft HEPA filters in the rear wall of the work station, and the flow rate through the filters is 100 ft per min.

The floor-to-ceiling work stations are used when the parts are too large for the bench-type stations. Like the latter, these are equipped with HEPA filters in the rear walls, motors and blowers. They may be mounted on casters.

The air flow in clean work stations can be either horizontal or vertical. Horizontal flow toward the worker has the advantage that most particles from the worker's body and clothing are removed from the vicinity of the work area without passing over the work area.

The above discussion has emphasized the air distribution system in laminar-flow clean rooms and work stations. However, many clean rooms are not of this type, and this may continue to be true for many not-so-critical applications. All the air entering such a clean room, recirculated as well as fresh air, should be filtered, preferably with both prefilters and very high efficiency final filters. The room air should probably be changed at least every three minutes for 8 to 12 ft ceiling height rooms.[1] Air conditioning should be provided as required for heating, cooling, humidification, or dehumidification of the clean room.

One advantage of the laminar-flow room is that it is necessary to operate the room only during actual working hours in order to achieve the desired degree of cleanliness. On the other hand, it is usually necessary to operate a non-laminar flow room continuously to maintain the desired cleanliness standards.

Sometimes such rooms have been compartmented into a series of small rooms with particular operations or types of operations assigned to each room. This helps control the contaminant level and aids in locating local sources of contamination.

One method of arranging the air flow in such a room utilizes a large perforated plenum along the center of the ceiling to distribute the air entering the room. The air leaves the room along the walls next to the floor and beneath work benches, where dust tends to accumulate. This system leaves pockets of eddying or nearly motionless air in the upper corner regions of the room.

Particles settling from these regions will reach the flowing air before reaching the floor, but not necessarily before reaching a work bench. Such an arrangement might be particularly useful for a clean room utilizing laminar flow work benches and would be less expensive to construct than a laminar-flow clean rom.

A number of non laminar-flow rooms have been described in the literature.[10,3] For example, such rooms were used extensively for building the Mercury manned satellites.[11]

Turbulent-air work stations have also been built, but these are little more than chemical hoods and there is little point in their use. There may be a need for hoods with in-flowing air when working with hazardous or irritating chemicals. Often a better solution than a hood for such an operation is a vertical-flow laminar clean room or work station.

Clean rooms must be designed for many different purposes and this produces a diversity of circulation problems. An extreme example is the control of contaminants in inert gas-welding atmospheres. High-melting metals such as columbium, titanium, tungsten, and tantalum are widely used in space technology. These metals are very reactive and must be processed in inert atmospheres. The fabrication of parts from such metals is carried out in rooms containing atmospheres such as argon, and the workers in the room must wear special suits and masks attached to air inlet and exhaust lines. The main contaminants to be controlled are oxygen, other oxidizing agents, and moisture. The circulation problems in this case are quite different from those of conventional clean rooms. In one room for handling these metals pure argon is brought in at the room floor and the contaminated gas is removed at the ceiling, since the impurities are lighter than argon and tend to rise to the top of the room.[12] Argon is about 1.33 times as dense as air. Since most of the work is carried out in the lower portions of the room, this circulation arrangement ensures that the operations are conducted in the purest air. The argon leaving the room is passed through a 600 cu ft/min purification plant before it is returned to the bottom of the room.

### Auxiliary rooms

Most clean rooms are equipped with one or two auxiliary rooms. These are a change room for workers and a decontamination room for supplies and parts that are used in the clean room. Change rooms are provided for the preparation of all persons about to enter the clean room. Such preparation is essential to prevent gross contamination of the air in the room. Change rooms should be designed with three sections:[2] a locker room, a semi-contaminated section, and an uncontaminated section.

The locker room is the first approach to the clean room area, since it is there that personnel about to enter the clean room start the personal decontamination process. The locker room is considered to be an uncontrolled area from the fine-particle viewpoint. It is the room (or the place) where overcoats, hats, overshoes, etc. are kept while the worker is in the clean room. Next, the worker enters the semi-contaminated section. A shoe-cleaner should be located at the entrance to this section. Washing and toilet facilities are provided here, and T.0.00-25-203 recommends that the washing facilities include foot-controlled wash stands, liquid soap, and air hand dryer. These are used rather than towels to avoid the production of airborne lint.

The uncontaminated section of the change room is next, and is so located that it can be reached from the clean room or the semi-contaminated section. A sole cleaner, which can consist of a sticky mat, is placed in this section, and an air shower and air lock are provided at the clean room entrance. This section also contains racks or lockers for clean-room garments. The garments will probably include shoe covers or clean-room shoes, so benches or foot rails should be provided.

The personnel air lock is essentially a closet with a door on each of two opposite sides, and large enough to hold several persons. It must be equipped with an interlock door system so that only one of the two doors is open at any time. An air shower can be used as the air lock by interlocking the entrance and exit doors of the shower.

The air shower is designed to remove particles from clothing and exposed skin. This is accomplished by air blasts from nozzles or slots. The exhaust air is removed by suction.

Supervisor areas should not be located in a clean room. If communication with the clean room from a supervisor area is needed, windows and an intercom system can be provided between the clean room and an office.

Numerous modifications of the above suggestions are of course possible. For example, a very large clean room, in fact almost a complete plant, was built by RCA at Cambridge, Ohio; it occupies one and one-half acres, much larger than is usually recommended. The locker rooms for this facility are equipped with sticky mats which remove dust and other dirt from shoes. Persons about to enter the clean room then walk through two corridors that are equipped with high-pressure blowers which remove dust and lint from their street clothes. They put on a snood or cap over the hair, a specially laundered, lint-free, no-closure smock, and booties over their shoes. They then pass into the clean room.[10]

Elaborate precautions such as these may cease to be necessary as improvements continue to be made in clean rooms and clean work stations. The use of laminar-flow circulation to isolate parts being processed from the contamination generated by the workers is a big step in this direction.

A second type of auxiliary room is designed to clean components or raw materials before they are admitted to the room. T.0.00-25-203 defines a materials cleaning room as "...a room immediately adjacent to the clean room, equipped with vacuum lines, ultrasonic cleaners, and/or other mechanical devices for cleaning parts, tools, and materials immediately prior to their entry into the clean room."

Actually, such a room should consist of two parts. The first can be an area rather than a room, where the parts are given a thorough cleaning. The second part is an air lock, which must be large enough to handle the largest materials to be used in the clean room. The doors should of course be equipped with interlocks.

Another, similar room can be set up if there is liklihood that equipment (as contrasted with parts) will have to be transferred in and out of the room. Again, two rooms or an area and a room are needed, one to give the equipment a rough cleaning and the other to serve the dual purpose of thorough cleaning area and air lock. This final cleaning can usually be achieved with vacuum cleaners. Whenever possible, the equipment airlock should only be used during non-working hours. If equipment is moved in or out of the room only on rare occasions, temporary air locks can be constructed. In fact, when laminar-flow rooms or work stations are used, air locks for equipment may not be necessary to maintain the desired cleanliness. If there is no air lock, the equipment can be moved only when the room is shut down, since the air lock is required to maintain the slight positive pressure.

The larger of the two rooms described by Bragg[8] and mentioned earlier was equipped with a dressing room downstream of the return damper modules and a parts pass-through built into the wall at the downstream end of the room. Parts which had entered the room through the pass-through were given a final cleaning, were vacuum oven-dried, inspected for contamination, and assembled into the end product. Each operation was performed at a station progressively closer to the end of the room equipped with the final filters. Testing was performed on the opposite side of the room.

A clean room described by T. F. Tanza[13] was equipped with a cleaning room where component cleaning, inspection, and prepackaging were undertaken. It was also equipped with an ultraviolet light to detect the presence of hydrocarbons and other contaminants on the cleaned surfaces. Component inspection and packaging facilities were located within the clean room, and the inspection included particle counts.

### Other details of design

The shape of the clean room is not important, but for a laminar clean room it is important that the internal wall surfaces be parallel to the direction of air flow and that the cross-sectional area and configuration of the room remain constant downstream of the final filters.[9] There should be few if any ledges, and windows should be flush with the interior wall surfaces. According to Whitfield,[9] size is not important, at least for vertical flow rooms, and some very large clean rooms have been constructed. However, the Air Force standard clean room is limited in size with the statement that rooms larger than 24,000 cu ft present difficulties for a number of reasons. For example, the traffic in large rooms combined with the long distances to exits tends to increase the dust level.

The floor of a clean room should be free of cracks and the edges and corners rounded so as to facilitate cleaning and minimize dust collection. When the air flow is laminar and vertical the floor is a grating; otherwise the floor should be smooth. In the latter case a vinyl or similar plastic sheet material is satisfactory. T.0.00-25-203 points out that floors are potentially one of the strongest sources of particles in a clean room, and that it is possible to generate 150,000,000 particles 1.0 micron in diameter by wearing away a thickness of 1.0 micron from an area the size of a postage stamp.

A number of alternatives are possible to the use of sheet material for floor covering. For example, several coats of polyurethane paint over existing asphalt tile floor was used for one clean room. Vinyl asbestos tile has also been suggested.

The walls of the room should be smooth to discourage particle adhesion, impact-resistant, and durable. Plastic panels or polymer-type paints are especially useful. There should be as few joints and corners as possible and they should be smoothly sealed. Prefabricated panels faced with "Masonite" and held in place with standard aluminum extrusions have been found satisfactory. Proper sealing of joints helps to ensure that particle-laden air doesn't enter the room, which otherwise would be a possibility, although a rather remote one, in spite of the positive room pressure.

Ceiling construction will depend to a considerable extent on whether vertical laminar flow is employed. If the ceiling does not consist largely of filters, acoustic material or the same type of material used for the walls is satisfactory. The ceiling support should be rigid, to prevent flexing accompanied by the production of dust by differential movement at installations such as light fixtures.

Clean-room lighting should produce at least 100 foot candles of illumination at the working level and should as much as possible be supplied from ceiling fixtures. These should be recessed into the ceiling so that the face plates are flush with the ceiling. Preferably, the fixtures can be serviced from outside the clean room, but servicing from below may be more economical.

Whitfield et al.[9] suggest that lamp fixtures for a laminar downflow room will generally cause little or no trouble when mounted in the ceiling between the filters and flush with the ceiling, as recommended above, or when they are mounted a short distance below the filter bank. The latter arrangement will produce some turbulence and is not particularly desirable. The turbulence will usually extend downward about three times the width of the lamp fixture, but little trouble will be caused by this turbulence if it does not extend down into a "dirty" area. Whitfield suggests that the decision between mounting light fixtures flush between the final filters or suspending them below the ceiling depends on the type of filter mounting assembly to be used, the manner in which the lights are to be serviced, lighting distribution, and ceiling height.

When the rooms have turbulent flow or horizontal laminar flow there is no reason why the lights should not be mounted flush with the ceiling.

Fixtures should be sealed in place to prevent leakage of the room air and a possible fall of pressure.

The lighting fixtures of the small clean room described by Bragg[8] were standard commercial flush units mounted on hinges so that they could be pulled down into the room for servicing. The fixtures in the large room were mounted above acrylic-plastic light diffusers, located between ceiling panels. These light fixtures were mounted on a sliding track which permitted pulling the fixture out beyond the exterior wall of the room for servicing. Thus these light fixtures could be serviced without interfering with clean-room operations.

The air-conditioning system must be capable of maintaining the positive pressure in the room and should probably be somewhat overdesigned to take care of various contingencies. It should be equipped with automatic controls so that temperature and humidity are kept within stipulated limits. The air-handling system should be designed to filter and introduce up to 25 percent make-up air into the clean room. Even higher percentages may be required to satisfy state or local health regulations.

The intake ducts for make-up air for the air-conditioning system should face away from the prevailing wind. As pointed out in the discussion of inertial effects in Chapter 2 (p. 103), such an arrangement may considerably decrease the uptake of large particles (those over a few microns in diameter). It is obvious that such ducts should not be near local sources of particles.

Lines for electricity, water, etc. should be enclosed and brought into the room through the floor or lower walls. The lines in the room should be as short as possible and they should be sealed into the entrance openings to prevent leakage.

The color scheme in a clean room is important to the workers. Air Force specifications suggest that this is important to prevent eye fatigue. However, probably at least as important is the favorable psychological effect of attractive surroundings.

Furniture should be selected with care, particularly with respect to the finish. Various plastic finishes are appropriate. Any surface which is particularly susceptible to producing particles by abrasion or to retain particles firmly should be avoided. Thus fabrics should not be used.

Most recommendations such as those described above are merely guidelines unless they are incorporated in a specific statement of requirements. Many unusual situations will require very special designs. For example, the Gemini two-man orbiting space vehicle was built in a clean room. A special "white room" was constructed to protect the space craft while it was being readied for its mission. It protects the craft both from dust and from corrosion while it sits on top of its launch rocket, Titan II, during the weeks while equipment is installed and tested[14] (Figures 5-8 and 5-9).

This room was designed to be mounted ten stories above the launch pad on an erector, used for the first time with a manned vehicle instead of the gantry. A gantry rolls back and forth on track but an erector moves away from the rocket and capsule by tipping down to the horizontal position. This white room is 50 ft high, 25 ft across at the base and 23 ft across at the top. Since, the room had to be made of very light material, aluminum was chosen.

Construction was such that the aluminum sheet itself was the supporting material, and the aluminum angles merely hold the sheets in place. The room is held together by rivets rather than welding, and even the pipe, conduit, and floors are aluminium. Glazed windows are used for radio communication rather than light, which is artificial. The room is three stories high and has three floors.

Temperature inside the room is kept at 72°F and the humidity at 50 percent. In keeping with good clean-room practice, positive pressure is

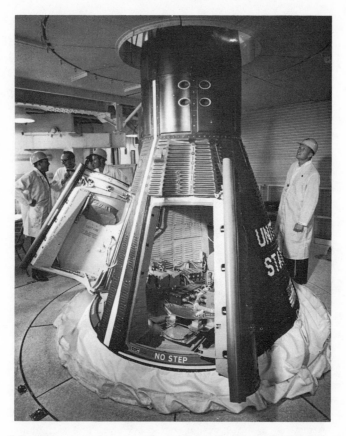

Figure 5-8. White room for protection of Gemini spacecraft while it is mounted on top of its launch rocket at Launch Complex 19, Cape Kennedy, Florida. (*Courtesy of NASA*)

maintained so that when the door of the aluminum elevator is opened, air will blow out and dust will not enter the room.

To prepare the vehicle and rocket for firing, the erector is placed in a horizontal position and the rocket is rolled into the erector through a door at the top of the white room. The entire complex is then raised to the vertical position.

Shortly before launch, when the erector is no longer needed, a door on one side of the room rolls into the roof, the central portion of the three floors are removed in a work elevator, and the remainder of the floors fold against the walls. The erector and white room are then lowered to the horizontal position.

Figure 5-9. Top floor of white room from Gemini spacecraft. Left to right are astronauts Armstrong and See, design engineer Wendt, and astronauts Grissom and Cooper. (*Courtesy of NASA*)

## CLOTHING

Ordinary fabrics readily shed fibers and dust and are a major source of particles in clean rooms unless covered in some manner. The hair and scalp are also a source of particles and should be covered. Shoes, of course, are notorious for tracking in dirt. Thus minimum clean-room clothing requirements are caps, smocks or similar garments, and special shoes or shoe covers.

The fabric should be of synthetic fibers; nonflammable, produce little lint, and not produce or retain an appreciable electric charge. Filament yarn rather than staple yarn must be used. Polyester, polypropylene, and polyamide fibers are usually satisfactory. The fabric should be chosen so that little linting occurs after cleaning. White materials are usually used, but there is no particular advantage to white, and colored uniforms may help to maintain worker morale or be used to identify various types of workers. For some purposes acid resistance may be important. Polypropylene and polyester fabrics have good acid resistance, but that of polyamide fabrics is poor. Except for antistatic qualities, cotton is a very poor fabric for clean room use, mainly because of the lint it produces, and should be avoided.

## REFERENCES

1. Federal Standard No. 209, "Clean Room and Work Station Requirements, and Controlled Environment," General Services Administration, Business Service Center, Washington, D.C. 1963.
2. Air Force Technical Order 00-25-203, "Standards and Guidelines for the Design and Operation of Clean Rooms and Clean Work Stations," July 1, 1963.
3. Lieberman, A., *Research/Development*, **13**, No. 1, 4 (1962).
4. Pate, J. B., in "Conference Proceedings," Third Annual Technical Meeting, American Association for Contamination Control, Los Angeles, May 5-8, 1964.
5. Agnew, B. I., "Laminar/Flow Clean Room Handbook," Agnew-Higgins, Inc., Garden Grove, Calif., 1963.
6. "A New Approach to Clean Room Design," Sandia Corp. Research Report No. SC-4673 (RR).
7. "Portable Clean Work Station," Sandia Corp. Research Report No. SC-4690 (RR).
8. Bragg, K. R., in "Conference Proceedings," Third Annual Technical Meeting, American Association for Contamination Control, Los Angeles, May 5-8, 1964.
9. Whitfield, W. J., J. C. Mashburn, W. E. Mitzel, and L. C. Trujillo, in "Conference Proceedings," Third Annual Technical Meeting, American Association for Contamination Control, Los Angeles, May 5-8, 1964.
10. Anony., Laboratory Management, p. 22, November, 1963.
11. Kline, G. R., *Air Engineering*, November, 1960.
12. Ritz, G. J., *Contamination Control*, **2**, No. 11, 18 (November, 1963).
13. Tanza, G. F., "Conference Proceedings," Third Annual Technical Meeting, American Association for Contamination Control, Los Angeles, May 5-8, 1964.
14. Anony., *Contamination Control*, **3**, No. 8, 18 (August, 1964).

# The Importance of
## *Chapter 6* Particle Size in Fine Particle Technology

Powders are used in a great many manufacturing processes and the particle sizes of the powders are often of considerable importance. The particle size distributions of powders for some technical applications must be known with accuracy and must be determined by making particle size measurements. Powders used for other applications may be known to be satisfactory if prepared in a certain manner, or if they perform satisfactorily in certain tests. Because of this wide variety of industrial applications and requirements, the importance of particle size to a few important industries is discussed below. Furthermore, each company within an industry may have its own problems and methods of solving them, so the following discussion is intended to provide examples rather than to provide any degree of completeness.

## THE PAINT INDUSTRY

### General

The paint industry, like many others in the United States, is made up of a few large companies controlling a considerable portion of the total market and a very large number of small companies. There are perhaps 1500 paint companies in the United States, about two-thirds of which have fewer than twenty employees. For details regarding structure of the paint industry see reference 1.

Coating materials having unusual properties are likely to receive most impetus from large companies. Examples are thixotropic coatings. Paints having thixotropic properties are quite fluid when vigorously stirred or applied but are much more viscous under slight stress (see Chapter 2, p. 114 ff.). Such paints have the advantage of being less likely to form drops from excess paint which runs down a wall or drips from brushes than more conventional paints. DuPont's "no-drip" "Lucite" wall paint is of this type and consists of a thixotropic acrylic emulsion.

New methods of applying paints have been the result of extensive research and have stimulated additional research. An example is the electrodeposition of organic coatings. The object to be coated is a conducting metal such as the body of an automobile, which serves as the anode while the tank body acts as the cathode. The pigment particles, negatively charged, deposit on the anode as a continuous film.

Automation in the paint laboratory has developed more rapidly than in the plant. Many operations that were previously carried out by manual methods are now done by various specialized instruments. Examples are various color-matching devices and color mixing computers which to a large extent can replace trial-and-error color blending and matching (Figure 6-1).

Figure 6-1. The quality and color of Pittsburgh ® paint formulations are checked constantly from raw materials to packaging. A recording spectrophotometer, center, a color difference computer, right, and a colorant mixture computer of the analog type, left, are used to help control paints. (*Courtesy of Pittsburgh Plate Glass Co.*)

The desirable properties of pigments for paint-making have been reviewed by Bell.[2] These properties must ultimately be specified in terms of the desirable properties of paints. The paint must be easy to apply as an even coating which upon "drying" produces a film about 0.001 in thick. Sometimes the individual films are thicker than this, but usually greater thickness is achieved by applying successive coats. The dried film must be smooth (but may be dull to glossy), uniform in appearance, tough, durable, and tacky enough to adhere properly to the surface. Paints vary markedly as regards the effects of the physical nature of the pigments. Some paint properties depend largely on the nature of the substrate in which the pigment particles are suspended, while others are affected by the nature of the pigments.

The substrate or medium is usually of high molecular weight or becomes so as the paint hardens. The "drying oils," such as linseed oil and tung oil, contain highly unsaturated fatty acid radicals in the glycerides of which they are constituted. These react readily with oxygen in the air to form three-dimensional, cross-linked, peroxides which are the tough solids that comprise the continuous phase of the dried paint film. Catalysts are often added to the paints to increase or otherwise control the rate of oxidation. Lacquers depend on the evaporation of a solution of the high molecular weight material in a volatile organic solvent to produce the desired film. The water-base paints are similar, but a colloidal suspension of a synthetic plastic in water is employed and evaporation of the water leaves the desired film. Many types of plastics have been used, including alkyds, vinyls, various cellulose derivatives, polyurethanes, and high molecular weight hydrocarbons. Some surface coatings, such as those used for certain types of furniture, may consist of nothing but monomer and catalyst, and polymerize *in situ* to form a transparent coating revealing the grain beneath. Obviously these different bases or media influence the choice of pigments, and in the latter case no pigment at all is used.

The many different types of pigments used in paints can be classified in several ways. One method breaks them down into classes based on color: white, black, and metallic. Another differentiates primarily between naturally occurring types and manufactured types. The former include iron oxides and extenders such as calcium carbonate and diatomaceous earth. The latter classification includes a multitude of synthetic organic dyes, various manufactured inorganic pigments such as the lead chromates, lamp and carbon black, and various powdered metals and alloys. An excellent, though somewhat out of date, discussion of paint pigments was edited by Mattiello.[3]

Pigments are prepared for use in paints in almost as many ways as there are varieties. Some, such as the chromate pigments, some iron oxides, and many organic pigments, are prepared by precipitation from solution. The particle size distribution of some pigments prepared in this manner is that of the particles immediately after precipitation, but this is not always so. The precipitates are usually filtered, washed and dried to produce compact cakes of pigment. These cakes are ground, and the size distribution of the product may bear little resemblence to that of the original precipitate. Other manufactured pigments are produced by calcining or by precipitation followed by calcining. Examples are chromic oxide, ultramarine, zinc sulfide, and titanium dioxide. Again, such pigments may ultimately be ground, the size distribution being determined by the grinding process. Some pigments are produced in the gas phase and used essentially as produced. Zinc oxide and antimony oxide are produced by the oxidation of the vapor of the metal, and carbon black is usually manufactured by the channel process, which involves burning natural gas and deposition of the carbon in metal plates or "channels." The "ultimate" particles produced in this way are usually very small; the arithmetic mean diameter of carbon black is often 0.01 to 0.03 micron as determined by electron microscopy. However, such materials have a marked tendency to form aggregates even while still suspended in the gas in which they were produced, and the effect of particle size on paint properties may depend in part on the size of the aggregates as well as on the size of the ultimate particles.

An upper limit to pigment and filter or extender size is set up by the desired thickness of the paint film. This is usually about 0.001 in. As Bell[2] emphasizes, a few oversize particles or aggregates can ruin a paint. Usually the upper size limit is about 20 microns diameter, based on this criterion. However, because of other considerations, such as flow properties and gloss, a much smaller maximum permissable particle size may be established. Bell mentions 5 microns as being typical. Fillers and extenders are usually coarser than pigments.

## Opacity of white pigments

The factors controlling the opacity of white pigments are the refractive index and the particle size.[4] Stutz and Pfund[5] investigated light-scattering of suspensions of zinc oxide in water and for a given weight concentration found a minimum light transmission (maximum scattering) when the particles were about 0.24 micron in diameter. Similar results were obtained for zinc oxide and zinc sulfide suspensions in water by Depew and

Eide,[6] who found that the optimum size was about 0.20 micron. As would be expected, particle shape was also very important. Particles of acicular form about 0.2 micron across and several microns long had greater light-scattering capabilities than spheres of 0.2 micron diameter.

Jacobsen[4] made a "practical" study of the effect of size on the hiding power of titanium dioxide (rutile type) pigments. A batch of pigment consisting of nearly spherical particles was divided into several fractions of differing mean size with a sedimentation technique. Particle sizes were determined with an electron microscope. Paints were prepared from the various fractions and the hiding power of each fraction was determined with a "contrast ratio" method. The relative hiding power as a function of particle diameter is shown in Figure 6-2. Again, the optimum diameter was about 0.21 micron. There was a much greater rate of decrease in hiding power per size increment for the finer fractions then for the coarser ones, probably because the former were in the Rayleigh light-scattering region.

Work[7] has suggested that for a pigment to possess good hiding power a large fraction of the material should be in the size range 0.2 to 1 or 2 microns diameter, and that a large difference should exist between the refractive index of the pigment and that of the vehicle. It is difficult to obtain by grinding the small sizes required, and the optimum sizes for maximum hiding power are usually produced by precipitation.

The tinting strength of white pigments has been suggested as an indirect

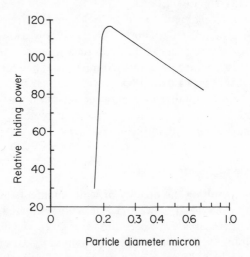

Figure 6-2. Particle diameter micron. Relationship between hiding power and particle size for a rutile titanium dioxide pigment.[4] (*Courtesy of Southam Business Publications, Ltd.*)

measure of the capability of rendering a paint opaque, especially for pigments of the same general type. For example, it was found[8] that continued wet milling of a basic carbonate white lead so that the surface mean diameter decreased from 5.86 to 1.10 microns increased the tinting power from 90 to 145. Jacbosen[4] investigated the relationship between particle size and tinting strength using carbon black and the sized fractions of rutile titanium dioxide mentioned above. The carbon black was added to each of the fractions to produce gray tints, the pigment-carbon black ratio being the same for each sample. Jacobsen found that the particle size fraction which produced the maximum hiding power (0.21 micron) produced a neutral gray tone of high reflectance. A predominantly blue-gray tone was produced with the smaller particle size fractions and brown-gray tones resulted with the larger particle size fractions. The tints were determined quantitatively with a reflectometer and blue, green, and amber filters. Relative readings with the green filter were considered to correspond to the relative reflectance as observed visually, and the maximum reflectance was obtained for particles about 0.2 micron in diameter. The decrease in reflectance per size increment was greater for the finer than for the coarser particles. The tone was judged from the reflectance with the blue and amber filters. A higher reading with the blue filter for the same particle size indicated a dominance of the blue tone, while a higher reading with the amber filter showed the dominance of a reddish tone.

### Durability

The durability of paints is considerably influenced by both the size and shape of the pigment particles. The effect of the size and shape of zinc oxide pigments on the durability of the paints containing them is the subject of a series of papers by Eide and his co-workers[9,10,11,12] as well as of other studies.[13] Zinc oxide is manufactured in a wide variety of sizes. The shapes are usually nearly spherical or acicular. Eide[7] found that the coarse acicular particles produce house paint which is especially resistant to both checking and cracking upon exposure. The coarse ("non-colloidal") form of zinc oxide in alkyd paints was found to be superior to the finer ("colloidal") form with respect to maintenance of luster, chalking and fading, and the amount of luster produced by polishing.

### Consistency

The consistency of a paint is markedly influenced by both the median particle size and the nature of the particle size distribution of the pigment it contains. A discussion of the importance of these factors on the rheology of a suspension was included in Chapter 2. Particle shape, of course, is also very important. A study of the influence of these factors on paint consistency was made by Dunn, Kushner, and Baier.[6] They prepared paints from a series of basic carbonate white lead samples which had been wet-ground to different surface mean diameters. The yield value* increased from 44 to 131 as the diameter decreased from 5.86 to 1.10 microns.

According to Goeb,[14] pigments suitable for paints have average particle sizes in the range 0.5 to 5 microns and he confirms the findings mentioned above that the maximum hiding power and tinting strength are found in pigments of 0.2 to 0.3 micron diameter. Smaller particles not only have poor hiding power but tend to agglomerate and produce paints having poor flow properties and low gloss.

The relation of yield value to particle size was also discussed by Green and Haslam.[15] They emphasized that the particles in a paint are usually irregularly shaped, many of them being in contact with one another to form loosely bound aggregates. This flocculation produces structure which in turn gives a resistance to shear that is quantitatively expressed as a finite yield value. Green and Haslam accept the hypothesis that the particles are held together as a result of interfacial tension, and suggest that when force is applied to the paint it will not flow until the force is great enough to cause a rearrangement of the particles, that is, to overcome the resistance to rearrangement resulting from the interfacial tension. According to this concept, decreasing the particle size increases the number of points of contact per unit cross-sectional area of paint for a given weight percent of pigment in paint, increasing the yield value. Similarly, increasing the weight concentration for a given particle size distribution should increase the yield value, since this increases the amount of interfacial area and the number of points of contact per unit cross-sectional area of the paint.

The pigments used to test these ideas were composed of zinc oxide, which has the unusual characteristic that when the powder is heated the large particles grow at the expense of small ones, producing a net increase in particle size. By heating zinc oxide at two temperatures, one fine-grained and one coarse-grained material were obtained. Pigments having various arithmetic mean particle sizes were prepared by mixing various proportions of these two materials. Each heating operation was undertaken twice, producing two series of samples. After heating, the oxides

---

*The minimum tangential force per unit area which, when applied to a plastic material, is able to produce flow.

were ground in a ball mill for one day to destroy aggregates. The pigments were dispersed in linseed oil and the dispersions allowed to age for a week so that wetting would be complete. Yield values were measured with a microplastometer.[16]

Some of the results obtained for a 75 percent pigment concentration by weight are shown in Figure 6-3. The decrease in yield value with increase in arithmetic mean diameter ($\bar{d}_{10}$) was expected, but it is also of interest to note the differences between the curves for the two series.

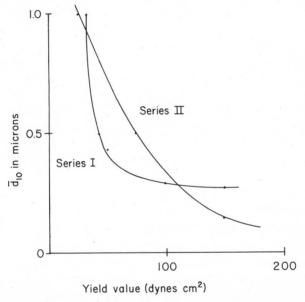

Figure 6-3. Effect of pigment particle diameter on yield value for a constant-weight concentration.[15] (*Courtesy of Industrial and Engineering Chemistry*)

The size distributions for the two series were quite different, and this may explain the deviations. Large deviations were also obtained when the plots were made on the basis of several other mean diameters ($\bar{d}_{21}$, $\bar{d}_{32}$, $\bar{d}_{43}$, $\bar{d}_{31}$, $\bar{d}_{20}$), although these are not shown in Figure 6-3. When the particle number concentration was kept constant but the particle size was increased, the interfacial area per unit area increased by definition and the yield value also increased. When the interfacial area was kept constant, the yield value increased very rapidly with increasing number concentration of the pigment particles. These results agree at least qualitatively with the proposed theory.

## Carbons

Carbon particles are in an entirely different size range from the particles in most other pigments. Venuto[17] studied the relationships among tinting strength, color (blackness), and particle size,  In general, the tinting strength increased with increasing particle size but the actual blackness decreased.  The size range was less than 25 millimicrons to about 60 millimicrons.  A similar study was reported by Wiegand,[18] who used a variety of colloidal carbons.  He found that while color intensity increased with decreasing particle diameter, tinting strength remained nearly constant for particle diameters less than about 24 millimicrons.

Jacobsen[4] emphasizes, probably quite correctly, that the sizes usually assigned to carbon blacks refer to the "ultimate" or "primary" particles. The particles are actually highly aggregated, but the aggregates are so loose that the ultimate particles are largely responsible for the tinting properties and the color, both of which are related to light scattering. The blackness of a carbon probably increases with decreasing particle size because the light scattering decreases and a larger fraction of the light is absorbed.  On the other hand, it is not at all obvious why the tinting strength of carbon blacks should increase with increasing particle size.

## Colored pigments

Numerous studies have been made of the relationship between tinting strength and particle size of colored pigments.  Barrick[19] found that such relationships exist for Prussian Blue and Molybdate Orange.  The maximum tinting strength for the former occurred for a particle diameter of 0.3 micron, and for the latter for a particle diameter of about 0.5 micron.  Just as in the case of white pigments, the rate of decrease of tinting strength was greater on the small-particle side of the tinting strength vs. size curve than on the large-particle side.

Color tone may also change with size, although the relationship, if any, is far from clear.  Goeb[14] found changes in the color of Siegle Red I with changing particle size.  He also observed that particle shape is important and found that acicular pigments such as monoclinic Chrome Yellow may exhibit pleochromism, show brush marks, and produce films of poor gloss.

## Extenders

Extenders can be considered to be pigments of low refractive index which are used to extend the hiding power of white and colored pigments. They may help to develop in the paint and paint film characteristics of importance to the application, durability, appearance and cost of the paint.[20] Extenders generally have little hiding power, but usually those having a high brightness and neutral tint are preferred. It is also important that the extender be light-fast and that it not accelerate the yellowing tendency of the paint vehicle.

Not much is known about the effect of particle size of extenders on their performance. Jacobsen[4] described unpublished results concerning the hiding power of a flat paint with variation of the particle size of the extender, calcium carbonate. The results suggested that extender particles 1 micron in diameter provided greater hiding power than those 8 microns in diameter. Piper[21] investigated the influence of variations of barium sulfate extender particle size on the hiding power of titanium dioxide paints. They contained 75 percent boiled linseed oil and 25 percent solids ($TiO_2$ plus $BaSO_4$) by volume. Most of the barium sulfate samples were prepared separately by precipitation from aqueous solution. For each $BaSO_4$ sample of different particle size, paints were prepared in which 85, 75, 65, and 50 percent of the total volume of solids present was barium sulfate. The paints were drawn out on hiding power charts and hiding power was measured by an ASTM method. The average diameters of the barium sulfate particles varied from about 1 to 6 microns while that of the titanium dioxide particles was about 1 micron. No significant variations in hiding power were observed that might be attributed to a particle size effect.

Jacobsen also described work which indicated that gloss may be influenced by the extender. For instance, one study showed that a finely ground limestone in which 80 percent by weight of the particles were below 10 microns produced greater gloss than a limestone in which only 35 percent by weight was smaller than 10 microns.[22] However, the effect of particle size on gloss may be overwhelmed by other influences, since in another study[23] it was found that a calcium carbonate having an average particle size of 2 microns produced a good gloss while another, having an average particle size less than 0.1 micron, produced a gloss that could be controlled by the pigmentation.

Kronstein et al.[24] prepared coatings based on a variety of latexes and alkyds pigmented with $TiO_2$, $MgSiO_3$, and mica of various particle sizes. The coatings were tested for blistering on wood, vapor loss through free films, and light transmission. Adding large, platy, mica particles to the $TiO_2$ pigment improved moisture resistance. Best results were obtained with a mixture of large and small mica particles, and the use of small particles alone decreased the sealing effect. The micas were characterized as being 325, 1000, and 3000 mesh. The influence of pigment particle shape and size on the moisture-sealing characteristics of organic coatings was the subject of another report by these authors.[25]  Specific characteristics investigated were blistering on wood, transparency, and permeability to salt-fog and water vapor of acetate latex and vinyl alkyd paints. Again it was found that the best moisture sealing was obtained with pigments having the greatest variety of pigment particle sizes and shapes.

Soul[26] has described the preparation and properties of whiting fillers and extenders from Cretaceous chalk.  Numerous grades of fineness are available, covering a size range of about 0.5 to 500 microns.  Most of the particles are between 2 and 5 microns diameter and variations among grades are largely variations in the proportions of large particles.  The proportion of particles between 2 and 25 microns is very important when considering the use of the whiting, and is used to assess plant operation and quality control.  Whiting is often used in putty; for this purpose it should have a wide particle size distribution to aid interpacking of the particles.

### Aluminum

Aluminum powder, particularly the flaky variety, is often used as a pigment.  It is usually treated with surface-active agents to give the particles a uniform orientation in the vehicle.[4]  At least two studies[27,28] have indicated that the hiding power of aluminum pigments increases as the particle thickness decreases.  This is not at all surprising, since the surface of the aluminum available for covering per unit weight of aluminum increases with decreasing particle thickness.

### Photoluminescence

Photoluminescent pigments are those which are either phosphorescent or fluorescent.  The luminescence of paints made from such pigments decreases rapidly with decrease in particle size.  A compromise must be made, since very large particles will produce a poor paint.  Diameters of 1 to 5 microns are conventional.

### Dispersion

The importance of the degree of dispersion of a finely divided material suspended in some substrate has been emphasized throughout this book, and this importance is nowhere greater than in the paint industry.  A finely divided material often forms clumps, especially in the dry form, and when the particles are of submicron size each package of pigment in a sense is a single aggregate. When dispersion of the ultimate or primary particles is incomplete, the paint may behave as though it contained primary particles the size of the aggregates, or in the case of some properties and some aggregates, as though it contained primary particles intermediate in size between the aggregates and the actual primary particles.

Usually at least part of the pigment material remains undispersed, and the minimum amount of this which is permissible depends on the type of coating. The degree of dispersion may influence the quality of the color, the gloss, and the texture in much the same manner as changing the ultimate particle size affects such properties when good dispersion is achieved.

Several factors influence dispersion. Small particles are generally more difficult to disperse than large ones, and pigments vary remarkably in the ease with which they are wetted by the paint vehicle. Some paints contain wetting agents to aid the dispersion.

A number of methods have been proposed and used for determining the degree of dispersion. Since dispersion is only important as it affects paint quality, tests of quality are indirect tests of whether or not dispersion has been satisfactory. If poor dispersion is suspected, microscopic examination is perhaps the quickest and most direct method of determining the degree of dispersion. Care must be taken, however, that preparing the sample for examination does not disperse any aggregates which may be present.

Agglomeration (flocculation) can of course also occur after a paint has been prepared, and the quality of a paint may be impaired if the agglomerates are very stable. This difficulty may occur as a paint ages during storage. Some aggregates or flocs are very loosely bound and seem to be in a state of quasi-equilibrium with the dispersed particles. Such flocs will often break up upon diluting the paint.

The effect of loose flocculation of pigments on the properties of lacquers has been studied by Dewey.[29] He used a microscope to observe the occurrence of flocculation in a film of lacquer. When flocculation of carbon black occurred, a brown tone resulted. Flocculation of Iron Blue caused a reddish or brownish tone. Also, pigment flocculation produced poor gloss in high-gloss lacquers. Jacobsen[4] studied the relationship between gloss and particle size distributions in enamels and found that enamels containing pigments of essentially the same size distribution differed considerably with respect to the resulting gloss depending on the degree of flocculation. Inferior gloss in general accompanied a high degree of flocculation.

## Printing inks

Closely related to pigments and extenders for paints are those for use in printing inks. Pigments for inks have their own requirements which are closely related to the types of printing processes. These can be divided into four groups.

Relief or letterpress printing is that used for most bulk work such as printing newspapers and books. The printing surface stands out in relief, as when using type. Ink is applied by means of rollers and transferred by pressure to the paper. The minimum thickness of the ink layer on the printed paper is between 1 and 3 microns.[30] These inks are usually oil-based and are very viscous, having almost the consistency of pastes. They usually dry by soaking into the paper, by oxidation, or both.

Lithography differs from letterpress printing in that essentially flat metal surfaces are used. The portion of the surface which is to transfer ink is processed so that ink adheres to it. The remainder is rendered hydrophilic. Rollers containing water or ink are passed over the surfaces and the ink adhering to the plate is transferred either directly to the paper or, in the case of offset lithography, to a rubber sheet. In the latter case printing is from the rubber sheet or blanket. The maximum thickness of the film deposited by offset printing is 2 microns.

Intaglio processes involve etching or engraving a metal surface. The ink, which is quite fluid, is forced to flow over the surface, filling the depressions. Excess ink is wiped off and that in the depressions is transferred to the paper with pressure. The ink deposit on the paper is quite thick (up to 20 microns), which permits a wide range of tone values. Since the inks must have a low viscosity, they usually have a volatile organic solvent base which dries by evaporation.

Screen printing (or just "screening") is a stencil process. The stencil is the screen, which is usually a fabric such as silk or nylon, with appropriate areas covered to produce the desired pattern. A thixotropic, organic-solvent based ink or paint is used, and the deposit may be quite thick, often as much as 50 microns. Screening has a large number of industrial applications.

The quality of printing ink is to a large extent controlled by the quality of the pigments and extenders, and an important aspect of the quality is the particle size and size distribution. Since the films of printed ink on paper or other objects are usually only about 2 microns thick, the particles should be not more than about 0.5 micron in diameter. When the printing involves the use of half-tone plates, even a small percentage of particles larger than 0.5 micron diameter will impair the tone rendering.[30] This is because the non-printing holes in the plates are only a few microns in diameter. If these holes collect oversize particles and fill up, they print along with the raised portions. It may be possible to save a badly clogged plate by washing it with a solvent. But starting a large printing press, washing, and starting up again is very expensive, and may have to be repeated unless a better ink is used. According to Bowles,[30] the size distributions and shape factors do not seem to be important if most of the particles are less than 0.5 micron in diameter. Of course, it must be possible to achieve the small particle size without sacrificing other desirable characteristics including high color strength; cleanliness; ease of grinding; fastness to light; chemical inertness; non-bleeding in oils, solvents, or water; and opacity.

Much the same considerations with respect to pigment and extender dispersion that apply to paints are true also of printing inks. However, once the pigments are properly dispersed in the vehicle, subsequent loose flocculation before printing is not harmful.

A simple test has been recommended to determine whether a printing ink contains coarse material.[31] An unused can is opened and the top layer of ink removed with a clean spatula.

The spatula is then scraped across the ink and some of the ink is rubbed on the spatula blade. Both surfaces are observed under a light at a 45° angle. If no grain is observed, the ink is probably well ground. A more accurate test involves putting a few milligrams of ink on a microscope slide, adding a drop of solvent for the vehicle, stirring in the paint, and covering with a cover-glass. Examination with a microscope using a high resolving power objective, oil immersion, and a calibrated ocular micrometer will reveal the presence of coarse particles. It is important that the refractive index of the solvent be markedly different from that of the pigment and of the extender.

## CEMENT

### General

The term "cement" is a general expression embracing almost all adhesives. However, its meaning is often limited to include only substances which bind together sand, gravel, stones or similar substances to form concrete, mortar, and related materials. The latter meaning is used here.

To many persons the term "cement" means Portland cement. But Portland cement is just one of a number of hydraulic cements, which can be defined as those which, when made into a paste with water and aggregate, set and harden as a result of chemical reactions between the water and compounds in the cement.[32] The setting and hardening are strictly results of the reactions and do not depend on the evaporation of water. In fact, some hydraulic cements will harden under water. While most such cements harden at room temperature when mixed with water, others require much higher temperatures. Taylor[32] gives as an example of the latter type a mixture of lime and finely divided quartz. This mixture acts as a hydraulic cement when water is added to form a paste and the mixture is subjected to steam in an autoclave.

Portland cement (or more properly Portland cements) is made by heating a mixture of limestone and clay at a temperature sufficiently high that sintering occurs. Substitutions may be made for the limestone and clay so long as essentially the same chemical composition is achieved. The product, or clinker, is ground and a little gypsum ($CaSa_4 \cdot 2H_2O$) is added. The types of Portland cement are usually differentiated by their properties such as the rate of hardening, the characteristics of heat evolution during hardening, and resistance of the final product to attack by solutions. The clinker contains four main phases, and these properties are greatly influenced by the relative proportions of the four phases and the size of the particles in the cement.[32] The phases are tricalcium silicate, $\beta$-dicalcium silicate, tricalcium aluminate, and a ferrite solid solution. The first three phases are often designated $C_3S$, $\beta$-$C_2S$, and $C_3A$. Using this symbolism, the fourth phase varies in composition between $C_2F$ and $C_6A_2F$, where F refers to the ferrite radical. This system expresses the chemical formulas in terms of oxides. Thus $C_6A_2F$ is $6CaO \cdot 2Al_2O_3 \cdot Fe_2O_3$. In most Portland cements the range of $C_3S$ is about 35 to 55 percent, of $C_2S$ is 15 to 35 percent, of $C_3A$ is 7 to 15 percent and of $C_4AF$ is 8 to 11 percent.[33] Other factors being equal, the ultimate strength of a cement is a function of the sum $C_3S + C_2S$ and this is almost always about 70. Apparently $C_3S$ is the phase providing early strength, while $C_2S$ acts later and only if the concrete is prevented from drying out.[33]

As Portland cements containing large amounts of $C_3A$ deteriorate when exposed to water or soil containing relatively high concentrations of sulfates, special sulfate-resistant Portland cements have been prepared which have a very low $C_3A$ content. However, $C_3A$ may have some value in cement since it reacts very quickly with water and thus may contribute to early strength. Grinding the clinker more finely will also increase early strength. The British Standard Specification[34] for ordinary Portland cement is that it is to be ground to a specific surface not less than 2250 $cm^2/g$, while rapid-hardening Portland cements must have a specific surface not less than 3250 $cm^2/g$.

The reaction of Portland cement with water is exothermic and the heat produced can be a nuisance, especially when large volumes of concrete are involved. Some dams have been built with pipes passing through the concrete through which water was circulated during the setting and hardening process. The largest contributions to the heat evolved are made by $C_3A$ and $C_3S$; low-heat Portland cements contain less of these phases than usual.

Numerous other Portland cements are manufactured. Very light-colored cements are made from raw materials that are relatively free of iron. Portland blast-furnace cement is a mixture of Portland cement and blast-furnace slag which have been ground together. The slag content is usually 25 to 40 percent. However, some such cements contain more than 85 percent slag. Various substances may be added to the cements to provide special properties. Thus the cement may contain pigments to color the resulting concrete or mortar, and waterproofing agents may be added. Slack lime may be added to cement to be used for mortar in order to increase the plasticity of the paste.

Numerous non-portland cements are used in the building trades, and only a few of these will be listed. A high alumina-content cement is made by fusing a mixture of bauxite (mainly hydrated $Al_2O_3$) and limestone ($CaCO_3$). This is a hydraulic cement based on calcium aluminate rather than calcium silicate and was developed as the result of a search for cements with improved resistance to aqueous solutions of various salts, such as sea water. Aluminous cement is indeed highly resistant to various aqueous solutions. Its setting time, which is defined as the initial stiffening, is greater than that of Portland cement, which is usually a few hours, but its hardening time is considerably shorter than that of Portland cement. It is highly heat-resistant and for this reason has been used for the preparation of various refractory materials, usually as the bonding agent.

Numerous processes are used for manufacturing aluminous cement including fusion in rotary kilns, reverberatory furnaces, electric furnaces, and converters.

Pozzolanas have been defined[35] as substances which are not cements themselves but contain substances which combine with lime and water to form insoluble substances that have cementing properties. Many of these substances are of volcanic origin but a number of others such as "fly-ash" can be used. Furriziam[35] classifies the natural pozzolanas according to the nature of the material which reacts with the lime: (a) volcanic glass, (b) zeolites, (c) hydrated silica. The mortars used by the Romans were made from lime and volcanic glass, and many Roman structures assembled with such mortar of course exist today.

Apparently, high resistance to attack by sulfates can be achieved with a proper mixture of pozzolanas, especially a mixture having a high content of silica.

A number of cements have been developed which produce pastes* that expand somewhat during setting and hardening. They are all hydraulic cements. The most important uses are production of self-stressed reinforced concrete and of concrete which retains at least the dimensions it had in the mold. Such cements are often made by adding a suitable material to Portland cement. Many contain gypsum ($CaSO_4 \cdot 2H_2O$) and others magnesium oxide. The former leads to the production of calcium aluminum sulfate hydrates and the latter to magnesium hydroxide (the periclase reaction).[36]

The manufacture of an expanding cement can probably be better controlled by mixing an additive containing an expansive constituent with an ordinary cement than by manufacturing a special "clinker" containing such an ingredient.

Magnesium oxychloride cements, also called sorel cements, are produced when magnesium oxide and an aggregate are treated with a concentrated solution of magnesium chloride.[32] They are often used as flooring materials.

Many plasters are produced by dehydrating gypsum. The gypsum can be dehydrated entirely to anhydrous $CaSO_4$ or partially to $CaSO_4 \cdot \frac{1}{2}H_2O$. The completely dehydrated calcium sulfate may have either of two crystal structures, $\beta$-$CaSo_4$ or $\gamma$-$CaSO_4$. Regardless of the form, setting occurs upon mixing with water as the result of rehydration to gypsum. The well-known plaster of Paris is largely $CaSO_4 \cdot \frac{1}{2}H_2O$.

Applications of particle-size determinations to the Portland cement industry have been reviewed in general terms by Rose.[37] For example, the time required for concrete to set decreases with increasing fineness of the particles. One would expect this, since chemical reactivity in general increases with decreasing particle size. From the standpoint of speed of construction and of strength, according to Rose, the use of the finest cement which has an adequate working time is desirable. However, the rate of evolution of heat, and apparently also shrinking and cracking, increase with decreasing particle size. Thus a particle size should be chosen such that the rate of setting and the strength are adequate, and yet there is no cracking or objectionable shrinking.

### Permeability

Mary[38] found that the permeability of concrete is only slightly influenced by variations in the nature of the inert ingredients, such as gravel,

---

*A paste is the slurry produced by mixing cement, water, and the discontinuous phase such as gravel.

and that for a given cement content the most important factor is the fineness of the cement. Mary emphasized, as did Rose, that in drawing practical conclusions from this it is important to remember that fineness has other effects on the concrete, some beneficial (greater ease of handling and high final mechanical strength) and some harmful (high thermal and hydraulic contraction). Also, the cost of additional grinding must be considered. The permeability of a concrete as determined in the laboratory does not necessarily indicate the permeability of the final structure made from it. However, laboratory-measured impermability is probably useful for protecting the concrete against corrosion by water.

In this regard, Kavcic[39] found that the most finely ground of four cements exhibited the greatest resistance to water but the least to 15 percent aqueous solutions of ammonium sulfate. He also found[40] that the electrical conductivity and the hydration velocity of cement increase with increasing fineness.

### Rate of hydration and strength

The effect of the fineness of Portland cement on the rate of hydration was also investigated by Hauenschild.[41] Cements were separated into fractions using an air centrifuge, and the diameters of the particles in the fractions were determined with a microscope. Cements having average particle diameters between 19.7 and 36.3 microns were found to give the highest strengths, while very fine cement was inferior because of the absorption of water and carbon dioxide soon after grinding. Hausenschild found that the finest fractions were richest in sulfate. Thus his research can be criticized on the basis that the fractions varied in chemical composition as well as in particle size.

The effect of the size of the particles in Portland cement on the strength characteristics was studied by Kuhl,[42] who separated two cements into seven fractions ranging from greater than 60 millimicrons to less than 10 millimicrons. Both tensile and compressive strengths increased with fineness. Increased strength can be obtained by grinding cement to a uniform particle size that is not too fine, or by adding a very fine to a very coarse cement.

The fineness of cement raw materials can be important. Thus the "burning" of cement may become easier as the grain size of the raw mixture is decreased, although the addition of fluorspar to a coarse mixture has been found to have more effect than an increase in fineness.[43] Also, increasing the fineness of the raw materials increased the strength and the rate of increase of the strength of 1:3 cement-sand mortars.

Oden[44] separated several commercial brands of Portland cement into several fractions of varying particle size using a sedimentation technique. The finest fractions produced very high compressive strengths for water-cement mortars, while the difference between fractions was even greater for 1:5 concrete mortars. The highest compressive strength obtained for a concrete mortar, produced from the finest fraction, was 700 kg/cm$^{-2}$. Tillman,[45] who obtained similar results, reported that cement grains larger than 50 microns diameter do not contribute to the binding strength. He also observed that the finer the grain, the greater the amount of water required to obtain the same strength.

A rather surprising finding is that Portland cement exposed to damp air loses its strength more rapidly when finely ground than when more coarse.[46] The strength is not affected by size when the cement is out of contact with the air. Kilossofov[47] found that the seven-day tensile strength of Portland cement increased with increasing fineness but that the 28-day and longer strengths passed through a maximum value with increasing fineness. Steiner[48] investigated seven cements of different finenesses and concluded that not only greater tensile and compressive strengths, but also lower weight per unit volume, greater water requirements, and earlier set accompanied increasing particle fineness.

Most of the experimental investigations reported in the literature on the effect of particle size on the properties of cement and concrete were conducted during the 1920's and 1930's. More recently, (1945) Magga[49] redetermined the effect of fineness on some physical properties of Portland cement. The results were not appreciably different from those described above. Thus he found that an increase in the specific surface of cement increased the speed of setting, the plasticity of mixes, the amount of water required, and the strength during the first week of aging. He found, however, that there was no increase in the ultimate strength if the specific surface exceeds a certain value, which for the cement he used was about 1800 cm$^2$gm$^{-1}$.

In 1950 Wuhrer[50] reported that cements having normal chemical composition and sintering developed the greatest strength when the particle diameter ranged from 0 to 30 microns. The compressive and transverse strengths after 28 days of setting and hardening were about 9100 and 1400 psi, respectively. When cements had this general size distribution, water requirements and shrinkage were normal. Wuhrer found that cement grains having diameters exceeding 30 microns hydrate very slowly and incompletely, and that grains larger than 60 microns hydrate scarcely at all. A similar result by Tillman[45] has been mentioned. When the maximum grain size was much less than 30 microns, even higher early strengths but the same ultimate strengths were obtained.  A cement with a size distribution in the range 0–7 microns exhibited excessive shrinkage and heat evolution, and one with a range of 0–2 microns set very rapidly. Cements with 40 to 50% of the particles greater than 30 microns, and containing particles as large as 2000 microns are conventional.  Wuhrer suggested producing cements of various particle size distributions by blending grinds of various degrees of fineness in order to achieve close control of cement characteristics.

## Grinding

Grinding the cement clinker with gypsum is undertaken as soon as the clinker has cooled.  The mill is usually a horizontal steel cylinder with ends which are closed except for orifices for feeding and discharging.[51]  It is usually loaded with steel balls, but balls of other materials are sometimes used.  The size of ball which is appropriate to achieve a given degree of fineness varies with this fineness.  Therefore, the cylinder is generally divided into three parts, with progressively smaller balls.  The mills are usually longer than they are wide (50 ft by 8 ft is typical) and they are usually called tube mills rather than ball mills.

The crushing action of a ball or tube mill is largely the result of one ball hitting another with material to be ground in between.  The intensity of action increases with mill speed until the balls are carried around during the entire revolution (the "critical" speed).  At speeds somewhat below this the balls fly clear across the mill and grinding is done at the expense of extreme wear of the lining.  Cement mills generally operate at about 70 to 80 percent of the critical value.[51]

Grinding methods that can be used to optimize the proportion of particles in the 3 to 30 diameter range have been described.[52]

## "AEROSOL" TECHNOLOGY

### General

The term "aerosol," as used in an important segment of modern industry, refers not to a suspension of a liquid or solid in a gas, but to a package with the capability of converting its contents to a spray.  In fact, the application of the term has been broadened to refer to a package which can convert its contents to foams or which can emit, upon release of a valve, streams, pastes, or creams.  The interior of the package is pressurized and this pressure acting on the contents expels part or all of them when a valve is opened. Because the term "aerosol," in this sense, is no longer limited even to sprays, the term "pressurized products" is sometimes used and hopefully it will one day replace the more conventional but inappropriate terminology.

The aerosol package is very popular because it is a very convenient device for packaging, transporting, storing, and applying a large variety of materials. It often removes requirements for special applicators such as brushes or nebulizers, since the applicator is in effect built-in. Since it is a general device for packaging and delivering, its use cuts across a large part of industry. A few examples illustrating the diversity of products packaged in this manner are pesticides, paints, shampoos, shaving creams, hair lacquers, fire extinguishing agents, whipped cream, window cleaners, and shoe polish.

The extensive use of aerosol packaging has largely developed since World War II. According to Shepherd,[53,54] it was given its greatest impetus during the war by the development and use of aerosol packages containing insecticides and using dichlorodifluoromethane as the "propellent" to produce the pressure. From almost zero units or packages sold before 1942, annual sales excluding foodstuffs and toothpastes had reached about forty million units by 1951, about three hundred million units by 1956, and were estimated to be about one billion in 1961.[53,55] A survey made by the Chemical Specialties Manufacturers Association indicated that about 670 million units were sold in the United States and Canada in 1960. By far the largest number of units (117 million) contained hair sprays and dressings while shaving lather and coatings were next with about 68 million containers each.

The aerosol packaging industry is roughly divided into two categories. One consists of those firms that engage entirely or partly in contract packaging. The other consists of firms that do their own packaging. Obviously these categories overlap, since some companies package both their own products and those of other firms.

### The aerosol package

The container may be fabricated of metal, plastic, or glass. The metal containers used in the United States have largely been tinplate. Aluminum is used occasionally in the United States and to a greater extent in Europe, and stainless steel is sometimes used. The inner walls of the containers are often coated, particularly to afford protection when the active ingredient is rather corrosive. Numerous types of coatings are used, usually synthetic resins such as those of the phenolic, epoxy, and vinyl types.

Generally such coatings are designed to protect the contents from dissolved tin rather than to protect the can against failure.

Physical strength of the containers is important since the contents are pressurized. The usual minimum bursting pressure is 125 psig.[57] The cans are either fabricated with seams which are welded, soldered, brazed, double-seamed, or swaged, or they are seamless, having been extruded or drawn. Some of the former barely meet the bursting pressure specification. The ends are usually concave or convex and made of harder metal than is used for the walls.

The most popular sizes of tinplate containers are 4, 6, 10, 12, and 16 fluid oz, but they are produced in a very large variety of sizes and shapes.

Many of the early containers were made of glass. Later, glass was virtually abandoned but it is now becoming more popular especially where pressure requirements are relatively low and there is an advantage to having containers with greater than average eye appeal. The latter advantage is especially important for cosmetic use. Glass also has the advantage over most metals of being highly resistant to corrosion, and has been used for pressure-packing various materials that could not be packed in metal containers.

Because of the possibility of a pressurized glass container exploding, especially upon impact, plastic-coated bottles are often used. The plastic may be either bonded to the glass or non-bonded. The glass may also be surrounded by a metal mesh or solid container. The shape of the bottle is important to pressure resistance; flat sides and highly irregular shapes are largely but not entirely avoided. Glass bottles are usually thicker than bottles used for non-pressurized purposes.

When plastic coatings are used they are usually vented to permit the release of pressure developing between the glass and the coating in the event that leaks or cracks develop in the glass. Such venting is most effective if the coating does not adhere rigidly to the glass surface.

Containers are also often made of plastic, which may be of either the thermoplastic or thermosetting variety. Various fillers, such as fiberglass, have been used to increase strength for a given wall thickness and to reduce distortion. Plastic containers have many of the advantages of glass containers such as the variety of shapes in which they can be molded and resistance to corrosion. The main disadvantage of plastic containers is their cost, which is greater than that of plastic-coated bottles and much greater than that of metal containers. However, this is somewhat compensated by their light weight and the fact that breakage is almost nonexistent, both properties considerably decreasing the cost of shipping.

The valve and nozzle are usually an integral unit. The valve is opened by pressure from a finger and usually remains open so long as the pressure is maintained. There are a number of configurations of valves, which depend to a considerable extent on the physical nature of the product (spray, foam, paste, etc.) and its anticipated use. Usually, when the valve is open the pressure in the can forces the liquid through a tube leading from the bottom of the can up through the valve and nozzle. The valve is spring-loaded, and closes upon removal of pressure from the finger. If the can is to be used in an inverted position, as in the dispensing of various toppings, the tube leading up from the bottom ("dip tube") is not used. Another variation is the metering valve, which stays open just long enough for a pre-determined amount of product to be ejected and then closes automatically, even if the finger pressure is maintained.[58,59]

Some valves are designed for the dispersion of suspensions of powders in a liquid propellent. There are a number of problems peculiar to the dispersion of such suspensions, such as caking and agglomeration of the particles and clogging or leakage of the valve. This is an application for which particle size may be of considerable importance. If the solid particles are too small, agglomeration and caking may be aggravated. On the other hand, if the particles are too large they will settle rapidly in the propellent and may not be of suitable size for the task they are to accomplish after they are dispensed. The size distribution appropriate for each material and application must be determined by experiment and experience.

Downing[60] states that powders passing through a 325-mesh screen are satisfactory at concentrations in the propellent up to 5 percent by weight and in some cases up to 10 percent by weight. Apparently, even powders passing a 200-mesh screen have at times been used at concentrations as as high as 10 percent. Downing points out that the orifice diameter in most valves is about 400 microns, and that 325 and 200-mesh screens will pass spheres smaller than about 43 and 75 microns diameter, respectively. Since clogging occurs even when the ultimate particle size is very small, agglomeration is apparently important. The presence of agglomerates may be the direct result of poor initial dispersion of the powder in the propellent. It may also be the result of caking in the bottom of the can, which is not entirely overcome by subsequent shaking of the container. And clogging may even result from the interception of very fine particles, especially of irregular shape, at the valve orifice.

Valves to be used for powder dispersion must have a high seating pressure to produce a seal against the dry particles. Also, the valve mechanism should ensure that it will always be wide open when activated to prevent collection of particles in the valve orifice.

Special valves are also needed for fire extinguisher packages. Some of these are one-shot devices. One type consists of a removable tab soldered over the outer end of a tube extending to the bottom of the liquid in the can, while another employs a plug in the inner end of the dip tube which is released by a stiff wire extending up the tube. The philosophy behind these one-shot devices is that the fire-extinguishing package, if any use at all, will always be fully pressurized. However, some extinguishers are equipped with repeating valves. Whichever type of valve is used, it is generally designed to liberate the contents of the container rapidly.

Some valves are reusable. These are particularly popular in Europe. The valves are retained by the customer and fastened onto replacement bottles.

The valves differ somewhat depending upon the construction material of the container. Obviously this will affect the type of seal between the valve and the container. In addition, the pressure must be relatively low if the container is made of glass and the valve assembly must operate satisfactorily at low pressures.


### The propellant

The propellants may be either liquid or gaseous at room temperature. If the propellant is a liquid it must have a very high vapor pressure at ordinary temperatures. When gaseous propellants are used they are often, but by no means always, selected because of their solubility in the liquids to be dispersed, since such high solubility gives them properties in the system similar to those of a volatile liquid.

Liquid or soluble-gaseous propellants serve the dual purpose of forcing the contents out of the container and helping to produce a spray or foam from the material emitted from the nozzle. Not only must they have the desired physical properties, but for most purposes they must be essentially non-toxic and non-corrosive. Also, they must not undergo chemical changes such as hydrolysis in the container, which would produce undesirable compounds.

At present the halogenated hydrocarbons are used as propellants more than any other class of compound. Most of these are of quite low molecular weight (85 to 240). The halogen in the molecule is usually either fluorine, or fluorine and chlorine; a fairly popular exception is dichloromethane. The vapor pressure of a halogenated hydrocarbon propellant is almost always between 15 and 100 psig at 70°F.

A few other liquids have been used or suggested for use as propellants. Some, such as vinyl chloride, are unsaturated halogen derivatives. The main disadvantages of vinyl chloride are its expense, flammability, and anesthetic properties,[61] but it has been considered for the formulation of lacquers and insecticides.

Dimethyl ether has also been used. Sciarra[62] has discussed its use for the dispersion of paint. It can be mixed with dichlorodifluoromethane, and the use of this mixture instead of a halogenated hydrocarbon alone decreases costs and permits higher concentrations of paint in the container. Scott and Terril[63] have shown that blends of dimethyl ether with various fluorocarbons are nonflammable if the concentrations of dimethyl ether are sufficiently low, usually less than about 10 percent.

Carbon dioxide, nitrous oxide, nitrogen, and air are the most commonly used gaseous propellants. Only the soluble gases carbon dioxide and nitrous oxide are of appreciable commercial importance, since the use of a soluble rather than an insoluble gas descreases the pressure drop as the discharge progresses, and evolution of the dissolved gas aids in breaking up the jet of liquid leaving the nozzle. The main advantages of compressed gases are low cost, and relatively small pressure change with change of temperature.

### Droplet size

With the exception of the sizes of solid particles which are to be dispersed, as mentioned above, the importance of particle size to the pressurized container industry is largely related to its importance to a particular application. For example, when paint is applied from a spray gun or pressure can, the droplets must be sufficiently fine to produce a uniform coating. Paint droplets in the 100 to 200 micron diameter range are usually produced by pressure cans; these sizes seem to be satisfactory but quite possibly are not ideal. There may be an advantage to even smaller droplets.

The size of the droplets is controlled by the size of the orifice in the nozzle, the pressure in the containers, the viscosity and surface tension of the solution ejected from the nozzle, the physical properties of the propellant, and the temperature of the contents of the container. When a jet of a non-volatile liquid or a liquid containing little or no dissolved gas is forced out of an orifice, and if the diameter of the jet is less than a few microns, the surface tension may overcome viscous forces in the jet, which then breaks up into droplets. If the liquid is highly viscous, strands or threads are formed. If the jet is of larger diameter and travelling at a sufficiently high velocity relative to air, threads of solution may be torn off the jet at the air-liquid interface. These threads may collapse into droplets.[64,65] The latter mechanism is especially important when the droplets are formed by an aspirating action, as in commercial nebulizers.

Droplet formation by an aerosol package is more complicated. As the solution leaves the valve orifice and the pressure restraining volatilization of the propellant is released, effervescence occurs. If the pressure is relatively low and the viscosity of the solution is high, a foam is produced. Otherwise the bubbles expand and break, forming droplets as the films between the bubbles collapse. The expanding gases may also draw out filaments which collapse to form droplets, but if so this is a secondary effect. Larger droplets resulting from these processes may be hurled violently into relatively stagnant air and break up by interaction with the air. Finally, any remaining propellant evaporates, leaving particles of the active ingredient suspended in air. Evaporation of the solvent does not produce a large decrease in the droplet diameter, since the diameter of a droplet varies inversely with the cube root of the mass. The mechanism of spray formation from pressurized containers has been discussed by York.[66]

The particle or droplet size distribution produced by pressurized packages can be controlled in a number of ways. When a powder is being dispersed, the particle size distribution is a function of the size distribution of the powder in the liquid, of the concentration of the powder in the liquid, and of the droplet size distribution as the propellent spray leaves the can. Unless the propellant is so volatile that droplets of propellant do not form, a given propellant droplet may contain several powder particles which cohere to form an aggregate when the droplet evaporates. If the suspension in the package is sufficiently dilute or the droplets sufficiently small, the probability that more than one particle will occupy a droplet is small, and excellent dispersion is obtained. Otherwise, considerable aggregation will occur.

The droplet size range can be controlled to a considerable extent by changes in pressure, composition, and valve design. Smaller droplets are obtained with higher pressures, which are controlled to a large extent by the nature and concentration of the propellant. Small orifices tend to produce small particles but also tend to clog easily and may restrict the delivery rate to an undesirable degree.

For the most part, little attention has been paid by manufacturers to the droplet size produced other than to make certain that the droplets are so large that they rain out. However, there are exceptions. One is the pressure packaging of insecticides. The U.S. Department of Agriculture specifies that insecticide sprays must contain no particles larger than 50 microns in diameter and that 80 percent of the particles must be less than

30 microns in diameter.[60] The upper size limits were established because large particles settle so rapidly that they would not be effective, and if many of the particles are large, the number concentration would be too small to provide a high probability of contact between particles and insects. Also, a large particle hitting an insect would provide much more insecticide than would be required to kill it, and insecticide would be wasted. Of course, very small particles would not settle or impact on an insect; but this is not a problem in the pressure packaging industry since no large fraction of the weight of the spray is associated with very small droplets, and the lower size limit of a powder is readily controlled.

Size control of therapeutic aerosols is also very important. In general, to achieve a high degree of penetration into the respiratory system the droplets should be as small as can reasonably be obtained from a pressure package. One way of achieving such a small size is to disperse a very dilute solution of the active ingredient in the propellant. If, for example, the concentration of the active ingredient is 1 percent, the mean droplet size after evaporation of the propellant will be about $1/\sqrt[3]{100}$ times the mean size of the droplets originally produced.

On the other hand, spray droplets for use on the surface of the skin should be relatively large so that impaction efficiency will be high and the droplets will spread. Kempe,[67] in a review of cosmetic and pharmaceutical preparations in pressurized packages, states that when aerosol droplets are used for skin treatment, particles larger than 50 microns are suitable.

Routine monitoring of the droplet size of sprays with reasonable accuracy requires considerable care. A method which has been proposed for insecticide aerosols involves drawing the spray into a wind tunnel and allowing the particles to impinge on a rotating microscope slide.[68] Droplets collected on the slide are measured and counted, and the sizes corrected for the spreading that occurs when the droplets hit the slide. A simplified, single-flash, version of the equipment for taking photomicrographs of aerosol particles *in situ*, described in Chapter 4, (p. 282 ff.) has been used by the author to determine the droplet size distribution of rapidly evaporating droplets in the size range produced by pressurized containers. Such equipment should be suitable for the routine monitoring of spray droplet size.

## POWDER METALLURGY

### General

Powder metallurgy can be considered to be the art of manufacturing items from powdered metals. It is actually a very old art, as in ancient times powdered metals were pounded or fritted into desired shapes. Powder metallurgy first became important in the present century as a means for producing tungsten filaments for incandescent lamps. The general use of powder metallurgy has increased rapidly since World War II. This has been largely brought about by improvements in compacting and sintering processes which not only have improved the products, but have also greatly decreased costs. The term "powder metallurgy" is often applied to the fabrication of articles by heating and pressing non-metallic as well as metallic powders.

The most common technique involves filling a mold with the powder and subjecting it to high pressures until a coherent article is produced. Whether the bonding at this stage is largely mechanical or chemical is controversial. The coherent mass is then heated, usually in an inert atmosphere or in a vacuum, to produce sintering. The voids are either reduced in volume or entirely eliminated and of course the "compact" becomes smaller. The result is a structure having physical properties similar to those of structures obtained from the same substance by fusion. Sometimes the characteristics are adequate for the finished product, but often additional compression, heating, or both is required. If additional heat treatment is given, it must be at such a temperature that the shape is not altered. This is usually an annealing process to increase the ductility or hardness.[69]

A wide range of sintering conditions is used, and the choice is determined by the nature of the powder and by the characteristics desired for the product. If the product is to be strong, it should be relatively free of voids. If the powder consists of a pure metal this is achieved by sintering at a temperature close to the melting point. A mixture of powders of metals of widely differing melting points can be sintered at a temperature between the two melting points.[70] This is called liquid-phase sintering, and is effective for removing voids and producing a very dense product. Another method of producing much the same final product involves sintering the higher-melting powder to form a spongy mass. The lower-melting material is fused and soaked up by the spongy material to form the final product. This process is called infiltration.

Essentially all the finishing processes that can be applied to parts made by more conventional methods can also be applied to parts fabricated by powder metallurgy, i.e., machining, buffing, plating, grinding, brazing, soldering, and welding. Ingots made from powders of many metals or alloys can be processed in conventional ways, and hot rolling or drawing of such ingots is not at all unusual. Many of the methods for processing metal powders are similar to those used in the ceramics and plastics industry.

Jenkins[70] lists four primary fields of application of powder metallurgy.

One, which has already been mentioned, is the manufacture of articles from metals or alloys which cannot be melted and cast, such as tungsten and tantalum. A second application is the manufacture of parts from mixtures of metals which do not form alloys and of articles which require the porosity which can be achieved by sintering powders. Metal filters for a number of purposes are prepared by sintering, and have a wide range of permeability and filtering efficiency which is largely obtained by controlling pore size. They are similar to those made of ceramics, but have superior mechanical strength and are more resistant to thermal and mechanical shock. Porous bearings, which contain lubricating oil within the voids, constitute another example. A third application is the production of alloys of precise composition for uses where certain properties must lie within very narrow limits. An example is alloys for making glass-to-metal seals in which the coefficient of thermal expansion is of prime importance. A fourth general application is the direct fabrication of finished parts using only powder metallurgy techniques.

### Powder production

Numerous methods, both mechanical and chemical, are used for producing the powders. The critical factors are considerations such as the shapes and size distributions desired, production costs, and physical or chemical properties of the raw materials which may limit the choice of method. Chemical methods are usually better suited to preparing metallurgical powders then those which are strictly physical. This is primarily because most mechanical methods, such as machining, crushing, and milling, produce particles that are too large and of too irregular shape to be satisfactory for powder metallurgy.

One chemical method involves reduction of the metal oxides. The oxides are first ground to an appropriate size distribution; this is readily achieved since the oxides of most metals are very brittle. This permits considerable control over the size distribution of the metal powder. The reduction is usually undertaken at a relatively high temperature with a gaseous reducing agent. The temperature must not be so high that sintering occurs, or a crust will form over the particles, slowing the reduction process. For instance, powdered iron oxides have been reduced at temperatures between 800 and 1000°C.

The reducing gases may be carbon monoxide, hydrogen, ammonia, or various hydrocarbons such as methane. The selection of the reducing agent may be based on chemical reactivity, availability, economy of operation, and need for high purity. The powders produced are usually rather spongy—a state which is very helpful to pressure compaction processes. The particle size of the metal is controlled not only by that of the oxide powder, but also by the conditions of reduction. When the reduction temperature is low the particles tend to be fine; when the reductions are carried out at high temperatures and the reducing gas has a high water vapor content, the metal particles tend to be coarse.

Reduction of metal oxides with hydrogen in an electric furnace is especially common. Some of the hydrogen, along with water vapor produced by the reaction, passes through the bed of oxide without reacting. Excess water is removed from this hydrogen and it is recirculated. The powders are often handled in metal trays, and the operation may be continuous, in which case the trays are introduced into the furnace an a continuous belt, or the operation may be conducted as a batch process.[70] This general process is used for preparing powders of iron, nickel, iron-nickel alloys, copper, cobalt, and molybdenum. The tungsten powders used for preparing lamp filaments are usually made in this manner.

The gaseous reduction of aqueous solutions of salts of the metals is somewhat more recent as an industrially important process. The raw materials are usually either scrap metals or ore concentrates, which are treated with acids or bases to extract the metals in the form of water-soluble salts. The pH is adjusted, catalyst added and the reduction carried out with hydrogen in autoclaves using elevated temperatures and pressures. This process produces metals of high purity, and a very narrow size distribution. Considerable control over the median particle size can be achieved by limiting the time during which the particles can act as precipitation nuclei. Median diameters between 40 and 100 microns are typical.

A more conventional and more widely used chemical method is thermal decomposition of the metal carbonyls. The process originated in Germany and was adapted in the United States as a means of producing extremely fine spherical particles of essentially pure iron for molding high-frequency iron core coils.[69] The carbonyls are prepared by treating the metals with carbon monoxide. Iron pentacarbonyl and nickel tetracarbonyl are liquids at room temperature, having boiling points of 103°C and 43°C, respectively. Both are very toxic. The iron carbonyl is usually produced from iron powder which had been produced by hydrogen reduction of the oxide. Carbon monoxide is passed over the powder at a high temperature and pressure, and the resulting gases, containing the carbonyl, are expanded to atmospheric pressure. This expansion causes dissociation of the carbonyl to produce a cloud of powdered iron.

The particles as first produced are very small, about 0.01 micron in the case of nickel. However, they serve as condensation nuclei and can be built up in size by allowing additional metal vapor to condense on them. The growth of iron particles is usually stopped before a large percentage of them exceed 10 microns diameter. Nickel particles are usually allowed to grow to much larger sizes.

The particles are spheres and do not compress very well, but they have excellent sintering characteristics.

Electrolysis is another essentially chemical method for producing metal powders. Deposition may be from aqueous solutions of metal salts or from fused salts. Organic substances are often added to the aqueous solutions to promote the formation of small particles at the cathode. By maintaining a high acidity and current density, hydrogen as well as the metal is liberated at the anode, and this imparts a desirable spongy consistency to the product. Particle size is controlled by removing the deposit continuously or at frequent intervals. The metal depositing at the cathode either falls to the bottom of the bath or is scraped from the cathode surface. When iron is produced electrolytically the deposit is brittle, and it is ground, cleaned, dried, and annealed before use. Alloys can be prepared by dissolving the salts of more than one metal in the bath.

Electrolysis of fused salts is usually restricted to metals with a high melting point such as tantalum and thorium.

The one mechanical method for producing metal powders which is used to an appreciable extent in powder metallurgy is "atomization." The process is similar to that used in perfume and pharmaceutical nebulizers in that a jet of air produces a pressure drop at the orifice of a nozzle which draws molten metal through the nozzle and into the air blast. In another, more modern, version the molten metal is placed in a vessel having an orifice in the bottom through which the metal flows. The stream of metal impinges on a jet of cold water which both disintegrates the metal and chills the resulting droplets. The solid metal particles are removed from the water by filtration. When the metals are apt to be oxidized the operation is conducted in an inert atmosphere. This process produces fairly large particles, for the most part in the range of the standard sieves.

### Size and size distribution

Goetzel[69] states that for practical powder metallurgical purposes, the powders can be classified into sieve and subsieve size ranges. He further suggests that powders in the sieve size range are usually used for the molding of various parts, magnets, bearings, etc., and that the finer powders are used for manufacturing refractory metals, cemented carbides, and magnetic cores.

Particle size and size distribution play an important role in the compaction process. Both the theoretical and experimental aspects of consolidation, including both cold compaction and sintering, have been reviewed by numerous authors.[69,71,72] Kuhn[73] has discussed this subject with emphasis on the behavior of submicron diameter particles. He suggests that there are three stages of sintering following the cold compaction. The first stage involves neck growth between particles and also the development of chemical bonds. The second stage produces an increase in density resulting from diffusion and plastic deformation, and the third stage involves the elimination of residual voids. The various theories concerning sintering generally include the importance of particle size. For example, Kuczynski[74] has developed an equation for stage (neck growth) based on the concept that the formation of necks can occur by four mechanisms, (a) viscous or plastic flow; (b) evaporation and condensation; (c) volume diffusion; and (d) surface diffusion:

$$x^n/r^m = F(T)t \tag{6.1}$$

$F(T)$ is a function of temperature and is characteristic of the flow type, $t$ is time, $x$ is the neck radius, and $n$ and $m$ are integers having the following values:

For viscous or plastic flow, $n = 2, m = 1$
For evaporation and condensation, $n = 3, m = 1$
For volume diffusion, $n = 5, m = 2$
For surface diffusion, $n = 7, m = 3$

According to this equation, the radius of the neck decreases with decreasing particle radius for a given time, regardless of the transport mechanism, but the neck radius does not decrease as rapidly as the particle radius. Thus a powder consisting of very fine particles might be expected to achieve a given rigidity more rapidly than one comprised of finer particles. Equation 6.1 is based on the assumption that the particles are all one size.

Kuhn's discussion of sintering[73] is based largely on a concept developed by Rhines,[75,76] which has the advantage that no assumptions need be made concerning particle shapes or size distributions. This concept assumes that sintering behavior for a given type of material is a function of the number of particles, $P$, in a given mass of powder and the number of points of contact, $C$, between particles. This function is called the genus, $G$:

$$G = C - P + 1 \tag{6.2}$$

In principle, $G$ can be evaluated experimentally, regardless of particle size or shape, by measuring $C$ and $P$. The genus is essentially the number of bonds or contacts that must be broken to return $G$ to zero. Two touching spheres have a genus of zero, three spheres touching in three places have a genus of 1, etc.

The first stage of sintering, described above, is a period of constant genus, except as a change in stacking arrangement may change $C$. During the second stage $G$ decreases to zero as pores become isolated, and during the third stage $G$ remains zero. In general, the genus of a given powder will increase rapidly with decreasing particle size.

Rumpf[77] has proposed the following basic equation for the first stage of sintering:

$$\text{T.S.} = \frac{9}{8} \frac{1 - \epsilon}{\pi d^2} kH \tag{6.3}$$

where T.S. is the tensile strength, $\epsilon$ is the void volume fraction, $k$ is the average number of points of contact between a particle and its neighbors, and $H$ is the average bonding force at each point of contact. It is assumed that the particles are spheres having the same diameter, $d$. Rumpf has proposed the following equation for particles whose sizes are normally distributed:

$$\text{T.S.} = 2 \left( \frac{H}{d_h^2} \right). \tag{6.4}$$

Here $d_h$ is an effective particle size. These equations indicate that the smaller the particle size and the greater the number of points of contact (and thus the greater $G$ of equation 6.2), the greater is the tensile strength following the first stage of sintering.

The density of the final product depends on the density in the absence of pores and on the percentage of pores in the product. The mechanism of shrinkage during the second and third stages is not well established. It may involve plastic flow or volume diffusion. Kuhn[73] states that when the particles are very small, a body is produced which is composed of very fine pores and grains which grow rapidly and tend to trap pores within single crystals. Possibly such trapping can be avoided by using a lower sintering temperature and grain-growth inhibitors. There is an advantage to having a fine particle size during the third stage of sintering since this seems to accelerate the density increase as a result of rapid recrystallization and grain growth. Kuhn also suggests that ultra-fine powders of poor packing and low bulk density may have high initial rates of "densification" compared with such powders of higher bulk density. The sintering rate may be reduced in later stages because of the development of large grain size and large pores, but this can in some cases be overcome by proper calcining.

An important application of powder metallurgy is dispersion strength-ening. A large part of the work in this field has been with sintered aluminum powder (SAP) but the technique is applicable to a number of other alloys and non-metallic materials.[73, 78, 79] The goal in many cases has been to produce alloys that can be used at temperatures closer to the melting point of the matrix material[78] than is normally possible. The usual technique is to mechanically mix two powders, one of which is to become the continuous phase and the other the discontinuous phase, which provides the strengthening action.

High-temperature rupture strength increases with decreasing distance between the insoluble refractory particles. This distance can only be made very small by using particles that are to become the continuous phase which also are very small. Metal powders of submicron particle size must be used if dispersion strengthening is to be effective. The dispersoid particles in SAP blends are about 0.3 micron apart. Cremens[78] has derived the following equation which relates interparticle spacing, $I$, volume fraction of the refractory material, $f_r$, and the ratio of volume to surface area, $R$, for the dispersoid phase in the finished composite alloy and is of course a function of particle size:

$$I = 4R(1/f_r - 1) \tag{6.5}$$

In terms of particle size of both the metal and the refractory particles, 6.5 can be written

$$I = d_r\left(\frac{f_m}{f_r}\right) + d_m \tag{6.6}$$

where $d_r$ and $d_m$ are the diameters of the refractory and metal particles, respectively. These are defined as the arithmetic means of the lengths of a line, projected at random through the powder, intercepted by the particles.

Cremens concludes that if the desirable interparticle spacing for the dispersion strengthening of alloys is in the range 0.1 to 1 micron, and the volume percent of dispersed phase is in the range 2 to 20, the metal particle diameters should be between 0.05 and 0.5 micron and the refrac-tory particle diameters between 0.005 and 0.1 micron.

Zwilsky and Grant[79] prepared a number of dispersion-strengthened copper alloys. Those having the finest dispersions were also the strongest.

## CERAMICS

### General

Ceramics can be defined as the art of making objects from essentially non-metallic minerals by firing at high temperatures. On the basis of this definition there is some overlap between the fields of ceramics and powder metallurgy, since the latter field is extended at times to include fabrication from certain non-metallic powders. In Europe the term "ceramics" is limited to manufacturing from clays and clay minerals, thus excluding the manufacture of glass, cement, and a host of miscellaneous products. In this discussion, only manufacturing methods which involve shaping or forming the objects before firing will be considered.

The most common materials in a ceramic mix are water, clay, feldspar, and potter's flint. The clay may be used directly as mined, or after some refining. Ancient pottery was almost always prepared from a mixture of clay and water without any additional material. Modern ceramics usually makes use of two clays: "ball" clays which are especially effective for imparting plasticity to the mix, and "china" clays, or kaolin, which have a lighter color. The clay serves two purposes: when wet it provides the consistency which permits shaping before firing, and after firing it provides much of the solid matrix.

Potter's flint is a very fine silica powder. It decreases the shrinkage that normally occurs when the wet clay dries and also the shrinkage occurring during the firing. Feldspar has a relatively low melting point and is added as a flux to reduce the temperature required for successful firing. The feldspar also serves as a cement during firing.

Clays used directly for making bricks or pottery contain ingredients in addition to the basic clay mineral which to some extent serve the same functions as the potter's flint and the feldspar.

Porcelain is made from a type of clay known as kaolin, found mainly in Germany. The clay, quartz, and feldspar are purified and then combined with water to form the plastic mix. The mix may be shaped by hand with or without the use of a potter's wheel, but such methods are now used only for art work. Jiggering is a much more common process. The plastic mix is thrown on a mold to form one side of the desired object. The mold is then placed on a wheel and the other side is produced by forcing a template against the rotating mass. This method is often used to mass-produce dinnerware. Another method of forming involves pressing the plastic mass into molds. Or the mixture can contain enough water to constitute a slurry (or "slip") and poured into plaster molds. The plaster absorbs water to such an extent that a sheath constituting the desired structure is formed against the inner wall of the mold. The excess slurry is then poured out. A deflocculant such as sodium carbonate or sodium silicate is usually added to the slip to make it more fluid before pouring it into the mold.

The shaped object is dried and any unevenness such as the casting seam is removed. It is then placed in a kiln and heated to about 950°C. This renders the object hard and watertight, but it still has a dull surface. During firing, chemically bound water is lost from the clay minerals, and they are transformed to mullite ($3Al_2O_3 \cdot 2SiO_2$) and silica. The flux melts and some of the materials present dissolve in the flux. The liquid phase is largely converted to a glass upon hardening, binding together the mullite and silicate crystals.

After initial firing, the object is ready to be glazed. It is dipped in a slurry containing the same ingredients from which the object was made, but containing much more silica and feldspar relative to the amount of kaolin than did the original mix. Firing is then repeated but at a much higher temperature (1350–1450°C). When the porcelain has cooled, which takes several days, it is ready to be painted with dyes mixed with a glass powder and given a final heating. An alternative procedure is to decorate before glazing, but this is limited to a relatively few colors.

Some ceramic objects are extruded through a die having the desired cross section, and the resulting ribbon is cut to the desired length. This process is often used in making brick. Other objects are formed by pressing, which involves compression in a mold the top and bottom of which are plungers to which force is applied. One advantage of pressing is that less water is used than in "throwing" techniques, so there is little drying shrinkage. Another variation is to combine the forming and firing operation using a process known as hot pressing. In this case the mold and the material in it are heated.

Many ceramics, even within the limited defination used here, do not involve the use of clay. This is particularly true of refractories, about 40 percent of which consist of heavy non-clay substances such as magnesite and chromite.[80]

In addition to the conventional porcelain, pottery, brick, and china, a number of non-silicate inorganic objects have been developed which are often called ceramics. One class may be termed the pure oxide ceramics produced from oxides such as alumina ($Al_2O_3$), zirconia ($ZrO_2$), thoria ($ThO_2$), beryllia (BeO), magnesia (MgO), spinel ($MgAl_2O_4$), and fosterite ($Mg_2SiO_4$). The ferrites have the general formula $MFe_2O_4$ and have the cubic crystal structure of spinel. These are magnetic ceramics and are used in memory components of large computers and in other electronic systems. Ceramic nitrides, such as aluminum nitride, silicon nitride, and boron nitride have been developed for special purposes, such as refractories. These are just examples; new inorganic products are being developed almost daily.

### Sintering

As mentioned above, there is considerable overlap between the fields of powder metallurgy and ceramics, and this is especially true of the importance of particle size to the sintering processes. For example, Herring[81] has considered the effect of change of scale on the sintering process in general, defining sintering as any change in shape which a small particle or cluster of particles undergoes when held at a high temperature. He suggests that in the absence of applied stress, the force producing the changes is surface tension since the surface free energy decreases as the particles grow together. The transport of matter can take place by plastic or viscous flow, evaporation and condensation, volume diffusion, and surface migration.

Herring developed scaling laws based on the following considerations. Two partially sintered clusters are considered which are geometrically similar. The linear dimensions of cluster number two are $\lambda$ times the corresponding dimensions of number one. The factor $\lambda$ applies not only to cluster diameter but also to the diameters of the regions of contact between the clusters. Herring considered the relationship between the time $\Delta t_1$, required to produce a given change in shape of cluster number one in the sintering process, and the time $\Delta t_2$ required, at the same temperature, to produce a geometrically similar change in the second cluster. He obtained the following scaling laws for the different transport processes:

(a) Viscous flow of an amorphous material

$$\Delta t_2 = \lambda \Delta t_1$$

(b) Evaporation and condensation

$$\Delta t_2 = \lambda^2 \Delta t_1$$

(c) Volume diffusion

$$\Delta t_2 = \lambda^3 \Delta t_1$$

(d)  Surface migration

$$\Delta t_2 = \lambda^4 \Delta t_1$$

For each process, the time required increases with increasing cluster size.

One application of such scaling laws is to establish the transport mechanism, for if a given type of sintering experiment gives results obeying one of the sealing laws, the predominant mechanism of transport can be inferred.

## Porosity

The porosity of the final product can often be controlled by controlling the size distribution and thus the packing of the particles in the unfired material.  For example, Gugel and Norton[82] have suggested this as a method for preparing high-density firebrick.  Schüller[83] investigated the effect of particle size on the structure of porcelain using an electron microscope.  The concentrations and sizes of pores were little affected by the size of the quartz particles (5 to 150 microns diameter), but were considerably greater if the feldspar particle diameters were increased from less than 60 microns to 120–150 microns.

The influence of silica (flint) particle size on the permanent moisture and thermal expansion in porous earthenware bodies was investigated by Palmer.[84]  Potter's flint was ground from quartz sandstone and separated into four fractions of differing size distribution by elutriation.   Two series of bodies were prepared: (a) a talc-pyrophyllite series and (b) a clay-flint-feldspar series, using the various flint fractions as the single varying component.  Moisture expansion was found to diminish as the flint particle size decreased, while thermal expansion increased with decreasing flint particle size.  The median particle diameters ranged from about 2 to 30 microns for the four fractions of flint.  Vieweg[85] studied the effects of grain size of china clays and concluded that the porosity of the fired product increases with increasing porosity, while firing shrinkage decreases with increasing size. The average particle diameters in the clays investigated ranged from about 1 to 40 microns (Figure 6-4).

## Strength

The particle size of the quartz in porcelain has a marked effect on its strength.  Krause and Klempin[86] investigated this effect using nine classes of quartz powder covering the diameter range 0 to 175 microns.  Maximum strength of the porcelain prepared from these samples was obtained

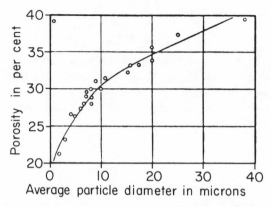

Figure 6-4. Relation between average particle diameter and per cent porosity of fired clay.[84] (*Courtesy of the American Ceramic Society*)

when the particles had diameters in the range 10 to 30 microns. Marzahl[87] made a theoretical study of this effect, based on the compressive stress impressed on the continuous glassy matrix of the porcelain by the greater thermal expansion of the undissolved quartz particles relative to the expansion of the glass. He found that a peak strength should occur for a quartz particle diameter of 12 microns and a thickness of glass between particles of 1 micron. A lower peak strength should occur when the glass thickness increases, and when it is 2.5 microns the peak strength is produced by a quartz particle diameter of 25 microns. These conclusions are in qualitative agreement with the experimental results of Krause and Klempin.[86]

The shapes and sizes of particles in clays have a marked effect on the quality of coarse ceramic ware made from the clays. Winkler[88] found that clays for ordinary brick should contain less than 20 percent of particles smaller than 2 microns and more than 60 percent of particles larger than 20 microns. When the particles are more complex and thinner, the proportion of fine particles should be increased. For roofing tile, Winkler suggested the proportions 23–51, 10–47, and 48–8 percent of particles less than 2, 2 to 20, and greater than 20 microns in diameter, respectively. The desired size distribution can often be achieved by blending different clays.

## Plasticity

The sizes of the particles in the clay affect its physical properties before firing, particularly the plasticity. The available surface is a function of the particle size, and Whittaker[89] obtained the empirical relationship

$$\text{Log } S = A P_1 + B$$

where $S$ is the specific surface, $P_1$ is the plasticity defined as the product of yield and strain, and $A$ and $B$ are constants. Whittaker emphasized that numerous factors other than particle size influence plasticity, including particle shape, temperature at the time of the test, time of application of the deforming force, amount of liquid medium, electrolyte content, and surface effects of the grains.

Moore[90] in 1930 reviewed the effect of particle size in clay products. He emphasized the manner in which clay particles can be packed together and came to the following conclusions. The best working properties are found for clays having enough small particles to form a continuous film around the large, "nonplastic" particles. Without such a lubricating film the clay tends to be crumbly or "short." On the other hand, if the larger particles are absent there may be a tendency to warping during drying. Moore suggested two ways of "opening up" the texture of clay having particles that are of nearly uniform size. One is to add a relatively small amount of large grains; the other is to reduce the proportion of medium-sized particles in the aggregate and increase the proportions of the existing large and small particles. Moore stated that the second method provides a stronger, more uniform mass which is free of flaws and internal cracks. This method may also improve the mechanical strength of the final product, such as firebrick. The best load-carrying texture for brick to be used at high temperatures is achieved with just sufficient fines to provide a firm bond. A high proportion of fines should be avoided since the motion of the larger particles over each other is aided by a thick film of fine particles. Moore also stated that the shape of the particles is very important, and the greatest strength is obtained with an interwoven mass of acicular particles. It is this structure which gives sillimanite refractories their high load-carrying characteristics.

### Miscellaneous effects

There are numerous miscellaneous effects of particle size in the ceramics industry. Control of particle size may improve the chipping resistance of bricks.[91] The development of pinholes in certain glazes can be minimized if the glaze particles are sufficiently small.[92]

Many of the considerations relating to particle sizes of pigments in paints also apply to the particles in the glazes and enamels on ceramic objects. Zwermann and Andrews[93] have reviewed the relationship between particle size and the characteristics of light reflected from porcelain enamel surfaces. Their general conclusion was that increased opacity could be obtained by extremely fine milling, largely because of the excellent dispersion of the "opacifiers."

### Ferrites

Particle size is of course important not only to the conventional ceramics just discussed but also to the manufacture of some recently developed devices. An example of the latter is the manufacture of components from ferrites. These are substances with the general formula $MFe_2O_4$. They are isomorphous with the mineral magnetite ($Fe_3O_4$) which can be termed ferrous ferrite. These substances are important because they are magnetic. The magnetic properties are retained if part of the ferric ions are replaced by other trivalent ions such as $Al^{+3}$, $Ti^{+3}$, or $Cr^{+3}$. While the magnetic properties of the ferrites are similar to those of magnetite, they have a higher electrical resistivity. Most applications are based on their low electrical conductivity compared with that of iron. A direct result is that energy losses resulting from induced currents at high frequencies are much smaller. Ferrite magnets can be used at frequencies up to the microwave region.

The use of ferrite magnets in computer memory systems has already been mentioned. They are also used in filters and transformers in radios, television sets, and other electronic devices, and for a variety of special electronic applications.

Ferrites are usually prepared by a solid state reaction between two metal oxides. Either the oxides or the corresponding carbonates which form oxides on heating are thoroughly mixed and heated at about 1000°C. Diffusion of the cations occurs to produce the desired product, but several regrindings and reheatings are required before the reaction is essentially complete. The powder is then pressed and fired at 1300 to 1400°C to produce the final shape.

The effect of particle size on the magnetic properties of ferrites was investigated by Schuele and Deetscreek.[94] It seems to be explained by the domain theory of magnetization. According to this theory ferromagnetic substances consist of regions (the domains) within which all the atoms are aligned with parallel spins. Thus each domain is magnetically saturated, but the directions of magnetization of the multitude of domains have a random distribution. When a magnetic field is applied to the substance, the direction of magnetization of most of the domains is changed to align with the field. This is accomplished either by a rotation of the atoms or a movement of the domain boundary so as to increase the volume of the domain in the direction of the field.[95,96] The former process is only important for high fields. When the particles are sufficiently small that each one is a single domain, the magnetic properties are markedly changed with respect to both coercive forces and permeability.

Schuele and Deetscreek studied these changes by preparing ferrites ranging in size from tens of Angstroms to microns. The former were so small that each particle consisted of but one domain. Such particles are called superparamagnetic. Conventional methods for preparing very small ferrite particles could not be used, since the sintering destroyed the fine particles and grinding does not produce sufficiently small particles. Therefore, three methods were used to prepare the ferrites, all of which involved a preliminary co-precipitation step to produce crystals containing two cations in the crystal lattice. One method involved dissolving sulfates or chlorides of the desired cations in hot distilled water and adding the stoichiometric amount of a solution of ammonium oxalate. The resulting precipitate was demonstrated to be the desired solid solution of oxalates. The washed and dried precipitate was heated at 400°C which decomposed it into the ferrite, carbon monoxide, and carbon dioxide. Average particle diameters determined by x-ray line broadening and from electron micrographs were between 300 and 700A.

A method which produced smaller particles involved adding the oxalate particles to molten potassium nitrate. The oxalate promptly decomposes and the escaping gases help to disperse the particles. The molten salt is then poured into a large volume of water. This method produced particles about 100A in diameter.

The third method involved adding an aqueous solution of the metal chlorides, heated to 80°C, to a boiling aqueous solution of sodium hydroxide with vigorous stirring. The resulting precipitate was shown by chemical analysis to be the desired ferrite. A nickel ferrite sample prepared in this way was found by electron diffraction techniques to have an average particle diameter of 18A. This method was adapted to growing ferrite particles of various sizes, taking advantage of the fact that the larger particles in an aqueous suspension tend to grow at the expense of smaller ones. This results from the fact that small particles are more soluble than large ones of the same substance. Since the rate of mass transfer is increased by raising the temperature, after part of the original precipitate was removed to provide the smallest particles, the remaining suspension was boiled under a reflux condenser. The refluxing was continued for several hundred hours, periodically removing samples.

Magnetic measurements were made on the ferrite particles to determine saturation magnetization ($\sigma_s$), the ratio of remanence to saturation ($\sigma_r/\sigma_s$) the coercive force ($I$), and the Curie temperature. Some of the results are shown in Table 6-1. On the basis of such results it was concluded that the critical single domain size for both nickel and copper ferrite is 400 to 600A.

TABLE 6-1. MAGNETIC PROPERTIES OF COBALT FERRITE POWDERS[93]

| Sample | Crystallite Size (A) | $\sigma_s \dfrac{emu}{gm}$ 300°K | $\sigma_R/\sigma_s$ 300°K | $I(oe)$ 300°K | $I(oe)$ 77°K | Curie Temp. (°C) |
|---|---|---|---|---|---|---|
| 1 | 72 | 24.3 | .04 | 160 | 2550 | 409 |
| 2 | 84 | 31.0 | .12 | 326 | 2550 | 494 |
| 3 | 120 | 34.0 | .18 | 570 | 1750 | 440 |
| 4 | 297 | 60.5 | .53 | 2500 | 6250 | 536 |
| 5 | 355 | 59.5 | .48 | 2280 | 6200 | 567 |
| 6 | 459 | 74.5 | .43 | 1380 | 5100 | 544 |
| 7 | 705 | 77.0 | .50 | 1390 | 6150 | 544 |
| 8 | 1030 | 74.3 | .45 | 980 | 5340 | 549 |
| 9 | 2000 | 77.5 | .12 | 326 | 2380 | 541 |
| Bulk Sample | | 81 | | | | 510 |

# ENCAPSULATION AND COATING OF PARTICLES

## General

Covering liquid or solid particles with a casing or coating is not a specific industry but it is such an important part of a number of technological operations that a separate discussion seems warranted.

There are many reasons for coating particles, but a major one is to keep them in a convenient form until ready for use. This is particularly true of liquids, since by encapsulating them they can be treated as solids until the capsules are broken. Encapsulation is a process that has been used for generations in the food (e.g. coloring) and pharmaceutical industries. However, the capsules are usually of the order of millimeters in size. During recent years techniques have been developed for encapsulating droplets of the order of microns or even fractions of microns in diameter. A result has been a host of new applications of encapsulation techniques. Materials which have been encapsulated include inks, dyes, perfumes, adhesives, medicines, and various chemical reactants. Many of the resulting products are spread on surfaces, such as paper, to liberate the liquid in the capsules when pressure is applied. For example, an encapsulated adhesive in powder form can be cemented in place over the surface of paper. When the paper is pressed against some surface the capsules break, liberating the adhesive and causing the paper to adhere to the surface. If the capsules contain ink, they can be used in the preparation of a "carbon" paper.

Particles produced in the pharmaceutical industry are often coated with some solid that slowly dissolves in the digestive tract so as to control the time and place within the body that the active ingredients are liberated. The particles may be either liquid or solid. The action of the coating is the same in either case, but the methods for applying it are quite different. Coatings may be used in the pharmaceutical industry and elsewhere to protect the contents, for example against atmospheric oxygen and moisture.

Coated particles are also becoming important in powder metallurgy. The coatings may act as lubricants; they help to ensure the production of a random distribution when there is more than one phase, and they may protect the particles from oxidation by the atmosphere.

### Production methods

To a very large extent, modern uses of small coated particles have been the result of effective and efficient production methods. A group of methods that has been especially useful for encapsulating very small droplets is based on the colloidal phenomenon of coacervation. It can be defined as the separation, by adding a third component, of a macromolecular colloid into two liquid phases, one of which is rich in the polymer and the other is an aqueous solution of the third component. The polymer-rich phase is called the coacervate and the aqueous solution is called the equilibrium liquid. The term "coacervation" was invented by Bungenberg de Jong and Kruyt[97,98] to differentiate the phenomenon described above from simple "partial miscibility," which is the separation of one phase into two co-existing phases. They believed that the colloidal system consisted of two phases even before the addition of the third component. It now seems likely that the system is a single phase before addition of the coacervating agent, but is differentiated from ordinary partial miscibility by the high viscosity of the coacervate.

If an emulsion of some oil is prepared in the single phase aqueous solution, the addition of the coacervating agent may cause the droplets of oil to separate with the coacervate and in effect to be coated with the polymer. Various modifications of this approach are possible. For instance, Brynko and Scarpelli[99] have patented a process based on this principle for encapsulating oils by two layers of solid material. The inner layer is a polymerized monomer and the outer is a hydrophilic colloid deposited by coacervation from a polar solvent in which the colloid has been dispersed. Brynko[100] has described a related technique. A polymerizable monomer is dissolved in an oil or other water-immiscible liquid in which the polymerized monomer is insoluble. The solution is then dispersed as droplets in a polar liquid, and the monomer is catalytically polymerized. The polymer deposits at the oil-polar liquid interface, forming a capsule around each droplet. The capsules are discrete, nearly spherical, and easily breakable under pressure.

Robbins, Thomas, and Cadle[101] studied techniques for encapsulating aerosol particles (liquid or solid) during or immediately following their dispersion into the gas phase. Several methods were found to be effective, as follows.

(a) The core material, dispersed as an aerosol, served as condensation nuclei on which the encapsulation material condensed from the vapor phase.

(b) A two-phase suspension or emulsion was spray-dried.

(c) An aerosol of solid core material was charged to one polarity and an aerosol of liquid encapsulating material was charged to the opposite polarity, followed by mixing of the aerosols.

(d) High turbulence was produced in an aerosol containing particles of core material and particles of encapsulating material. The turbulence was produced by using an aerosol of core material in place of the usual gas employed in an asperating-type aerosol generator.

(e) The core material, dispersed as an aerosol, was used as condensation nuclei on which organic monomers polymerized and condensed. The last method was studied using phosphoric acid as the core material. A number of organic monomers were tried. The most effective macromolecule production involved a mixture of isoprene and nitrogen dioxide.

Distinguishing between encapsulated and unencapsulated particles with a microscope was very difficult except for a few combinations, such as lauric acid condensed on dioctyl phthalate droplets. Therefore, a method for determining the degree of encapsulation was developed based on a comparison of the phosphoric acid available in the sample from the encapsulating runs with the acid available from blank (non-encapsulating) runs by titrating with aqueous sodium hydroxide solution using phenolphthalein. The most effective encapsulation achieved using this technique was 92 percent.

Matijevic *et al.*[102] have prepared aerosols consisting of a solid core on which a liquid shell was condensed in order to investigate light scattering by coated aerosols. The core particles consisted of silver chloride and were produced by evaporating solid silver chloride and condensing it in a stream of helium. The modes in the particle radius distributions as determined with an electron microscope were about 0.01 to 0.02 micron. The size distributions were relatively narrow; the standard deviations from the mean radius were about 20 to 25 percent.

Methods for coating powders for use in powder metallurgy and ceramics have been described by Goetzel.[69] Metal particles may be coated with a different metal to modify the chemical properties or the susceptibility to plastic deformation, while they may be coated with nonmetals to aid the pressing operation or to effect alloying during sintering. Goetzel lists four methods for coating metal particles: (a) ball milling, (b) electroplating, (c) precipitation, and (d) spraying.

Coating by ball milling involves milling relatively hard particles of the core material with softer, finer particles of the material that is to become the coating. An example is the coating of copper particles by tin. Electrolytic coating involves preliminary electrolytic preparation of the core particles which in turn serve as the cathode for deposition of the coating.[103] Precipitation coating involves the replacement of a metal ion by a metal (the core material) which is higher in the electromotive series, that is, is less "noble." For example, lead particles can be coated with copper.

In addition to the methods described by Goetzel, metal powders can be coated by sputtering or condensing metal vapors onto the core particles, oxidizing the particle surface to produce an oxide coating, or suspending the core powder in the heated vapor of a metal carbonyl.

Lamprey[104] has investigated methods for coating submicron size particles. For core material, he used a commercial grade of alumina ($Al_2O_3$) which was calcined to remove chemically combined water (presumably as $Al(OH)_3$), and leached with acid to remove iron. The average diameter, estimated from measurements of specific surface (by B.E.T.), was 0.03 micron. One method of coating involved stirring the alumina into a 10 to 20 percent aqueous solution of nickel chloride, and adding an aqueous solution of sodium hydroxide to precipitate nickel hydroxide on the alumina particles which hopefully acted as nuclei. The coated particles were removed by filtration, washed and dried, and then heated in hydrogen at 600°C to reduce the oxide to metallic nickel. Electron micrographs of the resulting material showed that the coatings were very uneven. Furthermore, the original deposition of nickel hydroxide on the alumina particles was equally uneven. Probably, because of the tremendous supersaturation that occurred when the sodium hydroxide was added, the particles of alumina did not act as nuclei, and precipitation was by self-nucleation. If this interpretation is correct, the coatings resulted from agglomeration of small nickel hydroxide particles with larger alumina particles, as Lamprey's photomicrographs suggest. Similar results were obtained when other metals, such as iron, molybdenum, copper, and silver, were substituted for the nickel.

Much more satisfactory coatings were obtained by "vapor plating." For example, the alumina was coated with 50 percent by weight of molybdenum by sealing alumina powder and the gas molybdenum carbonyl in a tube and heating above 350°C to decompose the metal carbonyl. Electron micrographs showed that the molybdenum deposited quite smoothly. An excellent silicon film was deposited by "fluidizing" the heated powder at 300°C with silane ($SiH_4$) vapor. The silane decomposed, and silicon condensed on the alumina particles. A similar coating of silicon on molybdenum was prepared, and by heating to 1100°C, chemical reaction occurred between the molybdenum and silicon to form $MoSi_2$, as established by x-ray diffraction techniques. Alumina was coated with tungsten by fluidizing it with a mixture of tungsten hexafluoride and hydrogen at 650°C, presumably forming hydrogen fluoride and tungsten.

Particles of micron size or larger can be coated by converting the outer portions of the particles to some other chemical species, and Lamprey found that this technique can be successfully applied to particles of submicron size. Tungsten, molybdenum, columbium, and nickel powders having average diameters in the range 0.02 to 0.11 micron were coated with the corresponding nitrides, oxides, carbides, sulfides, silicides, and borides. The coatings, however, provided little or no protection, as was indicated by the fact that the reactions producing the coatings could be continued until all the metal constituting the original particles was consumed.

An interesting semi-popular review of particle encapsulation has been written by Mattson.[100]

Particle size is important to the coating of particles in at least two ways. One is the method of preparation of the core particles. If the particles are at least a micron in average diameter, many methods including grinding, milling, and those discussed in the section on powder metallurgy are available. If the core particles are largely of submicron size, the number of available production methods is much more limited. Mechanical attrition is generally ineffective, although some high-speed mills will grind to the 0.1–1.0 micron diameter range. Particles of sub-micron size are usually produced by precipitation from the gas or liquid phase, either by chemical or electrical methods such as those described earlier in this chapter.

The other way in which particle size influences the production of coated particles is that it must be considered in developing the technique for handling the particles during the coating operation. For example, the velocity of gas flow through a fluidized bed of very fine particles must be less than through a bed of coarse particles; or entrainment of particles in the gas stream may occur.

Of course, the particle size must be compatible with the use. For instance if coated inks are to be used for reproduction processes, the particles must be much smaller than the lettering to be reproduced but large enough to be crushed and the ink liberated by reasonable pressure.

## PULP AND PAPER

### General

Paper is generally considered to be defined as felted cellulose fibers. This broad definition includes such primative materials as the papyrus of the Egyptions, and the tapas and kapas of the Polynesians. The application of the term is often limited to materials formed on a fine wire screen from a dilute aqueous suspension, but may be extended to include fibers of substances other than cellulose, such as asbestos and organic polymers.

Wood is the main source of the fibers used for making paper. The first step in the manufacturing process is converting the wood to pulp. There are three principal methods for accomplishing this, namely, mechanical, semichemical, and chemical. The latter includes the sulfite, sulfate, and soda processes. The choice of process is dictated by the type of wood, by the ultimate use of the paper, and by various economic considerations.

The mechanical method involves grinding in the presence of water with a grindstone. The strength of papers made from such pulp is low and it is usually blended with pulp made by other methods to impart additional strength. Even so, it is used for products such as newsprint that do not require exceptional strength.

The semichemical processes are relatively new. The usual procedure is to reduce the wood to chips, soften them by some chemical means, and complete the pulping process by mechanical means. Pulps produced in this way are usually used for newsprint, cardboards, and related products. Semichemical methods produce yields of pulp, based on the weight of wood, intermediate between those obtained by mechanical means (about 90 percent) and those obtained by purely chemical methods (40–50 percent).

The sulfite process involves treating the wood chips with an aqueous solution of sulfur dioxide (sulfurous acid) and a bisulfite. It is usually used for pulping softwood. The sulfate process involves digesting the chips with aqueous solutions of sodium hydroxide and sodium sulfite. It produces an especially strong pulp and can be applied to both softwood and hardwood.* The soda process is another alkaline chemical process which involves digestion with aqueous sodium hydroxide. It is usually used for hardwood, and the resulting pulp is not particularly strong.

In addition to wood pulp, esparto grass, cotton and linen rags, straw, and waste paper are used for making paper.

The size of the cellulose fibers affects both the uniformity and strength of the paper. Particularly large fibers or clumps of fibers are removed at the pulp mill by screening. The lengths of the fibers are affected by the type of wood (softwood fibers are longer than hardwood) and by the method of pulping.

The first step in paper making is beating, which crushes and splits the fibers, producing fibrils. During this process water is absorbed by the fibers accompanied by considerable swelling. This greatly increases the capacity of the fibers to bond to each other upon drying. After beating, the fibers are refined; this process breaks up knots and clusters, and cuts the fibers to a uniform length.

At some stage during the above stock preparation, various non-cellulosic materials are usually added. These may include clays, calcium carbonate, or other fillers; sizing; dyes; and wet-strength agents. After refining, a very dilute suspension is prepared which is fed to the continuous paper machine, either Fourdrinier or cylinder.

## Fiber size

The strength of the finished paper is related to the length and thickness of the fibers, but not in a simple way. This fact is not surprising since a number of factors other than fiber size contribute to the strength of the sheets. A very important factor is the strength of the bonds between the fibers, and when this is less than a minimum average value fiber size is of

*Softwoods are those obtained from coniferous trees of all species; hardwoods are from deciduous trees such as maple, ash, birch, etc.

little importance. The bond strength is determined by the physical and chemical nature of the fiber surfaces and by details of the paper-making process. The nature of the bonding has been reviewed by Van den Akker.[105]

Another important factor is fiber strength. This of course is closely related to the thickness of the fibers, but fibers of the same thickness but from different woods or separated from the same wood in different ways may have different strengths. Van den Akker *et al.*[106] investigated the importance of fiber strength to sheet strength. They determined the amount of fiber breakage that occurred during tearing and tensile rupture by microscopic examination of the paper before and after the rupture. Two techniques were developed for tagging fibers with dyes. Both tearing and tensile rupture were accompanied by considerable fiber breakage in the rupture zone, demonstrating that fiber strength is important to paper strength. When the breakage was produced by tensile rupture rather than by tearing, it was found that the amount of fiber breakage was related to fiber length and orientation, degree of bonding, and the amount of beating in the manufacturing process.

Numerous papers have been published describing the effect of fiber length and thickness on paper strength. Volokitina *et al.*[107] chopped long fiber cotton to varying average lengths (0.96, 1.8, 3.0, 4.4, 5.2, and 7.0 mm). Sheets of paper were prepared from these samples under standard conditions. The tensile strength of both wet and dry paper increased with increasing fiber length, and it was suggested that for each type of fiber there is a minimum fiber length below which a sheet cannot be formed. Haywood[108] also investigated the effect of variations in the size and shape of fibers on papermaking properties. He determined fiber-length distributions for a number of hard and softwood pulps. The average length of fibers from hardwoods was 0.8 to 1.3 mm and from softwoods was 2.0 to 3.3 mm. The ratio of length to width for the former fibers was 35 to 58, and for the latter 63 to 111. Pulp from the softwood gave a stronger paper than that from the hardwood, and this was partially a result of the greater fiber length of the softwood. It was found that birch and aspen pulps produce stronger papers than other deciduous pulps, probably because the fibers are thinner-walled.

Giertz[109] investigated the relationship between the properties of wood pulp from various sources and those of the corresponding papers. He concluded that tearing strength depends largely on the strength of the fiber and especially on the thickness of the fiber wall. Rapidly growing woods, particularly those with a high percentage of summer wood and long fibers, give a high tear strength but low bursting strength. Those pulps which contain a high percentage of amorphous cellulose produce papers having high tensile and bursting strengths.

Watson and Dadswell[110] studied the influence of fibers from early wood and late wood on paper characteristics. The chief differences were in the thickness of the fibers, the late wood having the thickest. Folding endurance, bursting strength, and tensile strength, which depend largely on bonding, were greater for paper prepared from early wood, while late wood from some species of trees provided better tear resistance. They concluded that when the properties of beaten pulps from 100 percent early wood and 100 percent late wood are known, the properties of mixtures of the pulps can be predicted.

The above results by a number of investigators seem to be fairly consistent with respect to the effect of fiber size on paper strength. The pulps in general were chemically prepared. However, the effect of fiber length is quite different when pulp is prepared mechanically. Morton and Alexander[111] found that sheets made from short fibers and fines of mechanical pulps have higher tensile strengths than those made from long-fiber fractions. They found just the opposite for chemical pulps.

Bobrov[112] has developed the following theoretical relationship among shearing strain (fiber on fiber), $s$, in kg mm$^{-2}$, specific fiber surface area, $f_0$, in cm$^2$gm$^{-1}$, breaking length $L$, in mm, and average length of the fibers $l$, in mm:

$$sl f_0 = 4L \qquad (8.7)$$

Fiber size affects other properties than paper strength. Density has been found to be directly proportional to tensile strength[111] and thus is a function of the dimensions of the fibers, although such a positive correlation does not establish a cause and effect relationship. An interesting modification of fiber size has been used to increase porosity and absorbency.[113] The fibers, such as cotton linters or wood pulp, are cross-linked by chemical bonding with a polyfunctional reagent such as a polyepoxide or polyaldehyde. This of course produces large "particles" consisting of chemically bound networks of fibers. The cross-linked fibers are refined and made into paper in the usual way.

Paper made from the short fibers of mechanical pulps have been found to have higher light-scattering coefficients than those from long fiber fractions.[111] But just as in the case of tensile strength, the reverse was found for chemical pulps.

## Sizing

Sizing may be defined as a viscid wash or other material applied to paper to produce a suitable surface. Arledter[114] investigated the relationship among particle size, degree of hydration, and the covering power of rosin sizing after it has been added to the pulp and water and a precipitate is formed. The size of the particles in the precipitate depends on the amount of free rosin in the sizing solution, the amount of electrolyte added, the type of protective colloid present, temperature, type of mixing, and the length of time the precipitate is allowed to stand. Rosin precipitates with the smallest possible particle size, other factors being equal, give the best over-all sizing.

Another study involved a comparison of the sizing properties of five rosins from different sources.[115] The rosin producing the largest particle size was the most effective for sizing the sheet. It is important to realize that these apparently are not the same particles that Arledter was considering.

## Loading and filling

The addition of finely divided mineral materials to the aqueous slurry of pulp before it is converted into paper improves the quality of the paper for many purposes and also decreases its cost. Fillers may be used to increase opacity, decrease the "show-through," improve receptivity, and give more body. They may also produce a smoother finish.[116] Fillers include clay, chalk, gypsum, talc, chemically precipitated materials such as calcium carbonate, and white pigments, such as titanium dioxide and zinc sulfide. Fillers used to produce high opacity and brightness should have the characteristics described earlier in this chapter as being appropriate for white paint pigments. The optimum particle size for producing paper opacity is about one-half the average wavelength of visible light, that is, the average diameter should be in the range 0.25 to 0.35 micron (for paint, see Figure 6-2). Also, as in the case of paint and for the same reasons, a filler of high refractive index will produce a brighter, more nearly opaque paper than one of low refractive index. A small particle size and narrow size distribution are essential to the production of a smooth surface.[116] Obviously, the filler should be clean, grit-free and have a good color.

The fillers are added to the pulp slurry before it is fed to the machine and much of it may be carried away from the forming paper as the aqueous solution drains through the wire mesh or filter. The pulp fibers retain the fillers by mechanical interception of larger particles, which may result in closing of large passages so that smaller particles are then retained, much as a filter bed is formed. Small particles may also be retained by polar forces acting between the fibers and the particles.

Cameron[116] states that the presence of filler in paper stock has two effects on filler retention. It increases the forces, which presumably are largely polar, holding the filler particles to the fibers, since cellulose and the filler are negatively charged and the alumina is positively charged. It may also act by causing flocculation of the suspended filler particles, so that they become large enough that mechanical interception is an effective mechanism of filtration by the cellulose fibers. A number of chemicals in addition to alum have been added to increase retention. They include various synthetic polymers and a number of naturally occurring materials such as guar gum, locust bean gum, and mannogalactans.

### Paper coatings

Paper coatings consisting largely of mineral matter are applied to render the paper opaque, to produce a smooth surface which is receptive to ink, and to change the color of the paper. The coating composition consists largely of inorganic pigment, an adhesive such as starch, and water. The viscosity and thixotropic properties of the mixture are very important to the successful application of the coating material to the paper surface. A mildly thixotropic mixture produces a smoother coating than a mixture exhibiting Newtonian viscosity, but a highly thixotropic mixture may be too viscous to be readily applied. When the coating pigment is largely clay, considerable control over the size of flocs and thus of both rheological properties and properties of the finished product can be achieved by the addition of predetermined amounts of dispersing agents. However, the production of suitable coatings is an art, and arriving at appropriate formulations is largely by trial and error.

The relationship between the flow properties of coating clays and particle size and shape has been reviewed by Albert.[117] He points out that deflocculation is probably not attributable to the presence of exchangeable cations associated with the particles, as has often been suggested, nor must free hydroxyl ions be present. The effectiveness of a deflocculant, such as a polyphosphate, seems to increase with increasing anionic charge. Sodium hydroxide seems to be an effective deflocculant when interfering ions have been removed from the surfaces of the clay particles. Instead of removing interfering ions, a substance capable of rendering the interfering ions inactive may be added.

Albert considers two types of systems represented by deflocculated and flocculated suspensions of kaolin. The former type contains small suspended particles which repel each other, and any disturbance of the system will be resisted, since it will cause particles to approach each other more closely than under equilibrium conditions. When the concentrations are high, a slight distortion may bring about mechanical interference between the particles; but when the concentrations are low, increased particle interaction as a result of disturbances is small or negligible, and the suspension may behave essentially as a Newtonian fluid over a considerable range of shear rate. As the concentration increases, the curve for rate of shear vs torque is no longer linear, but is concave with respect to the torque ordinate. This phenomenon is known as dilatency or shear-rate blockage. Its onset is much more abrupt when extremely small particles, in the conventional colloidal size range, are removed with a high-speed centrifuge.

The slurries (coating colors) should not possess the flow characteristics described above, but should be thixotropic. Thus the slurry should be a system in which attractive forces exist between suspended particles. These forces produce some rigidity in the system when it is at rest, and their disruption when shear is produced is responsible for the thixotropic behavior.

Albert studied a series of coating colors containing 60 percent total solids by weight, a chlorinated starch as the adhesive, and having a weight ratio of starch to clay of 12 to 100. Tetrasodium pyrophosphate was used as the deflocculant. Over 90 percent of the clay particles were less than two microns in diameter. When the suspensions contained less than 0.3 percent of deflocculant on the basis of the clay content, only partial deflocculation was achieved. They exhibited high shear resistance but were thixotropic, and probably could be used with high-speed coating operations.

Clays consisting of particles predominately larger than 2 microns diameter produce very fluid slurries when the concentration of solids is low. Such slurries exhibit a low viscosity even at high clay concentrations but are particularly susceptible to shear-rate thickening and shear-rate blockage.

Summarizing, coating formulations having desirable rheological properties are produced by the use of components which contribute mainly to the thixotropy while still maintaining as low a viscosity as possible. Additives such as soaps may be used to increase the thixotropic behavior, and the adhesive component may also contribute to it.

The importance of particle size to the optical properties of pigments used in coatings is very similar to the situation for paint pigments, discussed earlier in this chapter. The clay kaolin is the most widely used pigment, being particularly appropriate because of the leaf- or plate-like character of the particles which result from the parallel cleavage of the hexagonal crystals. Particles less than about two microns in diameter are usually plates and lie flat in a coating, producing a good gloss.[118] Larger particles are usually uncleaved, and since they lack the plate-like morphology do not produce a satisfactory gloss. The kaolin leaves are extremely thin, and although they are transparent they are highly effective in rendering paper opaque. This apparently results from the reflection of light from the numerous interfaces between kaolin leaves.

These effects of the size of the clay particles are shown in Figures 6-5 and 6-6. The former shows the relationship between particle size and opacity, while the latter shows the relationship between particle size and

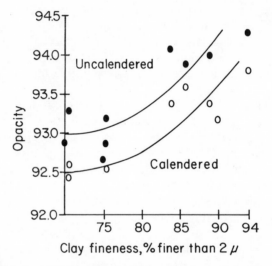

Figure 6-5. Relationship between particle diameter of kaolin and coating opacity.[115] (*Courtesy of the Society of Chemical Industry*)

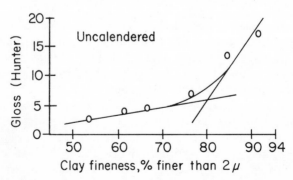

Figure 6-6. Relationship between particle diameter of kaolin and gloss.[115] (*Courtesy of the Society of Chemical Industry*)

gloss. They demonstrate that both opacity and gloss increase rapidly with increasing percentage of particles smaller than two microns, especially when the percentage is above about 80 percent.

## SOAPS AND SYNTHETIC DETERGENTS

### General

The soap and detergent industry, like the paint industry, is dominated by a few companies which are responsible for most of the production; many companies produce the rest. There are a number of other similarities between the two industries. Before the second world war, the soap and detergent industry was dominated by soap, the production of which remains largely an art, and although the large soap companies maintained large research and development laboratories, the emphasis was largely on development. Since 1945 the use of detergents has become much more general, and their production requires highly sophisticated synthetic organic techniques. Few of the small companies maintain research organizations, and most of them purchase the bulk detergent from large manufacturers.

Properly, soaps are detergents of a certain type, namely the salts of long-chain fatty acids. Most other detergents are synthetic organic chemicals and thus are called synthetic detergents or simply detergents. Actually, even the term detergent is quite ambiguous. A detergent produces an unusually large decrease in the surface tension of a solvent in which it is dissolved and may be defined as a substance which, as a result of this property, is useful for various types of cleaning.

The calcium and magnesium salts of most long-chain fatty acids are insoluble; when ordinary soaps consisting of the sodium salts are used with hard water a scum is produced. A major advantage of many synthetic detergents is that their calcium and magnesium salts are very soluble in water, and certain detergents, the nonionic detergents, do not form salts at all. Detergents prepared by combining kerosene with sodium benzene sulfonate were used during the second world war for washing in sea water.

Detergents are useful not only for washing, but also for a number of other purposes, for instance as germicides, emulsifiers, insecticides, foaming agents, and food additives.

### Soap and detergent powders

The particles of soaps and detergents are generally much larger than those considered throughout most of this book. For example, spray-dried washing powders consist of particles having diameters mainly between 0.1 and 1.0 mm.[119]

Soap powders may be produced by various types of grinding or spray-drying while synthetic detergents are usually spray-dried. Modern soap powders usually contain from 10 to 30 percent of dry soap, 25 to 50 percent of moisture, 25 to 55 percent of sodium carbonate, and much smaller amounts of one or more of a number of other substances such as borax, sodium silicate, sodium sulfate, and glycerol.[120]

A method for preparing a fluffy soap powder, common at least before 1950, involves mixing the hot liquid soap with an aqueous sodium carbonate solution and discharging the mixture onto a chilling roll. The hot mixture solidifies to form a thin sheet over the surface of the roll, and the water in the soap becomes water of crystallization of the sodium carbonate. The soap is cut away from the roll with a steel knife and falls onto a rotating screen which powders and sifts the soap. Particles which do not pass through the screen are transferred to a soap powder mill and ground.

One advantage of this process is that there is little production of extremely fine powder, which is annoying to the user when in the form of airborn particles, and little dust is distributed about the plant.

Many other types of grinders have been used for making powdered soap. These are usually equipped with dust bags or cloth-covered frames for collecting the airborne dust that is produced.

The spray-drying of detergents, and particularly of sodium alkylbenzenesulfonate, has been reviewed by Walter.[119] As in the case of powdered soaps, various "builders" are added to the surface active material. These include various phosphates, sodium silicate, sodium sulfate, and soil-suspending agents such as sodium carboxymethyl cellulose. A slurry of this material containing 40 to 50 percent moisture is sprayed into the top of a tall tower while hot gases are passed upward to evaporate the droplets. Many types of nozzles used for spray-drying of other materials are unsatisfactory for detergents since they produce a large percentage of particles smaller than 0.1 mm diameter and the product would be dusty when poured. A centrifugal pressure nozzle is usually used in the detergent industry. The slurry leaves the orifice at the base of the nozzle in the form of a film which breaks up to form droplets of appropriate size. The drops have dried by the time they reach the bottom of the tower, and after a short time to allow the particles to cool and the moisture content to reach equilibrium, the detergent powder is packaged.

Not only must the particles be free of extremely fine material, so that dusting is not a problem, they must be sufficiently fine that they dissolve rapidly and present an attractive appearance. Furthermore, the particles are hollow, but they must be sufficiently strong that they do not crumble during handling. Walter explains the fact that they are hollow on the assumption that as the drops fall through the hot air a dry skin forms on the surface. The thickness of the skin probably depends on the drying conditions and on the nature of the slurry. The liquid inside this coating vaporizes and the particles expand to form a hollow shell which eventually breaks open to liberate the vapor. Examination of such particles under a microscope often reveals the holes through which the vapor has escaped. Obviously, expansion due to this cause will not occur when the drops are so small that their radii are less than the shell thickness. Walter also states that as the droplet diameter increases, the percentage volumetric expansion also increases and the bulk density of the powder is reduced.

Other factors, such as the moisture content of the slurry and the final powder and the composition of the slurry, also influence the bulk density of the finished powder.

For a given type of atomizer the median diameters of the droplets produced and thus of the powders formed are largely dependent on the pressure under which the slurry is fed to the atomizer.

An important property of a finished detergent powder is its ability to flow freely. This can be controlled to a considerable extent by employing slurry formulations designed to produce free-flowing properties. For example, the presence of sodium silicate may be helpful. The flow properties can also be improved by adding fine inorganic powders to the finished powder, but this is done at the risk of producing a dusty product.

### Abrasive cleaners

Scouring powders, pastes, and bars contain an insoluble abrasive. The powders usually consist of soap powder, the abrasive, an alkaline salt such as sodium carbonate, and moisture.[121] Many different types of abrasives have been used. One of the oldest is ordinary sea sand. A very wide range of abrasive particle size is available so that scouring powders ranging from very harsh to very mild are available. Harshness depends, of course, on particle hardness and particle shape as well as on size.

Only mild abrasives should be used on surfaces such as glazed tile and china, while much harsher cleaners may be required for dirty pots and pans.

## CONCLUDING REMARKS

The above list of industries could be extended almost indefinitely. Many industries that depend heavily on fine-particle technology have hardly been mentioned or have not been mentioned at all. These include the manufacture of rubber goods, pharmaceuticals, various flours, fertilizers, sugar, spice, and cloth.

The preceding discussion in this chapter points up the fact that some of the industrial problems relating to the effects of particle size are common to many industries and have common solutions. An example is the importance of particle size to the opacity produced by pigments. Other problems are unique to a particular industry. An example of this is the effect of the dimensions of cellulose fibers on the properties of paper made from them.

Hopefully, the above discussion will be useful to engineers and scientists working in the industries described. However, it is also hoped that the examples of the practical effects of particle size, and of solutions to problems related to these effects, will aid in the solution of similar problems in other industries.

## REFERENCES

1. Kiefer, D. M., *Chem. Engr. News*, **43,** No. 5, 87 (February 1, 1965); **43,** No. 6, 80 (February 8, 1965).
2. Bell, S. H., in "Powders in Industry," Society of Chemical Industry Monograph No. 14, London, 1961.
3. Mattiello, J. J., ed., "Protective and Decorative Coatings," Wiley, New York, 1942.
4. Jacobsen, A. E., *Can. Chem. Process Inds.*, **33,** 124 (1949).
5. Stutz, G. F. A., and A. H. Pfund, *Ind. Eng. Chem.*, **19,** 51 (1927).
6. Depew, H. A., and A. C. Eide, *Ind. Eng. Chem.*, **32,** 537 (1940).
7. Work, L. T., in "Protective and Decorative Coatings," v. II, J. J. Mattiello, ed., Wiley, New York, 1942.
8. Dunn, E. J., M. Kushner, and C. H. Baier, *Ind. Eng. Chem.*, *Anal. Ed.*, **33,** 1157 (1941).
9. Eide, A. C., Official Digest, *Federation Paint & Varnish Prod. Clubs*, **145,** 164 (1935).
10. Eide, A. C., and H. A. Depew, *Paint, Oil, and Chem. Rev.*, **102,** No. 7, 26 (1940).
11. Depew, H. A., *Ind. Eng. Chem.*, **27,** 905 (1935).
12. Depew, H. A., and A. C. Eide, *Ind. Eng. Chem.*, **32,** 537 (1940).
13. Robertson, A., *J. Oil and Colour Chemists Assoc.*, **25,** 53 (1942).
14. Goeb, A., *Farbe U. Lack*, **57,** 14 (1951).
15. Green, H., and G. S. Haslam, *Ind. Eng. Chem.*, **19,** 53 (1927).
16. Green, H., and G. S. Haslam, *Ind. Eng. Chem.*, **17,** 726 (1925).
17. Venuto, L. J., *Paint, Oil, and Chemical Review*, **102,** No. 7, 32 (1940).
18. Wiegand, W. B., *India Rubber World*, p. 270, 1941.
19. Barrick, G., *Am. Paint Journal Convention Daily*, p. 12, Oct. 31, 1941.
20. Radcliffe, R. S., in "Paint and Varnish Technology," W. von Fischer, ed., Reinhold, New York, 1948.
21. Piper, H. D., Paper presented before annual meeting of Federation of Paint and Varnish Production Clubs, Chicago, Ill., Oct. 25–28, 1939.

22. Lukens, A. R., C. L. Cummings, and V. J. Babel, *Official Digest, Fed. of Paint and Varn. Prod. Clubs*, **228,** 306 (1943).
23. Craig, R. W., and C. B. Stetson, *Paint, Oil, and Chemical Rev.*, **102,** No. 7, 12 (1940).
24. Kronstein, M., H. Abramski, J. Rivera, and F. Weber, *Australian Paint J.*, **5,** No. 2, 13 (1960).
25. Kronstein, M., J. Rivera, H. Abramski, and F. Weber, *Paint Varnish Production*, **49,** No. 13, 33, 96 (1959).
26. Soul, D. C., in "Powders in Industry," Society of Chemical Industry Monograph No. 14, London, 1961.
27. Edwards, J. D., and R. B. Mason, *Ind. Eng. Chem., Anal. Ed.*, **6,** 159 (1934).
28. Wendon, G. W., *Paint Manufacture*, **17,** 373 (1947).
29. Dewey, P. H., *Paint, Oil, and Chemical Review*, **110,** No. 25, 9 (1947).
30. Bowles, R. F., in "Powders in Industry," Society of Chemical Industry Monograph No. 14, London, 1961.
31. Fuhrmann, O. W., L. O. Buttler, P. F. Duffy, F. G. Schleisher, and J. J. Mattiello, in "Protective and Decorative Coatings," vol. 3, J. J. Mattiello, ed., Wiley, New York, 1943.
32. Taylor, H. F. W., in "The Chemistry of Cements," H. F. W. Taylor, ed., Academic Press, New York, 1964.
33. Uttenthal, P., in "Powders in Industry," Society of Chemical Industry Monograph No. 14, London, 1961.
34. British Standard Specification 12:1958.
35. Turriziani, R., in "The Chemistry of Cements," H. F. W. Taylor, ed., Academic Press, New York, 1964.
36. Halstead, P. E., in "The Chemistry of Cements," H. F. W. Taylor, ed., Academic Press, New York, 1964.
37. Rose, H. E., "The Measurement of Particle Size in Very Fine Powders," Constable, London, 1953.
38. Mary, M., Compt. Rend., 17 me Congr. Chim. Ind., Paris, Sept.-Oct., 1937, p. 264.
39. Kavcic, J., *Zement*, **23,** 278 (1934).
40. Kavcic, *J. Arch. Hem. Farm.*, **8,** 72 (1934).
41. Hausenschild, A., *Zement*, **15,** 453, 469, 488 (1926).
42. Kuhl, H., *Zement*, **19,** 604, 630 (1930).
43. Sanada, Y., and G. Nishi, *J. Soc. Chem. Ind., Japan*, **39,** Suppl. binding 9 (1936).
44. Oden, S., *Teknisk Tidskrift, Upplaga C (Kemi)*, **57,** 70 (1927).
45. Tillman, R., *Mitt. Tech. Versuchsamtes.*, **33,** 23 (1934).
46. Nicolaesco, N., Rev. materiaux construction trav. publics, p. 401, 1929.
47. Filossofov, P., *Tonind-Ztg.*, **53,** 1302 (1929).
48. Steiner, D., *Zement*, **21,** 230 (1932).
49. Mazza, J. J., *Rev. Facultad Cienc. Quim. (Univ. nacl. La Plata)*, **20,** 155 (1945).
50. Wuhrer, J., *Zement-Kalk-Gips*, **3,** 148 (1950).
51. Pollitt, H. W. W., in "The Chemistry of Cements," H. F. W. Taylor, ed., Academic Press, New York, 1964.
52. Beke, B., *Zement-Kalk-Gips*, **12,** 529 (1958).
53. Shepherd, H. R., in "Aerosols: Science and Technology," H. R. Shepherd, ed., Interscience, New York, 1961.

54. Shepherd, H. R., in "Cosmetics: Science and Technology," E. Sagarin, ed., Interscience, New York, 1957.
55. "Package for Profit," Freon Products Division, E. I. du Pont de Nemours & Co., Inc., Wilmington, Delaware, 1958.
56. "Aerosol Pressure Products Survey," Chemical Specialties Manufacturers' Association, New York, 1960.
57. Forsman, Jr., R. A., in "Aerosols: Science and Technology," H. R. Shepherd, ed., Interscience, New York, 1961.
58. Sage, M. S., in "Encyclopedia of Chemical Technology," 2nd ed., vol. 1, Interscience, New York.
59. Herzka, A., and J. Pickthall, "Pressurized Packaging-Aerosols," Butterworths, London, 1961.
60. Downing, R. C., in "Aerosols: Science and Technology," H. R. Shepherd, ed., Interscience, New York, 1961.
61. Anonymous, *Mfg. Chemist*, **35**, No. 1, 91 (1964).
62. Sciarra, J. J., *Paint Varnish Prod.*, **53**, No. 3, 47 (1963).
63. Scott, R. J., and R. R. Terrill, *Soap Chem. Specialties*, **38**, No. 1, 142, 146, 148, 153; No. 2, 134, 136 (1962).
64. Green, H. L., and Lane, W. R., "Particulate Clouds: Dusts, Smokes and Mists," 2nd ed., Van Nostrand, New York, 1964.
65. Cadle, R. D., and W. C. Thuman, *Ind. Eng. Chem.*, **52**, 315 (1960).
66. York, J. L., *J. Soc. Cosmetic Chemists*, **3**, 204 (1956).
67. Kempe, W., *Soap, Perfumery, and Cosmetics*, **36**, 293 (1963).
68. "Tentative Official Method of Determination of the Particle Size Distribution of Space Insecticide Aerosol," Chem. Specialties Mfrs. Assoc., New York, 1957.
69. Goetzel, C. G., "Treatise on Powder Metallurgy," vol I, Interscience, New York, 1949.
70. Jenkins, I., in "Powders in Industry," Society of Chemical Industry Monograph No. 14, London, 1961.
71. Jones, W. D., "Fundamental Principles of Powder Metallurgy," Edward Arnold, London, 1961.
72. Pranatis, A. L., and L. Seigle, in "Powder Metallurgy," W. Leszynski, ed., Interscience, New York, 1961.
73. Kuhn, W. E., ed., "Ultrafine Particles," Wiley, New York, 1963.
74. Kuczynaki, G. C., *Trans. A.I.M.E.*, **185**, 169 (1949).
75. De Hoff, R. T., R. A. Rummel, F. N. Rhines, and A. H. Long, in "Powder Metallurgy," W. Leszynski, ed., Interscience, New York, 1961.
76. Rhines, F. N., Plausee Proc. 3rd Seminar, Reutle/Tyrol, 1958.
77. Rumpf, H., in "International Symposium on Agglomeration," W. A. Knepper, ed., Interscience, New York, 1962.
78. Cremens, W. S., in "Ultrafine Particles," W. E. Kuhn, ed., Wiley, New York, 1963.
79. Zwilsky, K. M., and N. J. Grant, in "Ultrafine Particles," W. E. Kuhn, ed., Wiley, New York, 1963.
80. Kingery, W. D., "Introduction to Ceramics," Wiley, New York, 1960.
81. Herring, C., *J. Appl. Phys.*, **21**, 301 (1950).
82. Gugel, E., and F. H. Norton, *Am. Ceram. Soc. Bull.*, **41**, 8 (1962).
83. Schuller, K., *Ber. Deut. Keram. Soc.*, **38**, 208 (1961).
84. Palmer, W. E., *J. Am. Ceram. Soc.*, **25**, 413 (1942).
85. Vieweg, H. F., *J. Am. Ceram. Soc.*, **16**, 77 (1933).

86. Krause, O., and U. Klempin, *Sprechsaal*, **75**, 229, 251, 273 (1942).
87. Marzahl, H., *Ber. Deut. Keram. Ges.*, **32**, 203 (1955).
88. Winkler, H. G. F., *Ber. Deut. Keram. Ges.*, **31**, 337 (1954).
89. Whittaker, H., *J. Am. Ceram. Soc.*, **22**, 16 (1939).
90. Moore, C. E., *Brick Clay Rec.*, **77**, 157 (1930).
91. West, R. R., D. H. Fleischer, N. Hecht, W. R. Hoskyns, A. Muccigrosso, and D. H. Schelker, *J. Am. Ceram. Soc.*, **43**, 648 (1960).
92. Laboratory of Ferro Enamels, *Keram Z.*, **12**, 626 (1960).
93. Zwermann, C. H., and A. I. Andrews, *J. Am. Ceram. Soc.*, **23**, 93 (1940).
94. Schuele, W. J., and V. D. Deetscreek, in "Ultrafine Particles," W. E. Kuhn, ed., Wiley, New York, 1963.
95. Kittel, C., and J. K. Galt, "Ferromagnetic Domain Theory," Solid State Physics, **3**, Academic Press, New York, 1956.
96. Stewart, K. H., "Ferromagnetic Domains," Cambridge University Press, London, 1954.
97. Bungenberg de Jong, H. G., and H. R. Kruyt, *Kolloid Z.*, **50**, 39 (1930).
98. Bungenberg de Jong, H. G., in "Colloid Science," vol. 2, H. R. Kruyt, ed., Elsevier, New York, 1949.
99. Brynko, C., and J. A. Scarpelli, U.S. Pat. 2,969,331, Jan. 24, 1961.
100. Brynko, C., U.S. Pat. 2,969,370, Jan. 24, 1961; H. W. Mattson, *Science and Technology*, p. 66, April, 1965.
101. Robbins, R. C., J. J. Thomas, and R. D. Cadle, *J. Colloid. Sci.*, **18**, 483 (1963).
102. Matijevic, E., M. Kerker, and K. F. Schulz, *Disc. Faraday Soc.*, **30**, 178 (1961).
103. Hardy, C., U.S. Pat. 2,182,567.
104. Lamprey, H., in "Ultrafine Particles," W. E. Kuhn, ed., Wiley, New York, 1963.
105. Van den Akker, J. A., *Tappi*, **42**, 940 (1959).
106. Van den Akker, J. A., A. L. Lathrop, M. H. Voelker, and L. R. Dearth, *Tappi*, **41**, 416 (1958).
107. Volokitina, N. A., S. S. Voyutskii, and A. D. Zaionchkovskii, *Bumazh. Prom.*, **27**, No. 9, 14 (1952).
108. Haywood, G., *Tappi*, **33**, 370 (1950).
109. Giertz, H. W., *Bull Inst. Paper Chem.*, **19**, 305 (1949).
110. Watson, A. J., and H. E. Dadswell, *APPITA*, **15**, No. 6, 116, 127 (1962).
111. Marton, R., and S. D. Alexander, *Tappi*, **46**, 65 (1963).
112. Bobrov, F. F., *Bumazhanaya Prom.*, **21**, No. 5/6, 5 (1946).
113. Hercules Powder Co., Brit. Pat. 871,205, June 21, 1961.
114. Arledter, H., *Das Papier*, **2**, 181 (1948).
115. Senger, F., *Das Papier*, **8**, 242 (1954).
116. Cameron, S. S., in "Powders in Industry," Society of Chemical Industry Monograph No. 14, London, 1961.
117. Albert, C. G., *Tappi*, **34**, 453 (1951).
118. Woodward, L. A., and S. C. Lyons, *Tappi*, **34**, 438 (1951).
119. Walter, S. T., in "Powders in Industry," Society of Chemical Industry Monograph No. 14, London, 1961.
120. Martin, G., "The Modern Soap and Detergent Industry," vol. 2, 3rd ed., The Technical Press, Surrey, England, 1951.
121. Price, D., "Detergents," Chemical Publishing Co., New York, 1952.

# Subject Index